DATE DUE

DEC 5 1971

NO 1972

STUDIES IN HISTORY, ECONOMICS AND PUBLIC LAW

Edited by the
FACULTY OF POLITICAL SCIENCE
OF COLUMBIA UNIVERSITY

NUMBER 397

DEISM IN EIGHTEENTH CENTURY AMERICA

BY

HERBERT M. MORAIS

DEISM IN EIGHTEENTH CENTURY AMERICA

BY

HERBERT M. MORAIS, Ph.D.

Instructor in History, Brooklyn College

NEW YORK
COLUMBIA UNIVERSITY PRESS
LONDON: P. S. KING & SON, LTD.
1934

To

MY PARENTS

"... Some American historian ought to re-relate to the world the full extent of [the] remarkable spread of skepticism in the eighteenth century ..."

—JOSEPH McCABE

"... [The] story of religious and philosophical thought in the eighteenth century is the story of the rising tide of deism, of the receding waves of orthodoxy ..."

—HOWARD M. JONES

PREFACE

ALTHOUGH deism was the axis about which the religious thought of eighteenth-century America revolved, studies dealing with it have been few. Interest in the subject, however, seems to be growing; in fact, only a few months ago, an excellent work covering the rise of an organized deistic movement appeared. In his *Republican Religion, The American Revolution and the Cult of Reason* (1933), Koch shows how the formation of deistic clubs, lectureships and newspapers made possible the popularization of deism. Interested especially in this phase of the deistic tendency, he does not concern himself with deistic speculation as such, with its origins, European background and relation to other types of rationalistic expression. The present writer, however, emphasizes these points as well as the development of an organized deism. In addition to these subjects, he points out the connection of the deistic trend with the French and Indian War, Freemasonry and the infiltration of French culture. The religious views of the signers of the Declaration of Independence, of other Revolutionary War figures and of prominent Republican and Federalist leaders are examined in order to determine how far these men traveled along the road of skepticism. Circumstances have forced the author to confine most of his discussion to deism in the North; he has, however, included some material on other sections and is indebted for suggestions in this connection to Professors H. M. Jones of the University of Michigan and J. G. de R. Hamilton of the University of North Carolina.

7

The author has set himself the task of defining the deistic movement in the light of its eighteenth-century environment, of giving a general picture of its rise, progress and decline and of interpreting its tenor in terms of its class support. To understand deism more clearly the writer has distinguished it from atheism and Christian rationalism, has noted its connection with anti-clericalism and has examined its development in Europe. Eighteenth-century deism accepted the sufficiency of natural (rational) religion and implicitly or explicitly rejected the need or truth of divine revelation. The author has sought not only to define deism but also to trace its progress from 1713 to 1805. A number of considerations led him to select 1713 as the proper starting-point for his study; in that year the first work on deism published by an American, Cotton Mather's *Reasonable Religion,* appeared; one year later, the first great collection of rationalistic works was sent to America. The year 1805 was regarded as a fitting close because in that year Elihu Palmer, responsible for the organization of a militant deistic movement, died. Moreover, by 1805, the second Great Awakening had run its course and had succeeded in making the country safe for Christianity. From pamphlets, sermons, diaries, travelers' accounts, library catalogues, and especially periodicals, information was secured to show the advent of deism in colonial America, the extent of its influence on the eve of the Revolution, its growing militancy after 1783, its spread from the intelligentsia to the masses, and its temporary collapse in early nineteenth-century America.

Lastly, the effort is made to interpret deism in the light of its class support. During most of the eighteenth century, deistic speculation circulated almost exclusively among " rich and well-born " liberals who used it for the purpose of overthrowing such vestiges of the old regime as the union of church and state. The upper classes, however, did not desire to destroy " religion " and therefore they minimized the anti-Christian implications of the deistic philosophy. When Palmer and his associates initiated an organized movement emphasizing these inferences and carrying them to the masses, deistically-inclined planters and " substantial " merchants generally refused to support the tendency. Stripped of its chief source of financial and intellectual backing and faced by a determined and well-organized evangelical Christianity, the deism of Palmer was doomed to failure. Yet, the deistic movement did not wholly disappear; in fact, from 1825 to 1835, it again came to the front and this time its denunciation of Christianity was outspoken and bitter. Its anti-Christian inclinations were grounded in the fact that its advocates were Owenite socialists who were convinced that one of the ways to eliminate the " evils " of the system of private property was to free the people from " the opium of religion." In another work, the author intends to show how deism was moulded during the early nineteenth century to suit the revolutionary aspirations of the advance guard of workingclass discontent.

The writer heartily welcomes this opportunity to acknowledge his many and varied obligations to others who have aided him; to Professor Evarts B. Greene, of the Department of History, Columbia University, for his patience, scholarly attitude, and stimulating direction; to Professor Herbert W. Schneider, of the Department of Philosophy, Columbia University, for his encouragement and expert criticism; to Mr. Solomon Bloom, his colleague in the Department of History, Brooklyn College, for his correction of the manuscript and for his many enlightening suggestions; to Professor Holland Thompson, of the Department of History, of the City College of New York, for the impetus given to this study and for his helpful literary hints; to Professor J. Salwyn Schapiro, of the same institution, and to Professor John Herman Randall, Jr., Department of Philosophy, Columbia University, for their suggestions on European deism; to Professor A. G. Fradenburgh, head of the Department of History, Brooklyn College, for his careful reading of various parts of the book; and to the Misses Lillian Morais and Dorothy Neugeborn for their patience in typing and retyping the manuscript. Whatever good points the work may have are due in a large measure to the constructive criticisms of these men and women; whatever faults the book may have are my own.

BROOKLYN COLLEGE,
DECEMBER, 1933.

CONTENTS

CHAPTER I

General Character of the Deistic Movement With Particular Reference to America

Deism in America shared the cautious and non-revolutionary temper of eighteenth-century liberalism of which it was an integral part. Although a few of its bolder spirits achieved some contemporary notoriety for their militant attack upon revealed Christianity, most of the deistic champions were willing to leave the question of divine revelation alone. Their apparent lack of gusto may be explained in one of two ways. In the first place, these men, caught up by the intellectual currents of their age, were swept into an acceptance of deism without fully appreciating its implications. Consequently, many of them—Hawley, a Northampton lawyer, Bliss, a New England clergyman and Edmund and John Randolph, prominent Virginian statesmen—eventually retraced their steps and returned to the Christian fold.

Secondly, it required courage to take up the crusade against revealed Christianity; it meant the loss of social respectability. To speak pretty nothings was one thing; to court martyrdom for one's views was quite another. Not that these militant deists were hanged or burned or broken on the wheel: no, this was the Enlightened Age of Reason and Progress and not the Dark Ages. Hence, little boys were told to stick out their tongues at these undesirables, while their more civilized elders were cautioned to shun them. Ethan Allen, hero of Ticonderoga and author of the first real anti-Christian work in America, became in his day " a vile and impious wretch " destined to burn eternally; Thomas Paine, the man who, as Jefferson wrote, " steadily labored " to secure

American freedom, achieved the dubious reputation of being an "atheist" despite his explicit assertion "I believe in one God and no more . . ."; while Elihu Palmer, the most aggressive of native-born deists, was described as "superficial, vain and affectatious." Social disapproval was expressed in subtler forms than those of vituperation. Militant champions of the deistic cause were concretely taught that deism did not pay. Isaac Hall, of Philadelphia, an agent for Palmer's deistic newspaper, the *Prospect*, was, according to rumor, refused the lease of a municipal wharf because of his membership in the "Tom Paine crowd." [1]

Moreover, another consideration made possible the victory of prudence over ardor. An attack upon the Christian system of faith and morals might be accompanied by undesirable social consequences. Such an eventuality was far from being relished by most of these liberal gentlemen. Drawn as they were from the "rich and the well-born", they did not oppose the spread of deism among the upper classes; they did, however, fear its dissemination among the masses. One contemporary clergyman, although condemning the anti-Christian inclinations of Hume, Bolingbroke and Gibbon, was nevertheless quite willing to praise them for the "good sense" they showed in confining their observations to "the more polished classes of the community. . . ." [2] Another eighteenth-century liberal was even more explicit; the upper classes used the "superstitions" of Christianity to enslave the masses. In a letter to the Editor of *The Temple of Reason* for November 27, 1802, "A Rich Deist" wrote,

Very few rich men; or, at least men in the higher grades of society, and who receive a liberal education, care anything about

---

[1] Koch, *Republican Religion, The American Revolution and The Cult of Reason* (New York, 1933), p. 144.

[2] From a sermon by Robert Hall on Modern Infidelity Considered with respect to its Influence on Society quoted *ibid.*, p. 75.

the Christian religion. They cast off the yoke of superstition themselves; yet, for the sake of finding obedient servants, they would continue to impose it on the poor.

Thus, the anti-Christian tendency of militant deistic ideology was too dangerous for the peace of society. It concealed tons of social dynamite which, if set off, would destroy not only organized religion but the social order.

Most American deists, therefore, contented themselves with the innocuous common-sense truths of " the pure and simple Religion of Nature " with its basic premise of a First Cause, its acceptance of a future state and its emphasis upon virtuous living. This threefold creed, however, was not entirely monopolized by the " Deistic Knights of the goose-quill "; it was also accepted by the rationalistic clergy of the age, Gay, Briant and Bentley in Congregational surroundings and Johnson and Smith in Anglican circles. Yet, these ministers held that the authoritative basis of natural religion did not rest in reason alone but also depended upon the Christian revelation which clarified its precepts and added weight to its teachings. So long as liberals were pleased to express their approval of the religion of nature, all went well. But the moment they neglected to mention the necessity of the Bible as an aid to " the new faith ", or, even worse, the moment they denied openly the need or truth of the Scriptures, the die was cast and the battle begun.

For the most part, however, the conflict was neither exciting nor dramatic because of the general lukewarmness of American deism which criticized Christianity in the guarded phraseology of the would-be reformer rather than of the determined destroyer. Desiring to make the Christian religion conform more fully with the intellectual currents of rationalistic science, most deists assiduously presented Jesus to their contemporaries as the first great deistic preacher, a man who, in the words of Jefferson, endeavored to recall the

Hebrews "to the principles of a pure deism, . . . to reform their moral doctrines to the standards of reason, justice and philanthropy, and to inculcate a belief in a future state. . . ." [3] Other exponents of the deistic philosophy were even bolder; they claimed that the simple carpenter of Nazareth was a "moral" deist who, like Paine, Volney and Palmer, desired men to love God and their neighbors.[4] According to the deists, the followers of Jesus lost sight of his teachings to the extent of replacing them with rituals, creeds and churches. Consequently, the religion of the Gospels was in need of redemption and in response to the necessity, deistic saviors appeared on the scene who proposed to strip Christianity of its "useless" accretions. By doing away with these additions, these deists hoped to see the restoration of the "pure and simple teachings" of Jesus, which teachings were "the best the World ever saw or is likely to see. . . ." [5] Since these sage precepts could be discovered by reason, all men could share them.

Prior to 1784, the American deistic movement made no real effort to examine openly and critically "the revealed word of God." During the colonial period, freethinkers were satisfied with the harmless approach of setting forth the tenets of natural religion without seeking an authoritative basis for them in the Bible. They made no attempt to popularize their views; rather than air their observations they confined them to letters and diaries. Fearful of social ostracism, many of the early disciples of deism—Hawley, Bliss and John Adams—sooner or later disavowed their "youthful fancies". The introduction of English ration-

[3] T. Jefferson, *Writings*, ed. Ford (New York, 1892), vol. viii, p. 224 (footnote).

[4] *Temple of Reason*, vol. i, p. 9. See issues for November 8, 15, and 22, 1800.

[5] B. Franklin, *Writings*, ed. Smyth (New York, 1905-7), vol. x, p. 84.

alistic works, the cosmic philosophy of Newton, the empirical psychology of Locke, the appearance of a liberal theological movement and some anti-clerical feeling prepared the way for the advent of deistic speculation in colonial America. Its progress during the provincial period was, however, very slow; in fact, up to 1776, deism was still an aristocratic cult confined to a few intellectuals residing in relatively large towns. In these cities as well as in the interior, it was regarded with a great deal of suspicion and hostility. Yet, in spite of its unpopularity, a large number of Revolutionary leaders either accepted it or came very close to doing so. Of the fifty-six delegates who signed the Declaration of Independence, the religious opinions of twenty were ascertained. Of these, three were deists, Jefferson, Franklin and Hopkins; two were veering towards deism, John Adams and Wythe; four, Robert Treat Paine, Bartlett, Rush and Thornton, entertained liberal, though not deistic, views; while the remaining eleven were orthodox in their principles. The same diversity of religious opinions which characterized the signers of the immortal Declaration prevailed among others who played an important role in the revolutionary struggle. Willie Jones of North Carolina, member of the Continental Congress, Edmund Randolph, prominent Virginian statesman, Ethan Allen, military leader and Thomas Paine, author of *Common Sense*, rejected either implicitly or explicitly the Christian revelation, while George Washington, James Madison and George Mason came dangerously close to doing the same thing. On the other hand, men like Samuel Adams, Patrick Henry and Henry Laurens were, in spite of their political liberalism, conservatives in religion.[6] During the Revolutionary era, deism became somewhat bolder in tone; in 1784, in his ponderous and repetitious *Reason, the Only Oracle of Man*, Allen rejected revealed

[6] See chapter iv, pp. 92-8, 100-3, 104-5, 113-8; chapter v, pp. 120-6, 141-2.

religion in general and Christianity in particular. Although not typical of the American climate of deistic opinion, he nevertheless represented a significant swing to the left, a swing stimulated by the rising anti-clerical spirit of the age. At the close of the Revolutionary War, established churches and religious discriminations existed in several American states. To the advance guard of deistic liberalism, liberty meant freedom not only from English but also from ecclesiastical interference. The forced payment of taxes to an established church and compulsory adherence to its dogmas were considered as derogatory to the nature of man as well as useless and pernicious to social welfare. According to the deists, it mattered little whether all men accepted transubstantiation or consubstantiation, infant or adult baptism, so long as they obeyed the laws of the land. Good citizenship based on freedom was of greater value to society than blind acceptance of a formulated creed which too often deluded its adherents. On the other hand, a general agreement as to dogmas was, they thought, necessary to the continuance in power of an established church which, whether Protestant or Catholic, would use the civil machinery to stamp out opposition. In the encouragement of fanaticism, the clergy, who were supported by forced contributions drawn from public funds subscribed to by believers and non-believers, were ever ready to " furnish their quota of imps " and transform Biblical phrases into weapons for killing. To the deistic liberal, the bloody struggles, which so often disgraced the pages of Christian history, could only be avoided in the future if clerical dogmatism were destroyed.

In order to put an end to ecclesiastical interference the deists sought to undermine priestly pretentions to authority. In the last analysis, these rested upon an acceptance of the Bible as a divine document. American deists might therefore be expected to attack the Scriptural revelation explicitly and boldly; but, during this period, with the exception of Allen, they did not. So vigorous was Allen's reaction against the priesthood that he declared himself to be no Christian " except as infant baptism made [him] so. . . ." Driven by the same anti-clerical spirit, the deistic Charles Lee, a general under Washington, directed his heirs not to bury his remains in a church or churchyard, while John Randolph of Virginia viewed with pleasure any victory of the Crescent over the Cross. Likewise Willie Jones, prominent Revolutionary leader of North Carolina, stated in his will that he wanted no priest to insult his body by saying anything over it. Yet, the North Carolinian did not go so far as to openly reject revealed religion. On the whole, his position was similar to that of his friend, Jefferson, who played a leading role in the disestablishment of the Anglican Church in Virginia. Like most American deists, the author of the Declaration of Independence was satisfied with drawing a nice distinction between the religion of the Gospels and that of the priests. He proposed to destroy the latter in order to restore the simple teachings of Jesus, which he thought, were essentially deistic. By this means, the dawn of the Enlightened Age of Natural Religion would begin.

Although anti-clericalism was prevalent during the Revolutionary era, it was not strong enough to produce an aggressive deistic tendency. This was postponed until after 1793 and was brought about by the activities of the ministry which forced more radical deistic liberals to invade the sacred domain of the Biblical revelation. Circumstances moved Paine and Palmer, the two outstanding deistic critics of Christianity in America, to throw caution to the winds. During the French Revolution, Paine felt that the clergy of France was allied with the descredited monarchical forces of reaction. In order to overthrow the alliance of throne and altar and to preserve republican and liberal principles, he

determined to destroy the priesthood by putting an end to the
source of its authority—the Scriptural revelation. The
growth of atheism, which appeared to him to threaten the
existence of the only true religion, deism, was another consideration motivating the Anglo-American radical to attack
the divine origin of the Scriptures.   In his view, disbelief in
God and a future state was due to the disgust men felt for the
fanatical and reactionary tendencies of the clerical party.
Thus, to save deism from atheism and republicanism from
despotism, the defender of the Rights of Man published his
Age of Reason (1794).   He had contemplated the writing
of such a destructive work for a long time but, true to the
cautious temper of eighteenth-century liberalism, he had hesitated to do so.   At a very early age, Paine came to doubt the
validity of the Christian revelation but was reluctant to
develop publicly the destructive implications of the deistic
philosophy.   Although he informed John Adams in 1776
that he intended to publish a work against the Old Testament,
he failed to do so.   Some ten years later, Franklin, in a letter
believed to have been addressed to Paine, prudently advised
him to give up this project and " display his Talents of
reasoning upon a less hazardous subject and thereby obtain a
Rank with our distinguish'd Authors. . . ." [7] It was not

---

[7] B. Franklin, *Writings*, ed. Smyth, vol. ix, p. 521. That this letter
might have been written to Paine appears probable for we know that the
Anglo-American intended to compose a deistic tract in 1776 and that he
informed John Adams of his intentions. What was to prevent him
from entertaining similar designs in 1786 and telling them to his friend
Franklin who, in line with his prudent habits, would advise against the
publication of any such work? That the above letter was written to
Paine to stop him from writing his *Age of Reason* (as was later contended) does not seem likely. Joseph Lewis, in his *Franklin the Freethinker*, attempts to show that this was not the case. He argues that
The Age of Reason was published a number of years after the above
letter was sent and that it was written, according to Paine, without any
one being consulted.

until he was almost sixty and in the shadow of the guillotine that the Anglo-American decided to modify his life-long resolve of never dishonoring religion nor of ridiculing " any denomination whatsoever."

Circumstances likewise made Elihu Palmer, teacher, minister and lawyer, denounce publicly the Christian religion. Forced to give up his pulpit in a Philadelphia Baptist Church because of heterodox views, prevented from holding meetings of his own because of clerical hostility, the blind preacher was ready in 1793 to accept the challenge of the French Revolution. Like Paine, this Dartmouth graduate proposed to save liberalism by fighting what seemed to him to be its bitterest opponent—the clergy. From 1793 onward, Congregational ministers of New England allied themselves with Federalistic conservatism and in order to stem the rising tide of democratic ideas, they cast aspersions upon the French Revolution and its principles of Liberty and Equality. To save these principles, Palmer, armed with that powerful engine of destruction, *The Age of Reason,* determined to put an end to the clergy by destroying belief in revealed religion. In short, the clerical forces of Old France and New England obliged more radical deistic liberals to attack what Paine was pleased to call

the Christian system of faith, including in it the whimsical account of the creation, the strange story of Eve, the snake and the apple; the ambiguous idea of a man-god; the corporeal idea of the death of a god; the mythological idea of a family of gods, and the Christian system of arithmetic that three is one and one is three. . . .[8]

The militant anti-Christian approach of Paine and Palmer, however, was not pursued by all deistic liberals. Most of them adopted the cautious procedure of Freneau and Jeffer-

[8] T. Paine, *Age of Reason* (New York, no date), pt. i, p. 57.

son who, while bitterly castigating the clergy, did not openly reject revealed religion. Likewise it would be misleading to assume that all of those who marched under the banners of Jeffersonian republicanism and equalitarianism were even moderate deists. In western Pennsylvania, Scotch-Irish Presbyterians, although active in the radical politics of their state, were conservatives in religion. William Findley and John Smilie, popular Republican leaders, represented the religious conservatism of their constituents; on one occasion, Findley and his associates were quite willing to bolt their party rather than accept a gubernatorial candidate reputed to be a member of the " Tom Paine crowd ". In New England, God-fearing Baptists and Methodists were usually Jeffersonians but at the same time were the backbone of the evangelical movement which more than anything else was responsible for the decline of deism. Likewise Republican leadership was not drawn exclusively from deistic ranks; Barlow and Sullivan entertained liberal, though not deistic, views, while Samuel Adams was so firm a believer in the Christian revelation that he observed with sorrow Paine's attempt to convert good American citizens to " so bad a cause " as deism. Conversely, not all Federalist leaders were religious conservatives; Timothy Pickering, Josiah Quincy and John Adams of Massachusetts held Unitarian views, while William Davie of North Carolina was a deist and Charles Cotesworth Pinckney of South Carolina was accused of being one.

Yet, because of the noisy aggressiveness of " Tom Paine and his infidels " and the attention bestowed upon them by a thoroughly frightened clergy, militant deism attracted an attention out of proportion to its actual influence. Convinced that the best defense was a good offense, it trained its siege guns of criticism upon the citadel of revealed Christianity. Deistic societies and newspapers were used at the turn of the century to demolish the Biblical revelation. Of these two

agencies, the former were by far more important since serving at first as cells of resistance, they were later to be employed as cells of organization for the establishment of " the
new faith ". They distributed deistic works free of charge,
initiated discussions, collected money and instructed their
members to turn their dogs upon unhappy Christian ministers. New York, Philadelphia, Newburgh, Baltimore and
the Genesee River country in western New York State had
such societies. Freethinking newspapers were also established to spread " the glad tidings of a new day "; *The
Temple of Reason* (1800-1803), published in New York and
Philadelphia, was designed to show the purity and soundness
of deistic principles, while *The Prospect, or View of the
Moral World* (1803-1805), printed in New York, proposed
to investigate fully the divine nature of Christianity. Back
of these two agencies of propaganda was Elihu Palmer who
offered to do for natural religion what St. Paul had already
done for Christianity. From Newburgh to Atlanta, this
apostle of missionary deism addressed enthusiastic audiences,
the size of which varied, as far as accounts go, in direct ratio
to the sympathies of his reporters. Incapable of making
anyone weary " within the sound of his voice " he was a
brilliant speaker, and, although he vigorously assailed the
Christian religion, his attack was according to one authority,[9]
even less daring than that of his New York co-worker, John
Foster.

Through the publication of popularized deistic tracts and
the formation of Freethinking societies, newspapers and lectureships, the deism of Paine made its way among students,
planters, doctors, teachers, merchants and farmers. Its
evident popularity caused consternation among the faithful
who were so alarmed that they felt only a miracle could save

[9] Francis, *New York during the last Half Century* (New York, 1857),
p. 92.

their religion.   This was reflected in an appeal made by the
New York Missionary Society in 1798.   Addressed to all
those who " love our Lord Jesus Christ in sincerity ", the
plea read,

> . . . Infidelity abounds.   It hath assumed an imperious air, and
> glories in the expectation of a speedy extermination of the
> religion of Jesus.   To confound its vain hopes, we are called
> upon to shew that the Spirit of Christ continues to animate his
> body . . . [The] Lord is about to build up Zion, and to appear
> in his glory.   Amen.   Even so: come Lord Jesus! [10]

Verily, the faithful were standing at Armageddon and batt-
ling for the Lord.   They conducted their defense of Christianity along two fronts, one rational and the other emotional.
The former was reflected in the appearance of apologetic
works intended especially to show the irrationality of Paine's
contentions.   Alongside of this rational tendency, there
emerged an evangelical movement whose message appealed
more readily to the people since it was addressed to their
hearts and not to their minds.   In its wake came missionary
agencies, orthodox magazines, theological seminaries, Bible
societies and Sunday Schools, all of which proved too powerful for the poorly organized deism of the militant forces.
Yet, the deistic movement made too much of an impression
to disappear entirely; it merged into the Higher Criticism
of the nineteenth century and even lives on today in the
discourses of modernistic clergymen and the harangues of
atheistic speakers.

English deism was marked by the same cautious approach
and internal division as the American tendency.   Like most
of their co-workers in the new Republic, English deists contented themselves with setting forth the sufficiency of natural

---

[10] *The Theological Magazine*, June, July, and August 1798, vol. iii,
pp. 267, 270.

religion and the consequent lack of necessity for revealed "truths". Tindal and Chubb identified the tenets of the religion of nature with the simple teachings of Christ which they hoped "to restore". Yet, a few champions of English deism strayed from the straight and narrow path and, like Collins and Woolston, openly denounced Christianity. For this they were bitterly condemned; Woolston, who portrayed Jesus as an impostor, sorcerer and magician, was fined and imprisoned, an act which constituted a slight miscarriage of the much-vaunted British spirit of tolerance. These men were moved to express themselves with such boldness because of their intense dislike for organized Christianity with its rituals, creeds and clergy. This anti-clerical feeling, however, was not strong enough in England to produce a widespread militant deism. The established Church of England pursued a liberal latitudinarian policy which, as a mode of thought, tended to promote deism by emphasizing rational religion and minimizing revelation.

Whereas a vigorous anti-clericalism was for the most part lacking in eighteenth-century America and England, that was not the case in France and, consequently, in that country the destructive implications of the deistic philosophy were most fully developed. Here, the Catholic Church, as a great landholder and recipient of privileges, was closely associated with the rapidly decaying feudal order. Abuses were prevalent within the Church and liberal philosophers seized upon these to strike at the mighty Gallican establishment in the hope of reforming the old regime. They viewed with envy and alarm the political power exercised by the Jesuit order, which power they thought was being used to advance bigotry and intolerance. They became convinced that this was the case when the Protestant Calas was tortured to death (1761) and when, four years later, the headless body of a sixteen-year old boy, La Barre, was cast into the flames on the ground that he had mutilated crucifixes. It was then, and only then, that Voltaire in the name of Reason and Liberty called upon his friends, Diderot, D'Alembert and others, " to destroy the infamy " by discrediting the source of clerical power—the Bible. Although the Church opposed external divergences of opinion even to the extent of stamping them out, she was conveniently oblivious to latitudinarian views within her ranks where a goodly number of deistic Abbé Gaimes and relatively few atheistic Abbé Mesliers could be found.

Yet, French freethinkers, like Voltaire, if left to themselves, might never have fought Christianity. The logic of events more than personal convictions forced the sage of Ferney to take up the battle. The fiery Frenchman, who came in contact with deism during his English visit (1726-1729), was led to doubt the validity of the Christian revelation at a rather early age but really made no serious attack on it until he was seventy and then only because of clerical activities in reference to the Calas incident. In his *Treatise on Toleration,* issued at this time, he let the cat out of the bag by stating that he would have borne with the absurd dogmas of the Church had she tolerated differences of opinion; but since she refused to do so the tacit understanding between them was at an end. In Voltaire's view clerical intolerance led to bloodshed, and therefore if peace within society were to be preserved, ecclesiastical power had to be overthrown by exposing Christianity's assumption of divine origin.

Although Voltaire remained a deist throughout his life, when he finished saying what God was not, the Supreme Being had few positive attributes left. Thus, it was an easy matter for his more radical associates to deny God and a future state; in short, militant deism in France led straight to atheism. This was more than Voltaire had bargained for; in spite of his professed boldness, he refused to take the next logical step in this battle of negations. True to his deistic heritage, he sought to combat the " false " reason of atheism with the " right " reason of deism. His rationalistic arguments, defending the existence of God, were derived from design and necessity. To Voltaire, the harmonious order of nature proclaimed the presence of a benevolent, just and intelligent Maker who had created the universe and had given it the initial impetus. As to the contention that the world presented a clear picture of its having been designed by an intelligent Architect, eighteenth-century skeptics held that even if this argument were true, it proved only the existence of a Being superior to man, whose workmanship might be faulty in comparison with that of other worlds. In opposition to Voltaire's argument that an independent and external Being was needed to set the heavenly bodies in motion, the Baron d'Holbach contended that such a moving force was inherent in nature itself. Holbach further maintained that the tendency of deism to ascribe fixed attributes to God, as benevolence, justice and intelligence, was useless because no one could have definite ideas about a Being who did not act upon the senses. Moreover, such characterizations were not only futile but pernicious since they sought to perpetuate ignorance under the guise of knowledge.

Yet, despite these atheistic contentions, Voltaire and his deistic friends felt that they still held a trump in their hand of tricks—the ace of social utility. Most people, they argued were virtuous because they hoped to be rewarded, or feared to be punished, in a future life, a consideration conducive to social welfare. The future state obviously pre-supposed the existence of a just and wise Deity who dispensed with fine precision individual rewards and punishments. Remove the idea of God and you destroy a belief in an after-life and with it a potent check upon the mob. This was behind Voltaire's famous remark, " If God did not exist it would be necessary to invent him ". On the other hand, the atheists contended that men could be taught to do good and avoid evil through channels other than those of fear. They proposed a system of education and legislation designed to inculcate virtue; their chief, d'Holbach, significantly observed that if men were bad, they were made so and not born so.

Thus, whether in Europe or America, deism retained in the end the essentially cautious temper of eighteenth-century liberalism. In France, where its negations were most fully developed, atheism resulted. Confronted with so dangerous " an enemy to social welfare ", French deists, led by their chief, Voltaire, prudently called a halt to the vagaries of reason and finished by accepting God and a future state. In America, where the attack upon revealed Christianity was not as pronounced because of a relatively less intense anti-clericalism, most deistic advocates judiciously rendered lip-service to the cause of natural religion without explicitly assailing the divine origin of the Biblical revelation. When a few bolder spirits did so, they were bitterly assailed by the faithful. In the last analysis, then, deism proved too con-servative and compromising for the atheist and yet, in its destructive phase, too radical and unyielding for the Chris-tian; thus it eventually passed into the limbo of unfortunate causes attempting to steer a middle course. For the reader to understand the intellectual source of the American deistic movement as well as its direction relative to similar tendencies the world over, it is essential to examine its European background.

CHAPTER II

EUROPEAN BACKGROUND

ONE factor in the rise of deism during the colonial period was the importation of English rationalistic works. In the early eighteenth century, Jeremiah Dummer, an agent of the Connecticut colony, sent over to America seven hundred books, donated by Elihu Yale, Isaac Newton and others, which formed the basis for the Yale library. Among these volumes were some of the writings of Shaftesbury, a deist, and Tillotson, a believer in both rationalistic natural religion and revelation. During the same period, Thomas Hollis, a liberal Baptist in England, gave a large collection of writings to Harvard College among which were many tracts on religion. Similarly English theological works, especially those of Tillotson, were transported to Virginia for the benefit of the Anglican clergy of that colony. Before his death (1751), James Logan of Philadelphia, statesman, scholar and scientist, collected from two to three thousand books, most of which he had purchased in England and all of which he left to his native city.[1] While English rationalistic works were not widely circulated, it is evident that they found readers. The literary contributions of such defenders of the faith as Tillotson, Locke, Clarke and Cheyne as well as those of English deists, Herbert, Blount, Wollaston, Shaftesbury, Collins and Bolingbroke, were frequently re-

[1] Wright, *Literary Culture in Early New England* (New Haven, 1920), p. 186; Schneider, *The Puritan Mind* (New York, 1930), pp. 162, 193; Meade, *Old Churches, etc.* (Philadelphia, 1861), pp. 354-5; and Lamberton, *Colonial Libraries of Pennsylvania* (Pennsylvania Magazine of History and Biography, vol. 42, no. 3 [1918], pp. 210-11).

ferred to in colonial periodicals, books, sermons and library catalogues.[2]   Obviously these works promoted the growth of deism; on the one hand, the importation of English deistic books taught colonial freethinkers the principles of the new movement, while, on the other, the introduction of the writings of the rationalistic school of English theology, which subscribed to natural religion and the Christian revelation, gave American readers like Franklin an easy opportunity to accept the first and reject the second.

The lack of a vigorous anti-clericalism as well as common cultural ties caused colonial deists to adopt the generally mild tenor of the English movement.   Most of the advocates of

---

[2] For references to these men see *The American Magazine*, August, 1744, November, 1744 and February, 1745; T. Clap, *Essay on the Nature, etc.* (New Haven, 1765), pp. 31, 33; J. Edwards, *Works,* ed. S. L. Dwight (New York, 1830), vol. ii, p. 84; E. Gay, *Natural Religion, As Distinguish'd from Revealed* (Boston, 1759), pp. 13-5; S. Johnson, *Letter from Aristocles to Authades* (Boston, 1745), pp. 7, 13, 19; *Introduction to the Study of Philosophy* (New London, 1743), pp. 19, 28-9; W. Smith, *Discourses* (London, 1762), p. 43 (Appendix) ; W. Livingston, *Philosophical Solitude* (New York, 1747), p. 35; J. Adams, *Works*, ed. C. F. Adams (Boston, 1850), vol. ii, pp. 23, 105 and B. Franklin, *Writings*, ed. Smyth (New York, 1905-7), vol. x, p. 148. For the works of Tillotson see *Harvard Catalogue*, 1725 (in Wright, *op. cit.*, p. 294), *Yale Catalogue* (Clap, *A Catalogue of the Library of Yale College in New Haven* [New London, 1743], pp. 27, 34), *Library Company of Philadelphia* (Philadelphia, 1764), p. 5, Byrd, *Writings*, ed. Bassett (New York, 1901), p. 427, and Knox, *Catalogue* (Boston, 1773). For Locke consult Byrd, *op. cit.*, p. 442, *Harvard Catalogue* (in Wright, *op. cit.*, p. 294) and *Library Company of Philadelphia*, p. 5.   For Clarke and Cheyne see *Harvard Catalogue* (in Palfrey, *History of New England* [Boston, 1897], vol. i, p. 384, note), *Yale Catalogue* (in Clap, *op. cit.*, pp. 10, 22), Johnson, *Catalogue of my Library*, 1726 (MS.), *Library Company of Philadelphia*, p. 63 and Knox, *Catalogue*, p. 11. For Herbert, Blount and Wollaston see *Harvard Catalogue* (in Palfrey, *op. cit.*, vol. i, p. 384, note), Byrd, *op. cit.*, p. 428), *Yale Catalogue* (Clap. *op. cit.*, p. 22), *Library Company of Philadelphia*, p. 34. For Shaftesbury, Pope and Bolingbroke consult *Yale Catalogue* (Wright, *op. cit.*, p. 186 and Clap, *op. cit.*, p. 42), *Library Company of Philadelphia*, pp. 73, 91, 129 and Knox, *Catalogue*, pp. 7, 28.

the deistic philosophy in England contented themselves with setting forth the tenets of the religion of nature without seeking an authoritative foundation for them in the Biblical revelation. Only a few dared to reject explicitly the miracles and prophecies of Christ. From an historical viewpoint, English deism was an important link in a chain of thought starting from the Reformation. In place of the authority of the Catholic Church, the Protestants substituted that of the Bible and, during the century succeeding the Protestant Revolt, Hobbes and other thinkers insisted that the Scriptures be subjected to an historical and rational criticism. The deists went further and, as they thought, deeper. They asserted that the basis of authority was to be found in reason and in the rational beliefs, common to all men, to which it universally led. Among the first to adopt such a stand was Lord Herbert of Cherbury (1581-1648) who attempted to state what these universal principles were. In his work on the *Religion of the Gentiles with the Causes of their Errors,* he formulated five fundamental articles of faith. His creed consisted of a belief in (1) the existence of God; (2) His Worship; (3) the practice of virtue; (4) repentance of sin; and (5) a faith in immortality. Herbert held that these tenets were self-evident and were equally available to all ages and every country. This was due to the fact that they were based on the rational endowment of all men. Reason, too, was the test of the validity of all books professing to be revealed.[3] Similarly, Charles Blount (1654-1693), in his *Oracles of Reason,* written toward the close of the seventeenth century, was more interested in asserting the ethical basis of faith than in assailing Christianity. " . . . Our Religion", he wrote, " must necessarily be this, to do good to [His] Creatures; for therein we concur with the will of

---

[3] Herbert of Cherbury, *Religion of the Gentiles, etc.* (London, 1705), pp. 3-4, 255, 257, 263, 268, 299-302, 327-8, 333.

God. . . ." Moreover, he was a firm believer in reason, " the greatest gift of the Deity ". Deism was " a good manuring of a man's Conscience " and if sowed with Christianity, would " produce the most profitable Crop." [4]

The approach of Blount and Herbert, characteristic of seventeenth-century English deism, continued to mark the movement in the eighteenth. Toland, Tindal, Chubb and Wollaston sought to advance the cause of natural religion but made no real effort to examine the Christian revelation under the microscope of rationalistic science. Like Blount and Herbert, they were satisfied that the Scriptures were not necessary to establish the true principles of religion which could be determined by reason. Both Tindal and Chubb carefully identified deism with Christianity and pictured Jesus as the first great deistic preacher. Between the last decade of the seventeenth century and the middle of the eighteenth, only a few deists, notably Woolston and Collins, rejected this harmless approach and explicitly denied the truth of Biblical prophecies and miracles. The outstanding difference between the earlier deism of the seventeenth century and the later one of the eighteenth was that the latter was by far more fashionable. Its evident popularity was due to a variety of causes. The general acceptance after the " Glorious Revolution " of a policy of toleration, which afforded freethinkers an opportunity to express their views, was conducive to the spread of deism. Although Socinians and Catholics were denied the right to worship by the Toleration Act of 1689, this affected only a small minority. Moreover, the Press Licensing Act of 1662, which forbade the printing of heterdox books, was eventually allowed to lapse

---

[4] C. Blount, *Oracles of Reason* (London, 1693), pp. 92-3, 95. To the practice of virtue he added the two other tenets of the deistic creed, the existence of God and the immortality of the soul, *ibid.*, pp. 90-1, 122, 124-5.

during the reign of William III. Yet, because of the increased activity of deistic writers, a statute was passed in
1698 providing for the punishment of any person brought
up in the Christian faith who published, taught or spoke
any doctrines denying the Trinity, or the existence of God,
or the divine authority of the Bible. Under the provisions
of this act, deists, like Woolston and Annet, were imprisoned
and the latter was also pilloried for " insulting language ".[5]
Yet, the prosecution of these two men was exceptional, since
the British ruling classes were generally tolerant towards the
opponents of Christianity.

Another factor favorable to the spread of deism was the
Latitudinarian movement which originated in an attempt to
broaden the Anglican Church so as to admit to its communion
a large proportion of Non-Conformists. Latitudinarianism, however, was more than a Church policy; it was a mode
of thought which emphasized rational religion as a basis of
agreement and frequently tended to minimize the importance
of revelation. It was founded upon the two-fold conviction
that the greatest possible freedom of discussion should prevail as to non-essentials, and that the basic principles of
Christianity were few. Liberty of expression was advocated
because it was believed that no one generation or church had
fully attained divine truth. The net result of this rationalistic movement, in spite of the genuine piety of many of its
leaders, was to stress a secular and rationalistic religious
life at the expense of spiritual depth and fervour. Emphasizing reason and free inquiry, the Latitudinarians investi-

---

[5] Bury, *A History of Freedom of Thought* (New York, 1913), pp.
139-40; McGiffert, *Protestant Thought Before Kant* (New York, 1911),
p. 192; Overton and Relton, *English Church from the Accession of
George I to the End of the Eighteenth Century* (London, 1906), pp. 38-9;
and Stephen, *English Thought in the Eighteenth Century* (New York,
1902), vol. i, p. 89.

gated the Bible in order to ascertain the basic tenets of Christianity as well as the divine authenticity of the Scriptural revelation.   They found the essential articles of the Christian religion to be the same as those of the religion of nature. Consequently, they unconsciously popularized the positive side of the deistic faith.   Although resembling the deists in their advocacy of natural religion, the " Latitude men" differed from them in their acceptance of the validity of the Christian revelation.

John Tillotson (1630-1694), Archbishop of Canterbury, was representative of the moderate Latitudinarianism shared by many thoughtful and religious churchmen of the eighteenth century.   Although the deistical Collins asserted that Tillotson was the head of all freethinkers, the Anglican archbishop fought the deists with reasonable arguments.   His position was that of a rationalist who was ready to accept the tenets of natural religion but who held that these must be supplemented by the Christian revelation.   He defined the religion of nature as " obedience to Natural Law, and the performance of such duties as Natural Light, without any express and supernatural revelation, doth dictate to man. . . ."   Its articles consisted of a belief in God, in the immortality of the soul and the practice of virtue.   Natural religion, the basis of revealed faith, needed the aid of the Christian revelation in order to strengthen its moral precepts.   To Tillotson, the divine origin of Christianity was attested by its fulfillment of the prophecies of the Old Testament, by its miracles and by its consistency with the nature of God.[6]   John Locke (1632-1704) adopted the same Latitudinarian views as did his contemporary, the Archbishop of Canterbury.   In his *Reasonableness of Christianity,* the apologist of the " Glorious Revolution" attempted to prove

[6] J. Tillotson, *Works* (London, 1717), vol. i, pp. 346, 350, 450-1, 616-22, 775; vol. ii, pp. 116, 119-26, 377, 527 *et seq.*, 575.

that the Christian religion was rational and yet divinely confirmed. Locke held that two things were necessary for salvation: " faith and repentance, that is, believing Jesus to be the Messiah, and a good life. . . ." This two-fold doctrine was the basis of the Christian system which was wholly consistent with reason, since, if a person attempted to live virtuously and believed in the divinity of Christ, allowances would be made for his imperfections. Moreover, Locke was convinced that the miracles performed by Jesus and his disciples proved the divine origin of Christianity.[7]

Similarly, Samuel Clarke (1675-1729), a close student of the Newtonian science and of the Scriptures, argued that the supernatural revelation of Christianity was required to aid natural religion; that it was in accord with man's notions concerning God; and that it was composed of rational doctrines. Moreover, he contended that the truth of Christianity was evidenced by the character of its founder, his fulfillment of the Hebraic prophecies, his performance of miracles, and the testimony of his apostles. Clarke maintained that the deistic attack upon revelation was essentially destructive in tendency and that atheism was its logical outcome.[8] George Cheyne (1671-1743), a doctor of medicine and a Fellow of the Royal Society, was another Latitudinarian who was read in colonial America. His *Philosophical Principles of Religion: Natural and Revealed* (1715) " though containing nothing great or original ", was " evidently the work of a zealous and pious man [whose] application of mathematics to theology [was] . . . very strange and fantastic. . . ."[9]

[7] J. Locke, *Reasonableness of Christianity* (no place or date given), pp. 19, 21-2, 40.

[8] S. Clarke, *A Discourse concerning the Unchangeable Obligations of Natural Religion; and the Truth and Certainty of the Christian Revelation* (in Watson, *A Collection of Theological Tracts* [London, 1791], vol. iv, pp. 115-123, 207-8, 213-7, 241, 243-4, 253, 285-7).

[9] *Life of George Cheyne, M. D., etc.* (Oxford, 1846), pp. 18, 30.

In this treatise, Cheyne described the elements of Newtonian philosophy in order to instruct young minds in the tenets of natural religion.   The proofs of this faith were derived from the " several Parts of this admirable Fabrick of the Universe. . . ."   Since man, however, was living in a state of degeneracy, the Scotch doctor held that the notions of the religion of nature required the assistance of the Christian revelation.   He urged all men to imitate the life and doctrine of Jesus, which were conducive to the love of God and the practice of virtue.   He also argued that universal charity was best reflected in Christianity.[10]

Besides the Latitudinarian writings of Christian rationalists, the Newtonian cosmic philosophy and the empirical psychology of Locke contributed to the greater dissemination of the deistic philosophy.   The *Principia Mathematica* (1687) of Sir Isaac Newton was to the Age of Reason what the *Origin of Species* has been to our own.   To the great English scientist, the universe resembled an infinite cosmic ocean containing island planets held in place by natural laws. In this cosmic sea, revolving about the sun, was a relatively small planet inhabited by man.   The entire machine was created at one stroke by a brilliant Mastercraftsman who bestowed upon it a set of excellent edicts and who was able to fix and mend His Machine, if He felt it to be necessary. That God existed was a hypothesis regarded by the great Englishman as beyond doubt.[11]   This cosmic philosophy emphasized just that aspect of theology which the deists made

---

[10] G. Cheyne, *Philosophical Principles, etc.* (London, 1715), pp. 89, 98-9 (Part II).

[11] Newton, *Mathematical Principles of Natural Philosophy*, tr. Motte (London, 1803), vol. ii, pp. 311-2; Burtt, *Metaphysical Foundations of Modern Science* (London, 1925), pp. 230-7, 281-95; Randall, *Making of the Modern Mind* (Boston, 1926), pp. 257-60; O. Lodge, *Pioneers of Science* (London, 1893), pp. 161-7, 180-99; and Whitehead, *Science and the Modern World* (New York, 1925), pp. 65, 68.

central. It provided them with their concept of the Supreme Being as an Efficient Cause of the universe. Although they agreed with Newton as to the existence of God, they disagreed on His method of governing. Whereas the English physicist held that the great Mechanic could and would tinker with His machine to perform miracles, the deists rejected this contention on the ground that any such interference would imply divine imperfection. Secondly, the deistic picture of human nature was strongly coloured by the Newtonian philosophy. Since the English scientist had displayed the universality of natural laws, the deists were led to feel that religious principles were also all-pervading. Inasmuch as the Supreme Being acted always according to general edicts, why should men feel that He would reveal Himself to any particular group? To think that God did one thing in respect to nature and another in regard to man was considered unreasonable. The spread of the deistic philosophy was further stimulated by John Locke's analysis of knowledge. Interested in acquiring certain and accurate, instead of supposed information, the great English empiricist made a plea for reason against reliance on blind authority in his *Essay Concerning Human Understanding* (1690). In line with his general position, he rejected the doctrine of innate ideas because it would " take men off the use of reason and judgment and put them upon believing and taking upon trust without further examination." Even the idea that God existed was not innate but came to the mind as the result of reason built upon the solid foundation of experience. Reason was to be used especially in matters pertaining to religion in order to purge the latter of all absurdities and superstitions. The truths of Christianity, he held, were to be found in its Biblical revelation which ought to be freely investigated to ascertain whether its statements were according to, above, or contrary to reason. Like Locke, the deists were willing to reject everything in the Bible that was contrary to reason; but, unlike him, they were unwilling to accept anything in the Scriptures which was " mysterious " or above reason. In short, deistic thinkers, though taking their cue from the renowned " scientist of human nature ", went beyond him by refusing to subscribe to anything in the Christian revelation which was out of harmony with their own views as to what constituted reason.

Locke's suggestion of freely investigating the Bible in order to find out if its statements were according to, above, or contrary to reason was taken up by one of his professed disciples, John Toland. So objectionable was Toland's *Christianity Not Mysterious* (1696) that it was condemned to the flames by the Irish House of Commons and declared to be a nuisance by the Grand Jury of Middlesex. In this book " the first important representative of the [deistic] school " [12] argued that if any miracle contained a logical contradiction it was false and consequently was not to be regarded as part of Christianity. Anything beyond the reach of rationality was likewise not to be included, for whatever the Deity did not desire to reveal clearly was not worth knowing. A " fictitious " miracle, like the birth of Christ, being contrary to and above reason, was to be rejected.[13] Still more outspoken in his attack upon traditional Christianity was another disciple of Locke, Anthony Collins (1676-1729), whose *Discourse of the Grounds and Reasons of the Christian Religion* (1724) called forth thirty-five answers. A " gentleman by birth, education and fortune ", Collins was a sincere freethinker who was driven to attack the religion of his birth because of his intense dislike of clerical activities.

[12] J. H. Overton and F. Relton, *English Church from the Ascession of George I to the End of the Eighteenth Century*, p. 35.

[13] J. Toland, *Christianity Not Mysterious* (London, 1696), pp. 6, 124, 150, 152.

His hostility toward the priesthood was summarized in the words of Grotius whom he quoted as saying, " Ecclesiastical history consists of nothing but the wickedness of the governing Clergy." In order to strip the priestly classes of their pretensions to authority, he proposed to examine one of the props upon which the divine origin of the Christian religion itself was based—the argument from prophecy. He held that many of the predictions which Christianity was to fulfill, specifically in regard to the Messiahship of Jesus, could not possibly be accepted. For instance, Jesus did not fulfill literally the prophecy that " out of Egypt have I call'd my son ", although Matthew told the story of Christ being carried to that land. According to Collins, the quotation referred only to the calling of the children of Israel out of Egypt.[14] The argument from miracles was then subjected to a searching analysis by Thomas Woolston (1669-1733) in his six *Discourses on the Miracles of our Saviour* (1727-9). So popular were these tracts that three successive editions of them were made, each edition consisting of ten thousand copies.[15] Because of the "levity" of his work, Woolston, a former Fellow at Cambridge, was fined and imprisoned for blasphemy. To prevent the clergy from hiding behind " the Miracles of Our Saviour ", he proposed to show that from a literal viewpoint those miracles were " full of Absurdities, Improbabilities, and Incredibilities. . . ." According to Woolston, even the Church Fathers felt that the supernatural acts of Jesus could only be taken figuratively and that if they were not so interpreted, they were both foolish and harmful.[16] Thus, just as Collins had cast doubt on a

[14] A. Collins, *Discourse of the Grounds and Reasons of the Christian Religion* (London, 1724), pp. 46-7. See also pp. 40-6, 47-8.

[15] Voltaire, *Letters on the Christian Religion* (New York, no date), p. 30.

[16] For Woolston's examination of the various miracles of Jesus consult his *A Discourse on the Miracles of Our Saviour* (London, 1727), pp. 22-30, 32-50.

literal explanation of prophecies, so had Woolston done in reference to miracles. In view of the work of these two men, clergymen approached the subject of miracles and prophecies more cautiously.[17]

While Woolston and Collins were attempting to destroy Christianity by pulling down its structure of revelation, Tindal, Chubb and Wollaston were endeavoring " to save " it by pointing out those elements in the Christian faith which could be retained as true. Matthew Tindal (1657-1733), a Fellow at Oxford, was by far the most important writer of the deistic school; in fact, his work *Christianity as Old as the Creation* (1730) was regarded as " the deist Bible ". To Tindal, both revealed and natural religion aimed to advance " the honor of God and the good of Man . . .", but the former differed from the latter in that it was not founded upon the " Nature and Reason of things, but . . . on mere will and pleasure. . . ." If any revealed faith varied from natural religion even in the minutest detail that alone was sufficient to condemn it and make support of it ineffectual. Moreover, serious questions could be raised concerning the truth of revealed religion, since there was always the possibility that it had been falsified by its disciples and changed during the centuries. In short, the deistic religion of nature was superior to the accepted supernatural evidences of Christianity. Tindal urged that all Christians should attempt to rid their religion of superstitious additions so that the true religion of Jesus—the religion of nature—might be restored.[18] Tindal's desire to return to the simple teachings of Jesus was echoed by Thomas Chubb (1679-1747) in his *True Gospel of Jesus Christ Asserted* (1738). Unlike most of the deists, who were drawn from the aristocracy or the

---

[17] McGiffert, *Protestant Thought Before Kant*, p. 219.

[18] Tindal, *Christianity as Old as the Creation* (London, 1731), pp. 52, 60, 222-3.

bourgeoisie, Chubb was an artisan and his views were naturally a reflection of his background. His position was the practical stand of a worker who saw in the Gospel a simple and hopeful creed stripped of all speculative niceties.[19] Chubb argued that the unadorned teachings of Jesus had been perverted by an emphasis upon established beliefs, rites and ceremonies as well as by the growth of an ecclesiastical organization more interested in temporal than spiritual matters. The true gospel was simple and easy to follow. It consisted of three things: (1) the practice of an eternal rule of conduct based on reason; (2) a repentance of and reformation from sin; and (3) a belief in immortality. Thus, like Tindal, Chubb, fearful that " virtue and religion were in danger of being plucked by the roots " desired to save both by returning to the simple gospel of Jesus, a gospel founded on reason and warmed by love.[20] Simplicity in religion was likewise the message of William Wollaston (1659-1724), a well-to-do schoolmaster who had taken Anglican orders. In his *Religion of Nature Delineated*, he held that all sin was ultimately the result of fallacious logic. So firmly convinced was he that correct reasoning or truth was basic to faith that he made it the essence of natural religion. This he defined as " the pursuit of happiness by the practice of reason and truth. . . ." For those who did not receive their just deserts in this world, Wollaston provided a future state where all would be compensated for their goodness. As all transgression was ultimately error, so the substance of religion was the rational worship of God.[21]

[19] Abbey and Overton, *English Church in the Eighteenth Century*, pp. 202, 204.

[20] Chubb, *True Gospel of Jesus Christ Asserted* (London, 1738), pp. 18-9, 104-5, 140-1, 155, 164-5, 167-8, 181-2.

[21] Wollaston, *Religion of Nature Delineated* (London, 1738), pp. 25, 40, 52, 126, 203.

Shaftesbury, Pope and Bolingbroke were in entire harmony with the mild tone of English deism. These men were chiefly interested in the problem of morality and only casually concerned with that of revelation. In his very popular *Characteristics of Men, Manners, Opinions, Times,* Lord Shaftesbury (1671-1713) based the distinction of right and wrong upon reason which showed men the need of doing good not because of the fear of future punishments but because of the promotion of their own happiness. Although convinced that a future state was not needed to make the good virtuous, this liberal nobleman prudently held that such a concept was necessary to compel the generality of men to live morally. Under the title of Christianity, Shaftesbury included superstition and fanaticism. Furthermore, he declared that the more he pondered upon its mysteries the more heterodox his opinions became.[22] Without realizing it, Alexander Pope in his *Essay on Man* (1733) reproduced the deistic position of Shaftesbury. The son of a Roman Catholic father, the celebrated poet was reared among Catholics who encouraged him to write. With literary success in London, he became a member of the Scriblerus Club. At about this time, his friend, Bolingbroke, who was likewise a member of the same organization, suggested to Pope that he write a philosophic poem. This he consented to do and the result was his *Essay on Man,* the arguments of which were probably furnished by Bolingbroke. In this work, Pope held that virtue made for happiness which, in turn, consisted not only in the good of one but in the felicity of all. Although he agreed that good deeds were not always rewarded in this world, he felt that virtue was too noble an object to be rewarded in temporal goods. In fact, all was right in this best of all possible worlds where everything

[22] Shaftesbury, *Characteristics, etc.,* ed. J. M. Robertson (London, 1900), vol. i, pp. 27, 66, 72, 252-3, 255, 267, 270-4; vol. ii, p. 88.

fitted into its place, all " parts of one stupendous whole, whose body nature is, and God the soul." [23]   When Pope found that this poem was generally interpreted as an apology for freethinking, he was greatly alarmed and was very grateful to Warburton when the latter defended his orthodoxy.   To the " tuneful Pope " the politically conservative Bolingbroke (1678-1751) addressed his *Essays Philosophical and Theological,* which were collected and published after his death. Voltaire's charge that the English Viscount held " the Christian religion in horror " [24] was only partly true because Bolingbroke believed the gospel of Jesus to be worthy of high praise.   To him, it was founded on the principle of universal benevolence and consequently was in accord with the laws of nature.   Yet, the simple teachings of Christ were corrupted by a " motley crowd of Jews and heathens " who added " a leaven of . . . theology."   With these views he assailed organized Christianity with its priesthood and theological subtleties.[25]

The publication of Lord Bolingbroke's essays (1752-4) marked the peak of the deistic movement in England.   Up to the middle of the eighteenth century, deism had spread widely among rich and poor, learned and unlearned.   About 1750, an orthodox German traveler, citing the *British Magazine,* stated that half of the educated people of England were deists.   Some twenty years before, a proclamation by the college heads of Oxford lamented the progress of deism among the student body.[26]   In a like fashion, deistic specula-

---

[23] Pope, *Essay on Man* (in J. A. Richards, *Outline of Knowledge* [New York, 1924], vol. xi, pp. 295, 316, 318).

[24] Voltaire, *Letters on the Christian Religion,* p. 32.

[25] Bolingbroke, *Works,* ed. Mallet (London, 1754), vol. iv, pp. 193, 267-8, 275-6, 282, 394, 629.

[26] J. M. Robertson, *A Short History of Freethought* (New York, 1906), vol. ii, pp. 136, 166.

tion had made its way among the uncultured and poorer classes, as the work of Chubb during the decade of the 'thirties indicated. Although deistic literature was read during the latter half of the eighteenth century [27] and a group of freethinkers opened a short-lived deistic chapel in London (1776), deism ceased to be a dangerous rival of orthodoxy. It was, however, still fashionable among the upper classes who seemed to have effected a cautious and tacit compromise whereby aristocratic freethinkers might be allowed to let their friends know quite openly their opinions on revelation but might not be permitted to publish any book on such a matter.[28] Thus, deistic thought merely declined in importance after 1750; it had made much too profound an impression to disappear entirely.

The decline of deism in England was due to its failure to appeal to the people and to its middle-of-the-road character. The deistic approach was so cautious, its speculation so vague that the possibility of its ever becoming a mass movement was negligible. In place of Christianity, the deists had nothing to offer. They urged the people " to follow nature ", the guide of true religion. This indefinite call scarcely impressed the public mind which desired a definitive presentation and an explicit set of rules and beliefs. Such a message was offered by Wesley's evangelical movement which gathered momentum especially after 1740. Wesley addressed himself to the hearts and not the minds of men, and his followers, unlike their deistic rivals, worked among the new industrial classes instead of rendering lip-service to the gospel of humanity. Their activities in this respect probably did a great deal to prevent skeptical thoughts from lodging them-

[27] Bolingbroke was widely read as late as 1790, while the translation of Voltaire's works kept alive the deistic spirit.

[28] Benn, *History of English Rationalism in the Nineteenth Century* (London, 1906), vol. i, p. 210.

selves in the minds of men, women and children found itself confronted not only by emotionalism in religion but by extreme rationalistic skepticism. Such doubters as Hume felt that the deists were too moderate in their treatment of the questions of the existence of God and the immortality of the soul. Thus, deism, caught between two uncompromising currents, was unable to defend itself successfully against the attacks of either evangelists or extreme skeptics.[29]

From England, deistic speculation made its way to France under the guidance of Voltaire. French deism, unlike the English, was so militantly anti-Christian that it paved the way for the extreme skepticism of the atheistic d'Holbach group. The aggressive deistic assault upon Christianity was chiefly due to the prevalence of an intense anti-clericalism. In eighteenth-century France, the Catholic Church held a great deal of land and her clergy were considered members of the privileged order, the First Estate. Her bishops, archbishops and abbots, drawn from the nobility, lived in ease and magnificence in direct contrast to conditions prevalent among the lowly curates. The abuses within the Church were seized upon by liberal philosophers, who, in the hope of reforming the old regime, hammered away at one of its most important props. French thinkers especially viewed with envy and alarm the political power exercised by the Jesuits whom they bitterly assailed. During the reign of Louis XV, the Society of Jesus was opposed not only by the philosophical party but also by Jansenists and Gallicans. Unlike the Jesuits, the former believed in the doctrine of conversion-by-the-will-of-God, while the latter claimed that the pope

[29] Benn, *History of English Rationalism in the Nineteenth Century,* vol. i, pp. 176-7; Abbey and Overton, *English Church in the Eighteenth Century,* pp. 236-7; and McGiffert, *Rise of Modern Religious Ideas* (New York, 1921), pp. 22-3, 41.

ght to depose or interfere with temporal rulers and that in spiritual matters a general council of bishops was superior to the pontiff. The struggle between these two groups and the Jesuits tended to undermine ecclesiastical and civil authority as well as religious beliefs. Much to the satisfaction of Jansenists and Gallicans Louis XV eventually suppressed the Jesuit order. The king's action was also hailed by the philosophical party which saw in it a victory for enlightenment and a defeat for bigotry. During the eighteenth century, the church naturally frowned upon external divergences of opinion and was even willing to take aggressive steps to stamp these out. Yet, she was conveniently oblivious to latitudinarian views within her ranks. Inside of the Church, a goodly number of Abbé Gaimes could be found from whom eager Rousseaus could learn their deistic lessons. Again, the Gallican establishment harbored some atheistic priests, men like the Abbé Meslier, who, during the French Revolution, was described in a decree of the National Convention as "the first priest who had the courage and honesty to abjure religious errors."

The deistic speculation of Voltaire, most renowned exponent of French deism, represented essentially a cautious compromise based on common sense. During his three-year stay in England (1726-29), the French thinker came in contact with the science of Newton, the psychology of Locke and the militant deism of Collins and Woolston; all of which he brought back to and popularized in France. Although in his *Letters on the English* and in his numerous novels, Voltaire showed his deistic leanings it was not until the Calas affair that he, then almost seventy, proposed to prove the invalidity of the Christian revelation and thereby destroy the base upon which clerical authority rested. Up to this time, Voltaire was willing to compromise with the Church even to the extent of enduring her "absurd" creeds and ceremonies. In return he asked only one thing of her and that was the practice of tolerance. When she flouted this in the case of Jean Calas, Voltaire decided to take the offensive. His *Treatise on Toleration,* written during this period, was followed up with a Niagara of pamphlets, histories, catechisms, dialogues, fables and sermons assailing the authenticity and reliability of the Bible upon which the Church rested her claim of divine power. In these works, Voltaire made no fine distinctions between Christianity and the Christian Church. Never vague, he openly declared that whereas it had taken twelve men to plant the Christian religion, it would only take one to destroy it. Representing the universe as a vast machine and mankind as " a very little thing ", he repudiated miracles as contrary to natural laws. Moreover, the supernatural acts attributed to Jesus were not superior to those performed by the ancients. Furthermore, Voltaire argued that the establishment of Christianity was accompanied by the introduction of intolerance and the rejection of such " a just man " as Jesus who himself was ill-treated " by envious doctors, and condemned to die by prejudiced magistrates." Holding that theological beliefs were conducive to bigotry, he vented his spleen upon them and charged that they led to atheism by concocting " the most absurd ideas of God." [30]

Voltaire's opposition to atheism was as intense as his hostility toward organized Christianity. To him, common sense dictated the existence of an intelligent Being who was responsible for the creation of the harmonious order of nature. Beyond the view that God existed, Voltaire came to no definite metaphysical conclusions. Always practical, he

[30] F. M. A. deVoltaire, *Philosophical Dictionary* (London, 1765), pp. 24-5, 87, 232-4, 280, 282, 314; *Romances,* ed. Komroff (New York, 1928), pp. 47, 125; *Toleration and Other Essays,* tr. McCabe (New York, 1912), p. 101; and *Letters on the Christian Religion,* p. 33.

refused " to waste his time " upon the problem of reconciling immutable natural laws with free will and contented himself with the common-sense reply that men possessed some liberty. In a like fashion, he at first satisfied himself with the consoling " tout est bien " philosophy in answer to the disconcerting question of how evil could prevail in spite of the existence of a good God.   However, the Lisbon earthquake in 1755 led him to reject this rather convenient response.   Faced by the old dilemma that God can prevent evil and will not, or He wishes to prevent it and cannot, Voltaire floundered about and ended by stripping the Deity of all His positive attributes. This led the less cautious Diderot and d'Holbach to the logical conclusion that the time had come to end the " myth " of God.   Such was the message of the latter in his *System of Nature* (1770), a book which was bitterly assailed by the thoroughly frightened Voltaire who felt that if the idea that God existed was done away with, the concept of a future state would likewise have to go.   This would mean the removal of a powerful check upon the actions of the " canaille " who chiefly did good either because they hoped to be rewarded or feared to be punished.   Thus, the prudent Voltaire concluded that if God did not exist, it would be necessary to invent Him.   To the atheists, this was common sense with a vengeance.

Voltaire was read in America especially after 1763.   His *Philosophical Dictionary, Letters on the English* and *Candide* were sold in Boston, New York and Albany.   At the same time, they were at the disposal of the members of New York and Philadelphia library societies.[31]   An interest in

---

[31] Voltaire's works were sold in Boston by Cox and Berry (*Catalogue*, 1776, probable date, p. 27) ; Blake (*Catalogue*, 1796, p. 41) ; and Knox (*Mass. Hist. Proceedings*, vol. lxi, p. 256) ; in New York by Rivington (*Mass. Hist. Proceedings*, vol. lxi, p. 256) ; Gaine (*Catalogue*, 1792, p. 14) ; and Berrian (*Catalogue*, 1803, p. 40) ; and in Albany by Thomas, Andrews

the treatises of the cynical Frenchman was reflected not only in library catalogues but also in newspaper advertisements and magazine articles. His writings were announced in the journals of Philadelphia, New York, Providence, New Haven and Baltimore,[32] while magazines discussed his life and conduct. Unsympathetic character studies of Voltaire appeared in numerous magazines [33] as well as anecdotes concerning his life.[34] The death of the great freethinker especially appeared to be of interest to Americans who desired to know whether he had been buried as a deist or a Christian. Newspaper and magazine articles appeared to agree that Voltaire died denying the divinity of Jesus.[35] His writings as well as his life were scrutinized and evaluated by American

and Penniman (*Catalogue*, 1798, probable date, p. 22). See also the *Library Co. Philadelphia Catalogue* 1770 and the *N. Y. Society Library Catalogue*, 1789. As early as 1771, Ezra Stiles was reading Voltaire's *Philosophical Dictionary* (E. Stiles, *Literary Diary*, ed. Dexter [New York, 1901], vol. i, p. 181).

[32] *Pennsylvania Journal and Weekly Advertiser*, July 6, 1769 (no. 1387); *The New York Journal*, December 22, 1768 (no. 1355); *The Providence Gazette, etc.*, May 7, 1785 (no. 1114); *The Connecticut Journal*, September 22, 1784 (no. 882); and the *Maryland Gazette or Baltimore Advertiser*, February 3, 1786 (no. 179).

[33] *The Pennsylvania Magazine*, January, 1775, vol. i, pp. 19-20; *The Boston Magazine*, July, 1784, vol. i, pp. 361-3; *The American Apollo*, April 20, 1792, vol. i, p. 171; *The American Universal Magazine*, August 7, 1797, vol. iii, pp. 204-6; and the *General Assembly's Missionary Magazine, etc.*, September, 1805, vol. i, pp. 455-6.

[34] *The Connecticut Journal*, Jan. 19, 1785 (no. 899); *The Moral and Sentimental Magazine*, July 3, 1797, vol. i, p. 24; and the *Literary Museum or Monthly Magazine*, Feb., 1797, p. 99.

[35] For newspaper narratives see *The Country Journal and Poughkeepsie Advertiser*, August 5, 1788 (no. 157) and the *Oriental Trumpet, etc.*, November 21, 1799. For magazine accounts refer to *The Boston Magazine*, July, 1784, vol. i, pp. 362-3; *The Columbian Magazine*, August, 1788, vol. ii, pp. 446-7; and the *General Assembly's Missionary Magazine, etc.*, January, 1806, vol. ii, pp. 30-2. Consult also, S. Payson, *Proofs of the Real Existence, etc.* (Charlestown, 1802), pp. 60-1.

critics.   While the aggressively anti-Christian Elihu Palmer
held that Voltaire was " entitled to the universal gratitude
and applause of the human race . . ." for having destroyed
"error by wholesale . . .", the more cautious John Adams
believed him to be " a little cracked."   In *The American
Museum, or Repository* for July 1792, a reviewer warned
his readers not " to cultivate any close acquaintance with so
erroneous and seductive an author."

The approach of Jean Jacques Rousseau toward revelation was more in harmony with the generally mild tenor of
American deism than was that of Voltaire.   Unlike his
skeptical contemporary, the citizen of Geneva approached the
problem of religion through the conscience and not the reason
of man.   The existence of God could not be demonstrated
like a geometric proposition but was traced upon every
heart in letters that could never be effaced.   " He remains at
an equal distance from my senses and my understanding ";
wrote Rousseau, " the more I think of him, the more am I
confounded . . . I feel him. . . ."   Moreover, unlike Voltaire, Rousseau's attitude toward Christianity was one of
reverential awe.   In his *Profession of Faith of a Savoyard
Vicar*,[36] the author of *Emile* said that the greatest works of
philosophy paled into insignificance besides the Gospels.
True enough, the New Testament contained contradictions
but before these one was to remain ever " modest and cir-
cumspect: [to] regard in silence what cannot be either dis-
proved or comprehended, to humble [one's self] before the
Supreme Being, who alone knows the truth. . . ."   To
Rousseau, the essence of religion was the worship of God
and therefore creeds based on books, prophecies and miracles

[36] The Abbé Gaime was the source of Rousseau's inspiration.   From
this clergyman the good Jean Jacques learned "lessons of pure morality"
which were "as so many seeds of virtue and religion."   Rousseau, *Confessions*, Hedouin Edition (London, no date), bk. i, pp. 79-81.

were of secondary importance. If Christians attempted to prove the validity of their own revelation, Jews and Mohammedans would do likewise. In the end people would not know which to follow. Thus, away with " artificial faith ", let men follow the correct path of natural religion.[37] On the whole, Rousseau's skepticism was superior to the biting mockery of Voltaire which only irritated all who were seriously religious. Yet, Rousseau's emotional approach gave the orthodox a weapon which they could equally brandish over the heads of atheists and deists. To the atheistic denial of God as well as to the deistic rejection of the Christian revelation the faithful could easily reply, " We believe! "

The prudent skepticism of Rousseau was more acceptable to American deists than the militant freethinking of Voltaire. In 1765, John Adams referred to Rousseau as an " opponent of feudalism "; by 1771 and 1772, the *Emile* was sold in South Carolina, Virginia, Pennsylvania and New York.[38] Anecdotes in praise of the " sublime Author of the Emilius " appeared in Philadelphia and Baltimore periodicals, while his literary qualities were likewise reviewed in the magazines of the period.[39] *The Amercan Museum, or Repository* for July 1792, however, contained an article which suggested that, while Rousseau should be read, he was not to be taken too seriously because he was an enemy of revelation. *The Connecticut Evangelical Magazine* for

---

[37] Rousseau, *Emilius and Sophia* (London, 1783), vol. ii, pp. 267-8; vol. iii, p. 49; *Profession of Faith of a Savoyard Vicar* (New York, 1889), pp. 34-5, 38, 56, 61, 64, 74-5, 76.

[38] B. Faÿ, *Revolutionary Spirit in France and America* (New York, 1928), p. 40 and L. Rosenthal, *Rousseau in Philadelphia* (*Magazine of American History*, vol. xii, pp. 51-2).

[39] *The Boston Magazine*, April, 1784, vol. i, p. 220; *The American Universal Magazine*, May 15, 1797, vol. ii, p. 224; and the *Baltimore Weekly Magazine*, July 19, 1800, p. 97.

August 1800 was willing to admit that the Frenchman had praised Jesus very highly but felt that if he had remained an unbeliever to the end, " the pangs of an accusing conscience [would] form a state of future misery equal to the highest descriptions of the Christian scriptures." Naturally American deists used Rousseau to further their cause and consequently they reprinted his *Profession of Faith of a Savoyard Vicar.*[40]

Comte de Volney (1757-1820) was more outspoken in his rejection of Christianity than was Rousseau. A member of the Estates-General and Constituent Assembly, he achieved a reputation as a savant through the appearance of his *Ruins: or a Survey of the Revolutions of Empires* (1791). Like Voltaire, he was moved by so bitter an anticlerical feeling that he rejected the Christian revelation and predicted the final union of all religions by the recognition of the common truth underlying them. In 1795, he came to America where he remained for two years. Here he was immediately assailed by the Unitarian Priestley then living in Philadelphia. So well was Volney's work received in America that along with Paine's *Age of Reason* it was said " to unchristianize " thousands. As a significant contribution to the rise of a more militant deistic movement in the new Republic, it will be more fully discussed in its proper place.[41] Two years after the publication of the *Ruins,* the atheistic Hébertists were praying before the altar of the Goddess of Reason, a ceremony which shocked Robespierre into proclaiming the Worship of the Supreme Being.[42] This

[40] *Prospect, or View of the Moral World* from May 5, 1804 (no. 22) to November 17, 1804 (no. 50).

[41] See chapter v, pp. 126-7.

[42] Robespierre's speech on the Supreme Being delivered on June 8, 1794 was reported in American newspapers. See chapter v, pp. 146-7.

struggle between the atheistic Hébert and the deistic Robespierre was symbolic of the battle deism had to fight in the intellectual circles of pre-Revolutionary France where its " real " enemy was the atheism of the d'Holbach group.

CHAPTER III

RISE OF DEISM IN COLONIAL AMERICA (1713-1763)

BESIDES the importation of European rationalistic works, the introduction of Newtonian science paved the way for the rise of deistic speculation in colonial America. The representation of the universe as a vast machine set in motion by an Efficient Cause and run according to immutable natural laws was reflected in the literature of the provincial period. In Calvinistic circles, the conservative Cotton Mather was amazed and charmed by the thought of an infinite universe with countless globes kept in place by the law of universal gravity, while Jonathan Dickinson, President of the College of New Jersey, praised "the glorious art and contrivance of [this] admirable frame of nature. . . ." The liberal-minded Mayhew, a Boston preacher, wrote likewise of the regularity, beauty and harmony of the natural. A young deist, Franklin, noted the insignificance of "this little ball on which we move. . . ." Some twenty-eight years later, John Adams, who in his youth showed deistic inclinations, wrote that the "solar system [was] but one very small wheel in the great, the astonishing machine of the world. . . ." In a like fashion, the influence of the Newtonian cosmography showed itself in Anglican surroundings. Samuel Johnson, President of King's College, saw a world system of fixed stars and our own sun "with his noble and splendid Chorus of Planets, Satellites and Comets. . . ." To William Smith, described by Ezra Stiles as "a consummate Hypocrite in Religion and Politics", it appeared ridiculous to watch "the atom-lords of this atom world . . . strut about in pride. . . ." [1]

[1] C. Mather, *Christian Philosopher* (London, 1721), pp. 16, 18, 21, 81-2;

54

The *Principia Mathematica* and popular tracts explaining it occupied a prominent place on the shelves of colonial libraries.[2] One provincial scholar, Cadwallader Colden, even proceeded to criticize and enlarge upon it. American students were advised by Mather and Johnson to read Newton, "our perpetual dictator. . . ." Clap, Rector of Yale, described the celebrated Englishman as a "great Genius", while the poetic Livingston, who was later to become Governor of New Jersey, sang of the "Immortal Newton; whose illustrious name will shine on records of eternal fame."[3] Since the Newtonian system was based on the Copernican theory, the latter was generally accepted; in 1714, Mather was preaching it from his Boston pulpit much to the distress of Samuel Sewall who thought that it was distinctly out of place. The Copernican theory was popularized in colonial almanacs, while the writings of its chief exponents, Brahe, Kepler, Galileo, Descartes, Boyle and Whiston were either to be found in provincial libraries or referred to in the litera-

J. Dickinson, *Reasonableness of Christianity* (Boston, 1732), pp. 17-9, 25, 27-8; J. Mayhew, *Two Sermons, etc.* (Boston, 1763), pp. 27, 41; B. Franklin, *Works*, ed. Sparks (Boston, 1836), vol. ii, pp. 1-2; J. Adams, *Works*, ed. C. F. Adams (Boston, 1850), vol. ii, p. 15; S. Johnson, *Introduction to the Study of Philosophy* (New London, 1743), p. 18; and W. Smith, *Discourses* (London, 1762), pp. 84-6 (Appendix).

[2] *Yale Catalogue*, 1714 (in Wright, *Literary Culture in Early New England*, p. 185) and 1743 (in Clap, a *Catalogue of Yale College*, p. 10); *Johnson Catalogue* (MS.), 1726; *Byrd Catalogue* (in Bassett, *Writings of William Byrd, etc.*, p. 441) and the *Library Co. of Philadelphia Catalogue*, 1764, p. 51. For works used to explain Newton see Byrd (in Basset, *op. cit.*, p. 436) and the *Library Co. of Philadelphia Catalogue*, 1764, pp. 33, 93.

[3] T. Clap, *Essay on the Nature and Foundation of Moral Virtue* (New Haven, 1765), p. 46; S. Johnson, *Introduction to the Study of Philosophy*, p. 28; W. Livingston, *Philosophic Solitude* (New York, 1747), p. 39; and C. Mather, *Student and Preacher, etc.* (London, 1789), p. 125. See also the *American Magazine*, January, 1745, for an account of Newton's life, pp. 9-18.

ture of the period.[4] As in England and France, so in America, the Newtonian cosmic philosophy furnished the deists with their central concept of God as a Passive Policeman. From this view, it was intellectually very easy to rule out miracles altogether, a position which was adopted by the champions of the new dispensation and which marked a significant deviation from the teachings of their professed Master. In still another way, American deists used the work of the English scientist to advance their own views. Newton had demonstrated that the Supreme Being always acted according to general edicts. Then why, asked the deists, should men feel that He should reveal Himself to any particular group and therefore do one thing in respect to Nature and another thing in regard to man? The advent of colonial deism was further made possible by the empirical psychology of Locke. Like Newton's *Principia Mathematica,* Locke's *Essay Concerning Human Understanding* had a great vogue in provincial America. It was listed in library catalogues and frequently alluded to in literary works.[5] By making

[4] N. Ames, *Astronomical Diary,* 1733 (Boston, 1733); J. Taylor, *Pennsilvania,* 1743 (Philadelphia, 1743); *Harvard Catalogue,* 1723 (in Wright, *op. cit.,* pp. 272, 279, 289); *Yale Catalogue,* 1743 (in Clap, *op. cit.,* pp. 8, 10); Byrd, *Catalogue* (in Bassett, *op. cit.,* pp. 436, 441); Lee Library, 1694; *Sharpe Catalogue,* 1713 (in N. Y. Hist. Collections for 1880 (New York, 1881), p. 362; *Library Co. of Philadelphia Catalogue,* 1764, p. 57; *Johnson Catalogue* (MS.), 1726; Mather, *Student and Preacher,* pp. 125, 128; *Christian Philosopher,* pp. 20, 44, 227; S. Johnson, *Introduction, etc.,* p. 29; and W. Nadir, *Mercurius Novanglicanus,* 1743 (Boston, 1743).

[5] *Yale Catalogue,* 1714 (in Wright, *op. cit.,* p. 185) and 1743 (in Clap, *op. cit.,* p. 5); and *Johnson Catalogue,* 1726 (MS.). Both Franklin and Adams possessed copies of the work. (B. Franklin, *Writings,* ed. Smyth, vol. x, p. 149 and J. Adams, *Works,* ed. C. F. Adams, vol. ii, p. 88). References were made to the essay by T. Clap, *Essay on the Nature, etc.,* p. 25; J. Edwards, *Works,* ed. S. L. Dwight, vol. ii, p. 207; J. Dickinson, *Reasonableness of Christianity,* p. 15; C. Chauncy, *Benevolence of the Deity* (Boston, 1784), pp. 92, 97-100; and S. Johnson, *Introduction, etc.,* pp. 8, 27.

reason the final standard of appeal, Locke supplied American deists with a weapon which could be used to destroy the validity of the Biblical evidences.

With the introduction of the new science and psychology as well as with the importation of English rationalistic works, a critical attitude emerged in Calvinistic and Anglican circles. In the former, an attack was made upon Puritan theology which ended in the rise of a deistic literature implicitly anti-Christian. From 1691 to 1763, the Puritan tradition in Massachusetts was considerably weakened. The participation of the ministry in the unfortunate Salem tragedy of 1692 tended to lessen clerical influence. It furnished liberals with an ever-handy citation designed to illustrate the dangers of ecclesiastical bigotry and superstition. At the opening of the eighteenth century, Cotton Mather, who played a prominent role in the Salem affair, feeling the power slipping from "the hands of godly men", attempted to protect the theocratic heritage of the Bay colony by advocating a closer union of the churches. In 1705, he proposed the formation of ministerial associations which were to give pastors advice, license clerical candidates and examine all charges against clergymen. Furthermore, Mather suggested that lay and ministerial delegates to these associations were to constitute standing councils to consider all matters arising within their limits. All decisions of these councils were to be final. These proposals, however, encountered opposition not only in Massachusetts but also in England where the Puritan commonwealths were especially unpopular. When it was suggested that a synod be called to determine church policies, the home government refused to consent. Imperial intervention not only dashed the hopes of the Mathers but also secured concessions for those dissenting from the Congregational order. By an act of 1727, Anglicans were allowed limited exemption in the Bay Colony. Although ministerial rates were to be collected as usual, the money of those who lived within five miles of an Anglican Church was to be turned over by the collectors to Anglican ministers. In 1728 and 1729, Quakers were likewise exempted provided they attended Church on Sunday, lived within five miles of a place of worship and declared their faith in the divine inspiration of the Bible and the Trinitarian doctrine.[6]

In Connecticut, the old order was more firmly entrenched. With the Church and State working together, a plan of " Consociation " similar to that of the Mathers was adopted. In 1708, the Saybrook Synod drew up a scheme which provided for the organization of the Congregational Churches through associations and consociations. The former were composed of pastors and elders in a rather extended territory, while the latter were unions of churches within more limited areas. In the same year, a Toleration Act was passed which cautiously declared that nothing in the act was to be interpreted to the prejudice of the established church or to the exclusion of any person from paying any ministerial or town dues, as might thereafter be requested. This Toleration Act was of little benefit to the Baptists, Quakers or Anglicans who as they increased in numbers demanded and worked for a greater degree of freedom. In 1727, Anglican churchmen were exempted from the payment of taxes used in the building of churches. Two years later, exemption was granted to the Baptists and Quakers. This, however, did not mean toleration for dissenters; in 1742, the Act of 1708 was temporarily repealed, only to be put in force again in 1760.[7]

[6] S. M. Reed, *Church and State in Massachusetts*, 1691-1740 (University of Illinois Studies in the Social Sciences, vol. iii, no. 4, Dec., 1914), pp. 132, 135, 139, 180, 185, 189; and W. Walker, *History of the Congregational Churches in the United States* (New York, 1884), pp. 202-4.

[7] M. L. Greene, *Rise of Religious Liberty in Connecticut* (Boston, 1905), pp. 138-43, 147, 154.

The outstanding event in the religious history of provincial New England was the Great Awakening. It began in 1734 with the preaching of Jonathan Edwards in the town of Northampton, Massachusetts. A few years later, this work was reenforced by the great Methodist preacher, George Whitefield. Both men attempted to draw individuals from the surface aspects of traditional dogma and formal observance to a deeper spiritual experience. The Great Awakening brought out two important tendencies in religious thought, both of which worked against the old Puritan system. One group, swept away by the emotional appeal of the evangelists, broke away from the established churches. The " New Lights " were bitterly assailed by a group of rationalists who drew their strength from the sophisticated society of the older towns. Some of these men, like Wigglesworth, were firm believers in the old ecclesiastical order, while others, like Chauncy, reacted strongly against some of the main tenets of orthodox Calvinism. Yet, both conservatives and liberals vigorously assailed "enthusiasm". In his *Seasonable Thoughts on the State of Religion in New England* (1743), Charles Chauncy, a Boston clergyman, called upon his clerical associates to eradicate such " dangerous " tendencies as itinerant preaching, "uncomfortable . . . Animosities " and physical agitations or " extraordinaries ". In order to check the revivalistic trend, he proposed that the " New Lights " be excluded from the pulpits of organized churches, that ministerial candidates be examined, and that certain basic doctrines be accepted after a rational investigation. He bitterly denounced the work of Whitefield as " a Dishonour to true Religion. . . ." Wigglesworth likewise condemned evangelicalism by asserting that it was subversive of Christianity, since every man imagined that any thought, which he strongly felt, came from God, although he had no proof of it.[8]

[8] Chauncy, *Seasonable Thoughts on the State of Religion in New*

The rationalistic movement was, for the most part, liberal in tendency; it criticized the principal tenets of the orthodox Puritan creed—original sin, predestination and, finally, the doctrine of the Trinity. It sought to humanize faith by representing the Deity as a benevolent Being and man as a responsible agent. According to contemporary accounts, its anti-Calvinistic or so-called " Arminian " teachings circulated in Cambridge, Northampton and other prominent Massachusetts towns. In the case of Cambridge, these reports seem to be somewhat exaggerated; at least, up to the Revolution Harvard was far from being liberal. An able scholar, Christie, has shown that, during the early eighteenth century, the fears of the Mather family concerning the progress of " Arminianism" at Harvard were groundless. In 1724, Cotton Mather felt that students at the Cambridge seat of learning were reading books fit for " Satan's library ". Yet, these works were indeed harmless; they were satanic only in so far as they were secular. About two years later, the same clergyman was unable to detect a single Congregational minister who entertained " Arminian " views. The college authorities at Harvard attempted to preserve the orthodoxy of their pupils. The overseers asserted the right to examine the theological views of the instructional staff and it was indeed an innovation for them to approve the appointment of John Winthrop without examination. Wigglesworth, the first professor to occupy the Hollis chair of divinity, was questioned by Leverett and Colman. The latter was no latitudinarian in theology; in fact, in 1732, he begged a New London clergyman to vindicate Yale from the aspersion of " Arminianism." Moreover, during the provincial period, the " pious youths " of the college were taught theology by such men as

England (Boston, 1743), pp. 36-40, 55, 78, 334, 336, 340-1, 397, 414-5, 422-4; and Wigglesworth, *A Letter to the Reverend Mr. George Whitefield, etc.* (Boston, 1745), pp. 3-4, 6.

Wigglesworth, Flynt and Holyoke, all of whom were " free from liberalism." Although the latitudinarian works of Tillotson and Clarke were to be found in the Harvard library, students did not take them out. Tillotson was not drawn out for nine years (1732-1741) and Clarke for two (1739-1741). Even though Locke was used as a textbook, all the other basic texts were orthodox.[9] Furthermore, Christie has shown that up to the middle of the eighteenth century there were few, if any, " Arminian " ministers in the Congregational Churches of New England. The moment anyone was suspected of " Arminianism," life was made so uncomfortable that, as in the case of Benjamin Kent of Marlborough, resignation from the pulpit resulted. Again, with the exception of Experience Mayhew's *Grace Defended* (1744), no " Arminian " book was published in America prior to 1749.[10]

Yet, from the middle of the eighteenth century onward, liberal doctrines became more current; they were preached by Gay, Briant and Mayhew at Hingham, Braintree and Boston. Ebenezer Gay, pastor at Hingham, was one outstanding New Englander who held opinions clearly outside of and distinct from Calvinism. In full sympathy with the rationalistic spirit of his age, he desired free inquiry and was opposed to all creeds. In 1759, Gay, a Dudleian lecturer at Harvard, addressed the undergraduate body on *Natural Religion as Distinguish'd from Revealed.* He defined the former as anything which reason alone discovered and the latter as anything which God had made known to man through immediate inspiration or prophetic teachings. The religion of nature consisted in adoring God and in helping His creatures. It was, however, in need of the Christian

[9] F. A. Christie, *The Beginnings of Arminianism in New England* (Papers of the American Society of Church History, 2nd ser., vol. iii, pp. 154-9).

[10] *Ibid.*, vol. iii, pp. 160-2, 165.

revelation because the reason of the average man was not equal to the task of discovering it.   Yet, if the evidences of Christianity were inconsistent with "the possibility of things", they were to be discarded.[11]   Lemuel Briant, pastor of the First Church in Braintree, also reacted against the traditional Calvinism of his day and repudiated the accepted doctrine of predestination.   He regarded "the pure and perfect Religion of Jesus" as built upon the assumption that man was a responsible agent whose happiness depended upon his personal actions.   To disparage moral goodness was to promote "infidelity", to encourage vice and to remove divine comfort.   The very aim of God was to advance the happiness of man.   Although Briant realized that his position was conducive neither to "popular Applause nor priestly Favours", he felt that if his stand was true, it would endure forever.[12]

The reaction against traditional Puritanism was revealed not only in the writings of Briant and Gay but also in those of Mayhew and Chauncy.   Influenced by Clarke and the milder English deists, Jonathan Mayhew, who, according to John Adams, "was a smart man, but embraced some doctrines not generally approv'd", sought to advance the cause of tolerance and rationalism.   To the Boston clergyman, the Deity ruled according to the standards of benevolence and wisdom.   The Creator was to be obeyed not through fear but through love.   His belief in divine goodness caused him to reject the idea that a majority of mankind was condemned to everlasting torments.   Moreover, Mayhew held that man was responsible for all his moral actions and was answerable

---

[11] E. Gay, *Natural Religion, As Distinguish'd from Revealed* (Boston, 1759), pp. 6-7, 21-2, 29-30 and Cooke, *Unitarianism in America* (Boston, 1902), pp. 58-60.

[12] Briant, *Absurdity and Blasphemy of Depretiating Moral Virtue* (Boston, 1749), pp. 7-8, 27-8, 30-1.

to God alone. He entertained the highest regard for the
teachings of Christianity whose good ends were " clearly
discernible. . . ." [13] Charles Chauncy carried on the work
of Mayhew. He was well versed in the deistic speculation
of England and clearly reflected the rationalistic, humani-
tarian and freedom-loving spirit of the new liberalism. Convinced that the Deity was the epitome of love, he rejected
the doctrine of the eternal damnation of sinners as contrary
to the divine scheme. Man had the capacity to do good,
and thus, to attain happiness. These doctrines sounded
strange, to say the least, in a Calvinistic pulpit and, for a time,
Chauncy hesitated to declare them openly. When he did
so, he was bitterly assailed. Some of the faithful described
him as a deist, while others, like Stiles of Yale, though rejecting this description, quite willingly granted that this
" Learned Character " possessed " some Singularities in
Theology. . . ." [14]

While these New Englanders were rejecting Puritan
beliefs but accepting the Christian revelation, others—
Franklin, Hawley, Adams and Bliss—were reacting against
Calvinistic doctrines to such an extent as to embrace the still
more " dangerous teachings " of deism. Yet, of this small
band, only one, Franklin, continued throughout his life to
subscribe to ideas which were more or less deistic. Even
before his departure from Boston (1723), Franklin was a
deist " vowed to the cult of Reason and Liberty." Having

[13] Mayhew, *Two Sermons on the Nature, Extent and Perfection of
Divine Goodness*, pp. 12, 14, 24, 35-9, 61, 65-6, 78; J. Adams, *Works,*
ed. C. F. Adams, vol. ii, pp. 4, 10; and Schneider, *Puritan Mind* (New
York, 1930), pp. 192-7.

[14] Chauncy, *Benevolence of the Deity*, pp. 18, 39, 51, 122-6, 141, 154
et seq., 244; Ezra Stiles, *Literary Diary*, ed. Dexter (New York, 1901),
vol. iii, pp. 255, 326; and Schneider, *op. cit.*, pp. 198-201. For a contemporary appraisal of his life and character see *The American Museum;
or Repository*, February, 1790, vol. vii, pp. 76-7.

poisoned himself with an extra-large dose of Collins and
Shaftsbury, young Benjamin regarded theology as a mortal
enemy and religion as a useful ally (provided it was not
employed to support tyranny and superstition). He im-
parted his deistic views to a fellow apprentice who fell deeply
in love with them. At the age of seventeen, Franklin left
Boston for Philadelphia where he met William Keith, Governor of Pennsylvania, an audacious freethinker whose deism
(as well as democratic politics) " shocked " the " substantial " Quaker element of the colony. Upon the advice of
Keith, the young man went to London where he found
employment as a printer. In the printing shop, Franklin had
an excellent opportunity to view the latest books on the deistic
controversy which was then reaching the peak of its popularity. One day, while setting up Wollaston's *Dissertation
on Natural Religion,* he ran across the phrase " The base of
all religion is the difference between the acts of men, be they
good, bad or indifferent." The clever Benjamin could hardly
restrain himself; eagerly he wrote an answer to this sentence,
a reply, which though not original, disclosed a penetrating
mind. His *Dissertation on Liberty and Necessity, Pleasure
and Pain* was a pretty little treatise composed in the geometric
fashion of the day. In one hundred axioms, he proved to
his own satisfaction that sin, liberty and personal immortality
did not exist. An " all-wise, all-good and all-powerful God "
would naturally allow only virtue to prevail and so the entire
question of evil was a foolish one. Moreover, every one
acted necessarily in accordance with the edicts of the deity
and therefore if a thief stole something, God had to find the
robber as virtuous as his victim. Yet, honest Benjamin
made haste to remark " I would not be understood by this
to encourage or defend theft; 'tis only for the sake of the
Argument and will certainly have no *ill effect.* . . ." Since
there was no difference between virtue and vice, the favorite

deistic argument in support of immortality—that a future state existed so that the Supreme Being might make amends for injustices suffered by the good in this life—was rejected. Moreover the soul ceased to exist after death.[15] Benjamin carefully printed one hundred copies of this work. Later in his life he did all he could to suppress this " clever . . . performance " of his youth.

Even in London, Franklin continued his practice of going to church, a habit which persisted throughout his life. He liked to attend church meetings, for here he met people and exchanged ideas. Moreover these services, according to one of his latest biographers,[16] helped him " to maintain his prestige as a serious man ". and, we might add, his reputation as a Christian. Like most American deists, Franklin was prudence personified. As a prototype of his own Poor Richard, he was too sensible to jeopardize his political and social influence by espousing views which an important group in the community abhorred. In a letter to his daughter Sarah, dated 1764, he stated that his political enemies were many. He urged his daughter to continue her attendance at church, since if she failed to do so, her indiscretions would be "magnified into crimes in order the more sensibly to wound and afflict me. . . ." With these practical considerations in mind, Franklin was likely to say very little about deism. His reserve in dealing with this topic was due not only to his desire to advance in the world but also to his growing indifference to metaphysical disputation which he came to regard as arguing for argument's sake. Doing good was far more important than proving a contention by theological or abstract subtleties.

[15] B. Franklin, *Dissertation on Liberty and Necessity, Pleasure and Pain* (in Riley, *American Philosophy—Early Schools* [New York, 1907], pp. 272-9).

[16] B. Faÿ, *Franklin* (Boston, 1929), p. 97.

Yet, in spite of his reticence in respect to deism, Franklin said enough, chiefly in confidential letters, to warrant his classification as a deist along the general lines of Lord Herbert of Cherbury.   Like that seventeenth-century Englishman, Franklin was persuaded that reason was to be used to ascertain the basic principles of sound religion.   These fundamental truths consisted of a belief in the existence of God, of the practice of virtue and of the immortality of the soul.   He held that in all ages mankind had accepted the existence of a good and wise Deity who created men so that they might secure happiness.   Felicity was to be achieved through the good life which was more important to the success of religion than was orthodoxy.   Convinced that the Supreme Being was concerned in the earthly happiness of men, the American statesman was also persuaded that God was interested in their future good fortune.   His belief in immortality grew stronger as he drew nearer the grave. Franklin also agreed with Lord Herbert in regard to the Christian revelation.   Although he did not desire to see Christian influence diminished, Franklin thought that his creed did not require the support of supernatural evidences. Furthermore, he argued that the Christian churches had been so perverted that " outward Appearances and Professions " were held in higher esteem than the simple teachings of Jesus.[17]   Franklin's deism was a reaction against the stern Puritan environment in which he grew up.   He especially repudiated the doctrine of Calvinistic determinism on the ground that it was inconsistent with the goodness and wisdom of God.   Furthermore, he was cynical of the strict-

[17] B. Franklin, *Works*, ed. J. Sparks, vol. ii, pp. 3-4, 6, 526; *Writings*, ed. Smyth, vol. i, p. 296, vol. ii, p. 215, vol. iii, p. 145, vol. iv, p. 248, vol. ix, pp. 267, 333-4, vol. x, pp. 84-5; B. Franklin, *Memoirs* (New York, 1839), vol. ii, pp. 14-6; and Curtis, *Outline of Philosophy in America* (reprinted from the Western Reserve University *Bulletin*, March, 1896, p. 5).

ness with which New England kept Sunday. This exact observance he contrasted with the freedom prevalent in Flanders where he

looked around for God's judgments, but saw no signs of them. The cities were well built . . . the markets filled with plenty, the people well favored and well clothed . . . which makes one suspect that the Deity is not so angry at that offence [non-attendance at church] as a New England Justice.[18]

In the meantime, four other New Englanders, Hawley, Adams, Bliss and Gridley were venturing along the road of skepticism. Joseph Hawley (1723-1788), a cousin of the famous Jonathan Edwards and a member of his church, went to Cambridge in 1744 and while there probably studied theology. Here, he came in contact with " a most dangerous and Corrupt Book " entitled *Grace Defended in a Modest Plea for an Important Truth.* This work was written by Experience Mayhew who held that, while salvation was only possible through the grace of God, man should be active in receiving and improving the grace that was offered. According to his own testimony, given many years later, young Hawley imbibed such " wicked principles " at Cambridge that he refused to accept " any Doctrine upon the mere authority of God's word. . . ." He showed a pronounced deistic trend in that he was unwilling to accept supernatural revelation unless it was consistent with the " Divine Light of Natural reason. . . ." By 1754, however, the embryonic deist began to retract, though it was not until 1762 that the Northampton lawyer, after an attack of religious melancholy, discarded the deistic infatuation of his youth. Hawley's change of heart was partly due to the untiring efforts of the Reverend John Hooker.[19]

[18] B. Franklin, *Writings*, ed. Smyth, vol. iv, pp. 185-6.

[19] J. Hawley, *Confession of his Belief in Arminianism* (MS.);

John Adams likewise indulged in skeptical utterances at this time. In the characteristic fashion of deistic speculation, the future President subscribed to a belief in the existence of God and in a future state. Like Bolingbroke, whom he greatly admired, the young Braintree philosopher believed that Christianity had been corrupted by synods, confessions and subscriptions. To him, the Christian churches were not producing good citizens; they were rather concentrating upon the manufacture of adepts in the solution of riddles. Although convinced that God governed the world according to universal laws, he conceded the possibility of Christian miracles.[20] Throughout his life, Adams was essentially a critical thinker who would disagree just as easily with the outstanding liberal philosophers of his age as he would with the Calvinistic clergymen of New England. He was a scholar and student who was extremely cautious in making any generalization. Like Adams, the Reverend William Bliss (1728-1808) became a skeptic during his youth. Ezra Stiles, who had quite a penchant for detecting deists, discovered that Bliss was " connected with deistical acquaintances, read deistical authors, and was deeply plunged in their system for many years. . . ." By 1765, however, the good clergyman repented of his evil ways and thereafter became a firm believer in revelation and an " earnest Advocate of Religion. . . ."[21]

Ezra Stiles was well equipped for the task of detecting the intellectual vagrancies of Christian clergymen. Like Bliss, the future president of Yale traversed as a young man the road leading from faith to doubt; yet in the end he too

Trumbull, *History of Northampton, Massachusetts* (Northampton, 1902), vol. ii, pp. 230, 543, 548; and Brown, *Joseph Hawley* (New York, 1931), pp. 19-21, 36, 41.

[20] J. Adams, *Works*, ed. C. F. Adams, vol. ii, pp. 5-8, 12, 17-8, 20.

[21] Stiles, *Literary Diary*, ed. Dexter, vol. i, p. 566.

regained the path of Christian belief. In 1750, the youthful Stiles exchanged views with another young man who
raised a number of skeptical questions as to the truth of
the Biblical revelation. These observations caused Stiles
to feel that the Scriptures were "a fable and delusion".
Yet, these doubts did not deter him from becoming a clergyman. In the ministry, however, Stiles was unable to find
peace and therefore he determined to study law. In 1753, he
took the oath of an attorney but his theological interests were
so intense that he continued to study the Bible. Some three
years later, his doubts were resolved and thereafter he became
a steadfast believer in the truth of the Christian revelation.[22]
Another New Englander was likewise so beguiled by the deistic philosophy that he too drifted from the pulpit to the bar.
Jeremy Gridley, well-known for his defense of the Writs
of Assistance against Otis and a prominent figure in the
American Masonic movement, was assailed by his contemporaries not only for his support of British policies against
colonial pretensions but also for his deistic tendencies.
Charles Chauncy felt that Gridley had no religion at all,
while Ezra Stiles described him as "a disciple of Shaftesbury
and Bolingbroke. . . ." From 1743 to 1746 Gridley published *The American Magazine and Historical Chronicle;
for all the British Plantations* and "with the gracious attitude of one deist to another" presented some of Voltaire's
non-controversial works.[23] Occasionally he allowed anonymous authors to use his magazine to spread deistic ideas.
In one issue an unknown writer completely ignored the
Christian revelation and urged his readers to follow nature
which always led to God and happiness. Believing that the
Deity intended to make men happy, he held that felicity could

[22] A. Holmes, *The Life of Ezra Stiles* (Boston, 1798), pp. 35-6.

[23] Richardson, *History of Early American Magazines* (New York,
1931), pp. 44, 48.

be achieved here and hereafter if people lived virtuously. Like Pope, the author argued that if any one contemplated the universe, he must be convinced that everything was excellently arranged.   Moreover, he agreed with the English deist that the prevalence of folly and vice were actually beneficial because these evils gave force to moral laws among " grosser minds." [24]   A few months later, in the same periodical, another anonymous author, " Eusebius ", wrote an article entitled " The Unreasonableness of Persecution " in which he indirectly assailed Christianity.   Maintaining that true religion promoted brotherly love, he argued that the Christian religion had encouraged strife and had " prov'd as brutal, bloody and inhuman as Mohametanism. . . ." " Eusebius " held that unless a tolerant attitude was adopted toward all religious beliefs, men would be driven into the ranks of " infidelity." [25]

That the seeds of deism were being sown in New England soil was the opinion of contemporary observers.   In 1755, John Adams noted that the "principles of deism" were making progress in the country town of Worcester where *The Moral Philosopher,* a work written by the English deist Morgan, was circulating widely.[26]   During the course of an evening's conversation, Adams heard a speaker lightly dismiss many of the miracles of Jesus as mere stories indulged in by " enthusiasts ".   Moreover, Mayhew in one of his sermons

---

[24] *The American Magazine,* December, 1744, pp. 678-80.

[25] *Ibid.,* June, 1745, pp. 255-7.

[26] Adams, *Works,* ed. C. F. Adams, vol. ii, p. 3 (note).   In *The Moral Philosopher* (1737), Thomas Morgan asserted that Christianity, as first preached by Jesus, was in reality deism.   He held that the simple teachings of Christ had been corrupted by his followers who had altered the gospels and had ascribed miracles to his doctrines.   He rejected not only the supernatural acts of Jesus but also the idea that Christ had fulfilled the Hebraic prophecies.   (T. Morgan, *The Moral Philosopher,* vol. i, pp. 350, 412, 440; vol. ii, pp. 220, 222, 225.)

felt it necessary to omit certain Biblical proofs because some
of his audience were unwilling to accept the authenticity of
the Christian revelation.[27]   In 1759, Ezra Stiles reported
that the " vitiated morals of Deism " were spreading.   In
order to stem the rising tide of " infidelity ", he urged men
to defend Christianity on the basis of its rationality.   He
attributed the progress of freethinking to the French and
Indian War which, he claimed, had brought Americans into
contact with British officers of deistic inclinations.   Stiles
exaggerated the skeptical proclivities of the British military
leadership in America as well as its influence upon the growth
of the deistic movement.   British officers, like James Wolfe,
when moved by a desire to do any extensive reading, turned
to books dealing with military history rather than to those
concerned with deism.   Even though some of the English
commanders were intimately acquainted with the leading
freethinkers of the day, their skepticism is not established
by this fact.   James Abercrombie, commander of the Anglo-
American forces in 1758, knew and corresponded with David
Hume, yet the latter did not write to his military friend on
such serious subjects as God and immortality.   On the
contrary, Hume satisfied himself with witty observations,
personal references and plans for practical jokes.[28]

In the meantime, the New England defenders of the faith
sought to check the progress of deism by pamphlets and
articles in newspapers and magazines.   Thomas Clap, who
was so " strenuous for Orthodoxy " that " he would have
supported it with the Inquisition & Arms " had he been " a
Cardinal or Pontiff ", defended the Christian revelation in
his *Essay on the Nature and Foundations of Moral Virtue*

[27] Adams, *Works*, ed. C. F. Adams, vol. ii, p. 13 and J. Mayhew, *Two
Sermons, etc.*, p. 14.

[28] Burton, *Life and Correspondence of David Hume* (Edinburgh, 1846),
vol. i, pp. 212, 222, 312.

and Obligations. In this work, the Yale Rector claimed that without the divine evidences of Christianity men would never have known the attributes of the Deity, the true basis of moral duties and the road to salvation.[29] A Boston periodical, *The American Magazine* for August 1744, urged the study of the New Testament in order to combat skepticism and supply young divinity students with correct ideas concerning the essential tenets of the Christian religion. One year later, this same magazine carried an article entitled, " Some Thoughts on Infidelity ", a reprint from the works of " a late Author." The writer urged that deistic principles be kept from the " Rabble ", who, for the most part, remained orderly chiefly through the force of religious teachings. He therefore requested all reasonable men to hold in contempt " infidels " who became the " Idols of the Mob. . . ." This article is illustrative of the cautious position of eighteenth-century liberals in respect to deism. So long as deistic principles were spread among " the sober and respectable " elements of the community, all was well. " Enlightened " members of the aristocracy and the bourgeoisie might play with them but not the masses, for in the hands of the latter they might be used for revolutionary purposes. Consequently, any intellectual who popularized deism stamped himself, so far as the upper classes were concerned, as an enemy of society. In the same Boston magazine, a few months later, a correspondent, " Ephraim Faithful " asserted that unbelief would make for injustice, tyranny and fraud. He deplored the anti-Christian tendency of his age and felt that only by rejecting skepticism could a country be prosperous and liberty achieved.[30]

From a literary viewpoint, deistic thought was less in

---

[29] T. Clap, *Essay on the Nature, etc.,* pp. 41, 47, 53.

[30] *The American Magazine,* January, 1745, pp. 21-2; September, 1746, p. 404.

evidence in the Middle Provinces than in New England; what little did prevail here was chiefly expressed in newspaper or magazine articles. The Middle Colonies generally accepted the idea of toleration and, except in New York, no serious efforts were made to establish any one church. Even there the attempt failed because the great majority of people belonged to churches other than the Anglican. Thus, a spirit of live and let live had to be adopted and liberty of conscience was extended to all but "papists". The Catholics were discriminated against not only in New York but also in Pennsylvania. Besides Anglicans and Catholics, there were in the Middle Colonies Quakers, Mennonites, Moravians, Lutherans and Calvinists. The last group included members of the Dutch Reformed, Presbyterian and German Reformed Churches and was the most important religious element in this section of British America.

In such relatively tolerant surroundings, religious liberalism was certain to raise its head. In the College of Philadelphia (later the University of Pennsylvania), founded by the deistic Franklin, rationalism, free from narrowness, flourished. This institution was headed by a liberal Anglican, William Smith, whose views were similar to those of the English Latitudinarian clergy. In his *General Idea of the College of Mirania* (1753) and in his *Philosophical Meditation, and Religious Address to the Supreme Being* (1754), Smith sought to advance natural and revealed religion. He praised the Deity as a wise and good Parent who had bestowed upon men "the noble Faculties of reason and understanding." These capacities, the Anglican clergyman argued, must be improved because upon their advancement depended the progress of truth and happiness. God desired men not only to better their mental powers but to love Him and His creatures. Such a feeling was inculcated by the teaching of natural religion which Smith urged in order to make young men more receptive to the truth and value of Christianity. He likewise suggested a closer examination of revealed faith.[31]

Over King's College in New York (later Columbia University) presided Samuel Johnson who in his youth entertained practically the same views as William Smith. In 1714, while a student at Yale, he heard that a new philosophy was in vogue and that Descartes, Boyle, Locke and Newton were its prophets. He was, however, warned to shun the new metaphysics because it was bound to bring in " a new divinity and corrupt the pure religion of the country. . . ." After his graduation, Johnson became a tutor at Yale where his most celebrated pupil was Jonathan Edwards. Forced to resign from the college in 1720 because of his " incompetence " as a teacher, he became pastor of a church in West Haven and thus was near enough to his Alma Mater to continue his studies. Meanwhile, he was reading the works of prominent Anglican clergymen and was beginning to doubt the validity of his Congregational ordination. By 1722, he determined to cross the Atlantic and take orders in the Anglican Church. In England, Johnson came in contact with the leading Anglican prelates and visited prominent places of interest.[32] He eventually became an Anglican minister and was satisfied that in this church he had found learning, order and urbanity.

In his youth, Johnson was receptive to the ideas of Locke, Newton and such milder English deists as Wollaston whose *Religion of Nature,* although well meant, was " a great stumbling block to many. . . ." It was Collins's *Discourse of the Grounds and Reasons of the Christian Religion* which

[31] W. Smith, *Discourses on Public Occasions in America,* pp. 45, 88-9, 101, 149, 152-5 (Appendix).

[32] S. Johnson, *His Career and Writings,* ed. H. and C. Schneider (New York, 1929), vol. i, pp. 6, 11-2, 15, 17-8.

encouraged the future college president to examine the evidences of Christianity. From this examination, Johnson emerged a good Christian who viewed with sorrow the " deplorable progress of infidelity " from " the well meaning but too conceited Mr. Locke, down to Tindal, and thence to Bolingbroke, etc. etc." [33] Although he observed during his lifetime that Latitudinarianism led to deism and deism to atheism, this did not prevent him from espousing Latitudinarian views. He was convinced that no conflict existed between the new science and older revealed truths; and therefore accepted, like Tillotson, the tenets of natural religion and the divine origin of the Christian revelation. In a sermon, delivered at Stratford, September 7, 1727, he illustrated the need of Christianity by arguing that " the light of nature " was insufficient and consequently he urged that reason be supplemented by divine revelation which taught the average man just ideas concerning God. Of all supernatural disclosures the truest was that of Christianity which was fortified by an excellent system of morality and was attested by miracles and prophecies.[34] Some sixteen years later, in his *Introduction to the Study of Philosophy,* Johnson likewise urged men to accept the Bible as an aid to " mere unassisted reason. . . ." Although insufficient, the rational was nevertheless to be used " to find out and know the Truth. . . ." Real happiness depended upon the cultivation of " right Reason " which was to guide one in the practice of virtue. The good life consisted in promoting individual and public welfare. Moreover, he believed that personal conduct determined the position each man would enjoy in the future world. His views as to immortality were naturally based on the assumption that God existed.[35]

[33] *Ibid.*, vol. i, p. 23.

[34] S. Johnson, *The Necessity of Reveal'd Religion* (MS.), pp. 6-12, 15.

[35] S. Johnson, *Introduction to the Study of Philosophy*, pp. 5-7, 20, 25.

Although the stand of Johnson in his youth was rather liberal and heterodox, by the time he became president of the New York seat of learning, his position was extremely conservative and orthodox.   Playing a prominent role in the establishment of King's College was William Livingston who did all in his power to liberalize the new institution. Graduating from Yale at the head of his class in 1741, Livingston came to New York to practice law.   When the Anglican Church attempted to gain control of the newly proposed college, he threw himself into the battle.   Opposing sectarian education, a limited curriculum and a privately supported institution, he suggested that the college be established by an act of the legislature.   This body was to be given the power of appointing trustees who in turn were to elect a president.   Although not completely victorious, the young lawyer had the satisfaction of seeing a governing board appointed representing other denominations besides the Anglican.   In the meantime, he became editor of a magazine, *The Independent Reflector* (1752), whose articles on religion so aroused the enmity of the clergy that Livingston was described as an atheist and deist.   The future Governor of New Jersey merited neither of these titles; he was far from being an atheist since he believed in the existence of a Deity and as for being a deist his acceptance of the Christian revelation precluded that possibility.[36]   On the whole, his religious views were liberal; he opposed intolerance and thought that a man might be a good Christian without belonging to any denominational church.   He believed sincerely in the divine authority of Christianity but urged that it be freely investigated.   If religion was to mean anything, it must be simple, plain and intelligible and con-

[36] In later life he published a satirical magazine article in which he ridiculed deism. See chapter iv, pp. 107-8 and Sedgwick, *A Memoir of the Life of William Livingston* (New York, 1833), p. 249 (note).

sequently was to be purged of all superstitious accretions and priestly inventions.[37]

Naturally Livingston encountered the opposition of the Anglican party in New York and soon his friends began to forsake him. Among the latter was James Parker who refused to support *The Independent Reflector* because he feared the loss of the government's printing business. Besides, in 1752, Parker found himself assailed by the orthodox of the city for an allegorical article published in his newspaper. In this composition, some Indian chiefs were used to popularize deistic principles. According to the account, a Swedish missionary, attempting to convert some Red Men in 1710, asserted that the Deity had revealed Himself in the Bible and that if the Scriptures were not accepted, eternal damnation would follow. In reply, the Indians stated that future rewards and punishments were allotted in proportion to the good or evil that was done in this life. They held that this idea had been disclosed to their forefathers or implanted in their own natures. Moreover, they argued that the supernatural testimony of Christianity had no advantage over their own because the Supreme Being had the power to reveal Himself to all men without the aid of any book. Any religion, teaching a special revelation, was blasphemous, since it represented the Deity as a tyrant who capriciously condemned most of His creatures to eternal misery, although they were not at fault. Even if the Bible were of divine origin, the Indians were thankful that God had not forced it upon them. In conclusion, they prayed to be saved from certain conceptions set forth in it.

That this speech was an implied rejection of the Christian revelation was so obvious that it was immediately answered by a defender of the faith. In a letter to the newspaper, an

[37] Sedgwick, *op. cit.*, pp. 55, 75-6, 86-7; and Richardson, *A History of Early American Magazines*, pp. 83-5, 89.

anonymous correspondent pointed out that the Swedish missionary was not represented " as a faithful minister of Christ " and that therefore the narrative was most misleading.   Yet, he left the entire controversy " to our able Divines, who were better able . . . to take the Author of the Paper to Task, about some impious Expressions in the conclusion." In a footnote to the above broadside, the editor, James Parker, stated that he meant no harm and had only desired to give the adversaries of Christianity a fair hearing.   This statement, however, did not satisfy the faithful and Parker was forced to call upon Franklin for aid.   Later, he publicly apologized for his " impious work " and appeased the orthodox by asserting his belief in the Trinity.[38]

Playing a part in the Parker episode was Cadwallader Colden, a prolific writer and tireless student who had few peers in the intellectual circles of provincial America. Franklin wrote to him in behalf of the persecuted printer and as usual approached just the right man for the business at hand since Colden was not only influential in New York politics but was also somewhat of a skeptic himself.   In his *Explication of the First Causes of Action in Matter and of the Cause of Gravitation,* he showed himself to be a materialist whose position was dangerously close to atheism.   The treatise, though exciting much discussion in Europe, hardly made a ripple here; on the whole, it illustrated a combination of erudition and originality and was an attempted criticism of an enlargement upon the work of Newton.   To Colden, there were three kinds of matter: (1) the resisting force opposing or suppressing motion; (2) the self-moving power always ready to change or endeavor to change its position; and (3) the elastic or expansive force reflecting or conveying

[38] *The New-York Gazette revived in the Weekly Post-Boy,* April 27, 1752 (no. 484) ; May 4, 1752 (no. 485) ; and August 3, 1752 (No. 498). See also B. Franklin, *Writings,* ed. Smyth, vol. iii, pp. 87-8.

any action from an agent. None of these three "species" of matter had within it the power to attract any other. Apparent attraction or gravitation was performed by "pulsion" which was the result of the joint actions of the resisting, moving and elastic powers.[39] This was an enlargement upon the work of Newton, who, according to Colden, did not in his writings attribute an attractive force to matter but merely spoke of an apparent gravitation, the perpetual effect of a cause of which he was ignorant. By implying that motion was inherent in matter, Colden was philosophically close to the atheistic contention that a First Cause was not needed to give the heavenly bodies their initial thrust. Yet, the future lieutenant-governor of New York explicitly denied this implication by asserting that some Intelligent Being was needed to create the celestial objects as well as to give them distinct kinds of motion. As to the problem of right and wrong, Colden was convinced that men had the power to follow their inclinations. Naturally they were responsible for their actions. Morality, he held, consisted in so living one's life as to achieve happiness.

According to observers, deism was making rapid headway in the Middle Colonies. In a Philadelphia newspaper, *The American Weekly Museum,* October 9-16, 1735 (no. 824), an article appeared lamenting the fact that skepticism was meeting with encouragement and was especially poisoning young minds. Had the readers of this Philadelphia journal taken the trouble to look about them, they would have found that deism had already "poisoned" more mature minds. On one of his visits to the city of brotherly love, the renowned evangelist, the Reverend Mr. Whitefield, preached a sermon which melted the hearts of some of the "most marvellous Offenders against the Great God." Among the

[39] Colden, *An Explication of the First Causes of Action in Matter and the Cause of Gravitation* (New York, 1746), pp. 21-2, 33, 51.

latter was a "notorious deist", Brockden, a recorder of
deeds, who was then sixty years of age and who had throughout his life zealously attempted to propagate deistical principles among "moral Men". Prevailed upon by another
deist, Brockden had consented to attend Whitefield's meeting. He came, he saw and was conquered! [40]   Philadelphia
apparently had quite a number of deists because on another
occasion Whitefield addressed a gathering of "Reasoning
unbelievers" who were far from impressed by his attacks
upon natural reason. At about this time another clergyman, Jonathan Dickinson, noted that frequenters of inns and
coffee houses were indulging in skeptical conversations. In
a letter, dated 1764, Franklin pertinently remarked to one
of his cynical friends, " . . . If you had Christian Faith,
quantum suff., [a proof of immortality] might not be necessary, but as matters are, it may be of some Use." [41]   In
the meantime, apologists were endeavoring to check the
progress of deism by vindicating the truth of the Christian
revelation. In 1732, Jonathan Dickinson, later president of
the College of New Jersey, published a work, *The Reasonableness of Christianity,* designed to prove that Jesus was
the divine Messiah and son of God and that no religion
except his own could be attested by miracles. Although
Dickinson allowed for the sake of argument that " the
Patrons of Infidelity " could produce the " fabulous Histories " of Mohammed and the " infamous legends " of the
Popes, he claimed that these stories were merely " the bare
reports of . . . unknown Authors. . . ." Furthermore, he

[40] Whitefield, *A Continuation of the Rev. Mr. Whitefield's Journal,
etc.* (London, 1744), pp. 66-7.

[41] J. Dickinson, *Familiar Letters* (Glasgow, 1775), p. 2; B. Franklin,
Writings, ed. Smyth, vol. iv, p. 250 (Letter to William Strahan, June 25,
1764).

challenged the deists to draw up a system which could explain man's lost innocency and which could keep man submissive.[42]

Some thirteen years later, Dickinson returned to the counter-attack in his *Familiar Letters upon a Variety of Religious Subjects*. In this pamphlet, he asserted that even the deists were forced to admit that the religion of Jesus was worthy both of God and man. To prove that it was revealed by the Deity, this " great Divine, who was not much of a Scholar ", as Ezra Stiles put it, showed that Christ had fulfilled the Hebraic prophecies, that he had performed miracles, and that he had given to the world a practical morality.[43] Dickinson was aided in his defence of Christianity by magazine contributors. In a Philadelphia periodical, a correspondent defended the excellence of the gospel, the superiority of Christianity and the existence of a miracle-working Providence.[44] In another issue of the same magazine, there appeared a communication from a clergyman who pointed out that all followers of Christianity were assured of eternal salvation. Later a writer, commenting on this letter, observed that the death of " the very feeblest of true Christians " was superior even to that of a Socrates.[45] In a similar vein, " Publicola ", in a Woodbridge (New Jersey) periodical, *The New American Magazine*, August 1758 (no. 8), informed his readers that while the religious man had little to lose if his faith were built on weak grounds, the " infidel " had everything to forfeit, if he were wrong.

[42] J. Dickinson, *Reasonableness of Christianity*, pp. 54, 78-85, 95, 100-1, 106, 120-1, 160-1.

[43] J. Dickinson, *Familiar Letters, etc.*, pp. 11-16.

[44] *The American Magazine and Monthly Chronicle for the British Colonies*, March, 1758 and September, 1758 (nos. 6 and 12), vol. i, pp. 290, 331, 600-2.

[45] *Ibid.*, March, 1758 and April, 1759 (nos. 6 and 7), vol. i, pp. 291-4, 331.

In the South, the deistic movement was still less conspicuous than in the North.   Here the Church of England was established by law and, except in North Carolina, the Establishment was fairly effective.   Taking the provincial period as a whole, the Anglican Church lost ground as compared with the Dissenters, of whom the strongest and most aggressive were the Presbyterians.   The latter were to be found chiefly in the back country and, although intensely partisan, their contact on the frontier with peoples of different denominations gradually developed in them a spirit of toleration. During this period, the Anglican Church in Virginia, although outwardly prosperous, was considerably weakened. This was due to a steady increase in the number of Dissenters, the spiritual laxity of the clergy and the exaction of clerical salaries.   Hostility to the clergy flared up in the famous Parson's Cause (1755-1758) occasioned by an act of the assembly providing for the payment of church taxes in money, instead of tobacco, at a rate below the market value. The clergy protested and failing to get relief in Virginia, appealed to the King who annulled the objectionable law. To test whether the royal order affected salaries payable between the passage of the act and its repeal, a case was made in which Patrick Henry, retained by the parishioners, practically secured a favorable decision.   During the trial, young Henry, though a member of the Anglican Church, made a violent attack upon its clergy.

Yet, in spite of this incident, up to 1763, a vigorous anticlerical movement was lacking in Virginia.   In the absence of such a tendency and in the presence of a general indifference to theological speculations, deism had little chance to gain ground.   According to Bishop Meade, the lay readers of the Anglican Church used none but Tillotson's sermons.[46]

46 Meade, *Old Churches, etc.*, vol. ii, p. 355.

These discourses, generally cold and unanimated, dealt with " moral virtues " and were not calculated to stir the heart. In 1722, James Blair, president of William and Mary College, stated that the Anglican ministry of Virginia had " little occasion in [their] sermons to enter the lists with Atheists, Deists . . ." etc. because the colony was not " infested with the enemies of the Christian faith. . . ."[47] At about this time, Sir John Randolph of Williamsburg was being reproached by his friends because of reputed deistic ideas. Sir John, however, was far from being a deist; in fact, in his will, he made a public profession of faith to the contrary. He believed that Christ was born miraculously and came into the world to persuade men to love their neighbors. He was convinced that people would be judged in the future world by the life they led rather than by mistakes in matters of speculation. In conclusion, Randolph condemned " learned Doctors " for striving to make the religion of Jesus a religion of " mysteries ".[48] The unpopularity of deistic speculation in the South was also reflected in newspaper articles. In the *Maryland Gazette* for November 22-29, 1734 (no. 90), an anonymous writer attempted to prove that the action of God, in commanding the sacrifice of Isaac, was consistent with His character. The correspondent argued that the narrative furnished an example of faith and obedience as well as a prediction of the future life of the Saviour. Moreover, in answer to the deistic contention that Abraham was acting contrary to natural law in attempting to kill his son, the writer held that the Patriarch was motivated to do what he did by reasonable and moral considerations and consequently his actions were justifiable.

[47] Quoted in the *History of the College of William and Mary from its Foundation, 1660 to 1874* (Richmond, 1874), p. 45.

[48] *General Magazine and Historical Chronicle*, May, 1741, vol. i, pp. 346-7.

In North Carolina, a general indifference, if not hostility, to organized religion prevailed. In Edenton, a town on the north side of Albemarle Sound, Colonel Byrd of Virginia was surprised to find neither a church nor a place of public worship.[49] He discovered that the people here were opposed to priests, christening ceremonies and sermons. In a similar fashion, the celebrated Wesley, who came to America to convert Indians and returned to England with the realization that he needed conversion, found that the people of Frederica, near Savannah, Georgia, were " cold and heartless . . ." to religious concerns. Yet, even more distressing to the famous founder of Methodism was the appearance of deists in Georgia. On May 18, 1737, Wesley discovered, as he believed, "the first Convert to Deism " made in Savannah. At first this unnamed skeptic had been " zealously and ex-amplarily religious " but unfortunately soon lost both zeal and faith. Thereafter, others followed with such rapidity that by September of the same year, Wesley was forced to read to his congregation a number of sermons with the hope that these might prove " a timely Antidote against the Poison of Infidelity, which was now with great Industry propagated among us. . . ." His fears for the safety of Georgia became so pronounced that he felt called upon to state in his *Journal* that deism was more dangerous to the existence of the new colony than Catholicism.[50]

---

[49] The construction of St. Paul's Church, Edenton, was begun eight years after Byrd's observation. Although work was started on the edifice in 1736, it was not until 1760 that church services were held in the building for the first time. By 1774, the church was finished at an estimated cost of $25,000 to $30,000. (*North Carolina Historical and Genealogical Register* (Edenton, 1900), vol. i, pp. 608-9.)

[50] J. Wesley, *An Extract of the Reverend Mr. John Wesley's Journal, etc.* (Bristol, 1739 [?]), pp. 32, 35, 41-2, 53.

CHAPTER IV

Deism in Revolutionary America (1763-1789)

From 1763 to 1789, the section north of the Mason and Dixon line made great progress in the matter of " soul freedom "; but religious discrimination of one kind or another still persisted. The Massachusetts state constitution required the governor to declare himself a supporter of the Christian religion, and though every citizen could claim the right to worship as he pleased, equal protection under the law was limited to Christians. Likewise Massachusetts practically excluded Catholics from holding office. In Pennsylvania, much to the disgust of the deistic Franklin, the state constitution required all legislators to declare their belief in the divine inspiration of the Bible. Moreover, state churches still persisted in New England; the Massachusetts constitution compelled each town to support " public Protestant teachers " and required its citizens to pay taxes for the support of some kind of Protestant service. According to this provision, if Baptists, Quakers and others maintained their own churches, they were not forced to support the Congregational Establishment. In Connecticut, a general toleration act was passed in 1784 which allowed every religious body to manage its own affairs. To this provision, however, was affixed the condition that all Dissenters, desiring exemption from the payment of Congregational taxes, were required to produce certificates to the effect that they were supporting their respective denominations. These were granted by church and civil officials with the result that many times Baptists, Quakers, Anglicans and others were forced to support the Establishment or suffer the punishment of imprisonment or fine.

Yet, in spite of these discriminations, toleration was more prevalent in the North than at any previous time. Amid these more tolerant surroundings, religious liberalism made rapid progress. In New England, the Unitarian tendency was making such an appeal that, according to one exaggerated observation, it was unfashionable to discuss the divinity of Christ because the subject was considered antiquated. Boston, Cambridge and Salem were the principal centers of the anti-Trinitarian movement. In 1767, Simeon Howard, succeeding Mayhew as minister of West Church, Boston, rejected the doctrines of the Trinity, predestination and the total depravity of man. Some eighteen years later, under the guidance of James Freeman, a reader in the Anglican Church, King's Chapel revised its Prayer Book in order to strike out any references to Trinitarian beliefs. Influenced greatly by William Hazlitt, an English Unitarian, who was then visiting Boston, Freeman believed that Christ, although not a member of the Godhead, was still more than a man and consequently, he addressed Jesus as his Saviour and Redeemer. Joseph Willard, President of Harvard, also showed Unitarian tendencies and was in constant communication with such English leaders as Priestley and Price. At Salem, worldly-wise merchants engaged in the East Indian trade listened approvingly to the liberal doctrines of the Reverend William Bentley. Out of Salem's twenty-four most prominent families twenty were Unitarians. Commercial contacts with the Orient probably made these families receptive to latitudinarian ideas in religion. At least, their minister was quite liberal in his views. Although not a deist, Bentley circulated deistic works. On one occasion, he lent Tindal's *Christianity as Old as the Creation* to a friend who promised to read it in private. It was left under his pillow, was discovered by a woman who gave it to an aunt, who, in turn, read it to her husband. Although himself a believer in the Christian revelation, Bentley was willing to admit that anyone who sincerely thought that Christianity was wrong honored God by rejecting it. In 1790, he preached a sermon at Stone Chapel, Boston, in which he rejected the Calvinistic doctrine of special election and upheld the excellence of natural religion. To him, all men were, and always had been, capable of attaining salvation and happiness. Furthermore Bentley held that " the honest devotion of a heathen " was more acceptable to God than " the hypocrisy of a Christian ". The " most excellent religion " was that of nature which consisted in doing the will of God and which was revealed to man through the dictates of reason. Christianity was not to be considered as an enemy to natural religion but rather a supplement to it.[1]

Universalism, like Unitarianism, was beginning to gain ground in the North. During the Revolutionary period, both Universalists and Unitarians believed that it was the purpose of God to save all men irrespective of creed, but, whereas the Unitarians rejected the doctrine of the Trinity, the Universalists generally expressed no opinion as to the equality or subordination of Jesus to God. After 1805, however, most of the Universalist ministry publicly defended anti-Trinitarian beliefs.[2] The leading Universalists of the period were John Murray and Elhanan Winchester. John Murray, an Englishman who came to America in 1770, promoted the rise of Universalism. In 1774, he was drawn to the town of Gloucester, Massachusetts, because of the religious sentiments of its inhabitants. Unlike some other Uni-

---

[1] Allen and Eddy, *History of the Unitarians and Universalists in the U. S.* (New York, 1894), pp. 180-5; Cooke, *Unitarianism in America* (Boston, 1902), pp. 66, 71-2, 76-9; W. Bentley, *Diary* (Salem, 1905), vol. i, p. 98, *A Sermon Preached at Stone Chapel in Boston, September 12, 1790* (Boston, 1790), pp. 8-9, 11, 15, 17; and Schneider, *The Puritan Mind*, pp. 204-6.

[2] Allen and Eddy, *op. cit.*, p. 429.

versalists of his time, he did not believe in future punishments since the evil that men did in this life was washed away by their belief in Christ who died for all. Among the early Universalists, the most eminent for learning and intellect was a former Baptist clergyman, Elhanan Winchester. In 1780, there was division in the ranks of his church in Philadelphia, and the following year he organized his dissenting brethren under the name of the Society of Universal Baptists. In his dialogues on *Universal Restoration* (1792), Winchester interpreted the Bible so broadly that its passages seemed to prove his contention that all men would be ultimately saved. He based his doctrine of restoration on the principles that " God [was] the universal and only creator . . .", that He was benevolent, and that His Son had died for all. In 1789, the Universalists of Philadelphia, over whom Winchester presided, addressed a letter to friendly societies asking them to meet in convention. This gathering met the following year and drew up certain articles of faith. Among these was a belief in the divine inspiration of the Bible, in the existence of one God, and in the salvation of all men through the death of Christ.[3]

Religious liberalism in the North appeared not only in the form of Unitarianism and Universalism but also of deism. From 1763 to 1789, the deistic movement became more significant than ever before and although still essentially moderate in speculation, it showed an increasing militancy. Fundamental to deistic thought was the idea of a general Providence which operated in accordance with universal laws. A corollary naturally deduced from this basic assumption was the inference that if God ruled the world according to general edicts, He would not go out of His

---

[3] Allen and Eddy, *op. cit.,* pp. 388, 390, 394-5, 405, 407-9, 414, 420-1; E. Winchester, *The Universal Restoration* (Bellows Falls, Vt., 1819), pp. 119-123; and Cooke, *op. cit.,* pp. 67-9.

way to reveal Himself to any particular people through such supernatural events as miracles. In June 1769, a Philadelphia periodical, *The American Magazine, or General Repository,* published a letter defending this deistic contention. The author argued that since worldly evils might all be for the best, man had little need of any particular intervention by an external Being. Reflecting the liberal revolutionary spirit of the age, the writer asked, " Why then should God interpose to alter the determinations of human will, more than the operations of nature? Cannot man be happy unless his liberty be over-ruled? " Furthermore, evidences of any intervention were merely assertions and although such events might have taken place, there were no criteria to judge of their wisdom or foolishness. In conclusion, the writer cautiously stated that what he had said did not preclude the possibility that if the Deity desired to reveal Himself by suspending His general edicts, He could do so. That the letter was an implied rejection of revelation was so evident that it was immediately answered. In the August 1769 issue of the same periodical, a " particular Providence " was defended on the ground that, since the Deity cared equally for all His children and disposed of all events, such foresight did not imply any partiality on His part. In subsequent issues, the original contributor defended his thesis and re-affirmed his faith in a general Providence and free will.[4] Since it was the policy of Lewis Nicola, curator of the American Philosophical Society and editor of the *American Magazine, or General Repository,* to publish nothing " derogtory to the principles of the Christian religion ", other articles did not evoke much controversy.

About this time, Nathaniel Ames, moved by anti-clerical feeling, indulged in the deistic phraseology of his time and

---

[4] *The American Magazine or General Repository,* June, 1769, August, 1769, September, 1769, pp. 174-7, 237-42, 304-6.

although not definitely a deist, was distinctly liberal in religion. To this publisher of almanacs, true religion was the essence of correct reason, while morality was the vital spark of all faith. Moreover, " to defend the Christian religion [was] one thing and to knock a man on the head . . ." for disbelieving in it would be another. Furthermore, hypocrisy generally flourished under the guise of orthodoxy. Another printer, Theophilus Cossart, a German, was regarded by his contemporaries as " a Freethinker and Philosopher . . .", who believed in the existence of God and a future state. According to Ezra Stiles, Cossart thought that " the Morals of the Mohametans [were] superior to those of the Christians in general "—a favorite argument employed by deists to indicate their dislike for Christianity. Having resided at one time or another in Charleston, Philadelphia, New York, Newport and Boston, the German printer had an excellent opportunity to spread his heterodox views.[5]

While deists were declaring their independence from a miracle-working Deity, the thirteen American colonies were doing the same in reference to England. At the outbreak of the struggle, deism was still a cult limited to a few members of the intellectual classes residing in relatively large towns. Outside of these cities it was scarcely known; in fact, John Leland, a Baptist clergyman who was then living in a small village only forty miles from Boston, observed that he had never heard of " Deism and Universalism . . . and of course was what is called a believer in revelation." If, by chance, the deistic philosophy made its way into the interior, it was certain to be regarded with a great deal of suspicion. On the eve of the Revolution, Joseph Clarke of Northampton requested Henry Knox, a Boston bookseller,

[5] N. Ames, *Essays, Humor, and Poems, with Notes and Comments* by S. Briggs (Cleveland, 1891), pp. 387, 403, and Stiles, *Diary*, ed. Dexter, vol. i, pp. 179-80.

to send him Hume's *Essays* and Leland's *Views of Deistical Writers*. Clarke urged his dealer to take every precaution to insure secrecy and directed Knox to deliver the books to a Mr. Smith. Since the latter proceeded to Boston a little too early, the purchase was not made. Fearing that Knox might send the books by another messenger, Clarke instructed the Bostonian not to dispatch them until Smith again visited the city. The prospective buyer explained that he was forced to adopt such measures because of the " bigoted attachment of the people in this part of the country to the particular principles in Religion that they had been educated in . . ." and because of " the Infamy they would Cast upon any man who differed from them in so material a point, as they would readily conclude he did, were he known to be possessed of books on Theism. . . ." [6]

The unpopularity of deism was also reflected in the actions of the Pennsylvania Convention of 1776 called to draw up a state constitution. The deistic Franklin, who presided, was apparently unable to stop the Convention from incorporating a constitutional provision stating that every representative was to declare his belief in the divine inspiration of the Bible. Some eight years later, in a letter to Priestley, the English Unitarian, Franklin told of his opposition to the above clause and felt called upon to remark that there were " several Things in the Old Testament impossible to be given by divine Inspiration. . . ." [7] Since no vote was recorded on this constitutional provision, it is impossible to say how the delegates stood. Probably the Scotch-Irish of the interior favored the clause because of their conservative religious views. William Findley, who could have been easily elected to the convention had he wished it, typified

[6] Massachusetts Historical Society *Proceedings* (Boston, 1928), vol. lxi, pp. 250-1, 259-60.

[7] Franklin, *Writings, ed.* Smyth, vol. ix, pp. 266-7.

the religious conservatism of these God-fearing Presbyterians. A deeply pious individual, he was a bitter opponent of deism. The piety of the Pennsylvania Convention was further displayed in the passage of a resolution providing for the initiation of divine services in order to praise "Almighty God . . . for the peculiar interposition of his special providence. . . ."[8]

In the same year that the Pennsylvania Convention met to write a state constitution, the American colonies in Congress assembled announced their freedom from England. Though the majority of those who signed the Declaration of Independence were agreed as to the desirableness of "soul freedom", their views on other religious questions were so diversified that they ran the gamut from the deism of Jefferson to the orthodoxy of Sherman. The author has examined the religious opinions of a little more than a third of the fifty-six delegates who affixed their signatures to the document. Of these, three were deists, two showed distinct deistic leanings, four entertained liberal, though not deistic, views, while the remaining eleven were definitely orthodox in their principles. Benjamin Franklin of Pennsylvania, Thomas Jefferson of Virginia, and Stephen Hopkins of Rhode Island espoused more or less openly the cause of deism, while John Adams of Massachusetts[9] and George

[8] Channing, *History of the United States* (New York, 1924), vol. iii, pp. 438-9; *Proceedings Relative to the Calling of the Conventions of 1776 and 1790... With a View of the Proceedings of the Convention of 1776* (Harrisburg, 1825), pp. 46-7, 53 (note), 58. Biographical sketches of the Cumberland, Westmoreland and Berks County delegation can be found in McMaster and Stone, *Pennsylvania and the Federal Constitution* (Lancaster, 1888), pp. 733, 735; Albert, *History of the County of Westmoreland, Pa.* (Philadelphia, 1882), pp. 78-9 (note); and Montgomery, *History of Berks County, Pa.* (Reading, 1894), pp. 223-4, 232-3, 235-6, 237-8, 247-50.

[9] For the deistic views of Franklin see chapter iii, pp. 63-7; for those of Jefferson chapter iv, pp. 116-7; for those of Hopkins chapter iv, p. 105; and for the deistic inclinations of Adams chapter iii, p. 68 and chapter v, pp. 141-2.

Wythe of Virginia, were close to the deistic philosophy.
Wythe of the Old Dominion (1726-1806) was a friend of
Jefferson and a professor of law at William and Mary.   On
the subject of religion he was strangely silent because,
according to Jefferson, he was afraid to trust anyone with so
important a matter.   His contemporaries suspected him of
" infidelity ".   So prevalent was this suspicion that when
Wythe died, his friend, William Munford, stated publicly
that the former professor was a believer in the truth of the
Christian religion and that before his death he " ' often prayed
to Jesus Christ his Saviour, for relief ' " [10]   Significantly
enough, Munford mentioned that Wythe had informed him
of his acceptance of the validity of Christianity only one or
two years before his death.   Robert T. Paine, Josiah
Bartlett, Benjamin Rush and Matthew Thornton held liberal
religious views.   Robert Treat Paine of Massachusetts
(1731-1814) was the son of a minister and in his youth
received " the best moral and religious instruction ".   He
was interested in theological matters and occasionally
preached.   Paine regarded Christianity as a system of moral
truths and righteousness given by God to man.   His
approach to the question of religion was practical; he thought
that if Christianity did not make men virtuous, it was of no
benefit.   Like Paine, Bartlett (1729-1795) was a liberal
in religion.   The future governor of New Hampshire, while
still a young man, was given the opportunity of using the
library of a liberal clergymen of Salisbury, the Reverend
Dr. Webster.   He soon came to doubt the traditional doctrines of Calvinism and during the greater part of his life,
believed that man was free to do as he pleased but was to
be held responsible for his actions.   By profession Bartlett
was a doctor of medicine but in this field he was less widely

[10] J. Sanderson (ed.), *Biography of the Signers to the Declaration of
Independence* (Philadelphia, 1823), vol. ii, pp. 180-1, 184.

known than Benjamin Rush of Pennsylvania (1745-1813), friend of Franklin and Jefferson. The Virginian carried on quite a correspondence with the Philadelphia physician and often exchanged with the latter his advanced religious views probably with the thought that Rush would understand and be sympathetic towards them. The doctor, however, was not a deist; in fact, *The Age of Reason* was so repugnant to his principles that he showed no desire to renew his friendship with Paine upon the latter's return to the United States. In short, the scientist was a Christian who revered the Bible, urged the excellency of Christianity and attended church. Like Rush, Thornton of New Hampshire (c. 1741-1803) was a physician and a religious liberal. He refused to affiliate himself with any religious denomination, believed in the existence of God, accepted the divine mission of Christ and, in short, would have classed himself as a Christian.[11]

Along with Livingston, Jefferson, Adams and Franklin, Roger Sherman was a member of the committee appointed to draw up the Declaration of Independence. Sherman of Connecticut (1721-1793) did not have much of a formal education but attained as a result of his own industry a considerable knowledge of science, law and theology. According to the testimony of his friend, Dr. Jonathan Edwards the younger, Sherman was an excellent theologian. Upon one occasion he argued a fine theological point with the renowned Reverend Samuel Hopkins on the theory of " disinterested submission ". Sherman held that men would not be willing to give up their " eternal interest " of salvation for the glory of God and the good of man. The Connecticut statesman believed in the Bible as the revealed word of God, in the fall of man and his consequent sinfulness and in the final day of judgment when the bad would be sentenced to

[11] Sanderson (ed.), *op. cit.*, vol. ii, pp. 211-4, 244-5; vol. iii, pp. 136-7; vol. iv, p. 283; and vol. v, p. 67.

ERRATUM

p. 95 line 7 for Oliver Scott read Oliver Wolcott.

everlasting punishment and the good would be rewarded with eternal life. Although tolerant of differences in religious matters, Sherman intensely disliked "irreligious" men. He opposed the confirmation of Morris as minister to France because he objected to Morris' practice " of speaking irreverently of the Christian religion. . . ." Like Sherman, his colleague, Oliver Scott (1726-1797), was deeply orthodox but at the same time tolerant in his religious views. According to one biographer, the future governor of Connecticut was pure in morals and faith; he was a " humble christian, untainted by bigotry or intolerance." William Williams (1731-1811), another Connecticut man, was likewise rigidly orthodox in his principles and yet was a firm believer in religious liberty. A member of the Congregational order, a deacon from his youth to his death, Williams attended church regularly and contributed money to missionary societies designed to spread Gospel teachings. Richard Stockton of New Jersey (1730-1781) was also tolerant of the opinion of others, although he himself was a strict Calvinist. He subscribed to the doctrine of human depravity and exhorted his children to remember that the fear of God was the beginning of wisdom. Carter Braxton of Virginia (1736-1797) advocated likewise the cause of religious liberty. Educated at William and Mary, he was an intelligent man who, while favoring independence from England, feared the democratic " ravings " of a goodly number of Americans. In 1785, he supported the cause of " soul freedom " in the Old Dominion in spite of the fact that he was an active churchman. Like Braxton, Francis Hopkinson of Pennsylvania (1737-1791) was an Anglican who was interested in ecclesiastical matters. In 1789, he served as secretary of a convention of the Episcopal Church. Samuel Huntington, Philip Livingston, John Witherspoon, Abraham Clark and James Smith were all orthodox Christians. Huntington (1732-1796), destined to become governor of Connecticut, was a "friend" of religion and a "member of the Christian Church". His faith in Christian principles was said to have been unshaken and he was accustomed to preach sermons on them. Like Huntington, Livingston of New York (1716-1778) was "a firm believer in the sublime truths of religion, and a humble follower of our divine Saviour." Witherspoon (1722-1794), President of Princeton, was a strict Presbyterian divine whose orthodoxy was unquestioned. His colleague from New Jersey, Clark (1726-1794), was also a devout Presbyterian, while Smith of Pennsylvania (c. 1713-1800), although inclined to joke, never allowed himself to utter a witty remark at the expense of religion or the clergy.[12]

Differences as to religious opinions prevailed not only among the signers of the Declaration of Independence but also among other Revolutionary leaders. Willie Jones, a member of the Continental Congress from North Carolina, Edmund Randolph, a prominent Virginian statesman, Ethan Allen, hero of Ticonderoga and Thomas Paine, writer of *Common Sense* rejected either implicitly or explicitly the Christian revelation. Even though George Washington, James Madison and George Mason did not go so far, their views on religion were distinctly liberal. On the other hand, Samuel Adams, Patrick Henry and Henry Laurens were religious conservatives. A Puritan of the Puritans, Samuel Adams desired the good people of Boston to follow in the paths of Bradford, Winthrop and other early New England worthies. He also urged that the state should carefully supervise the morals of its people. Moreover, in line with his Puritan heritage, Adams showed himself most hostile

[12] Sanderson (ed.), *op. cit.*, vol. iii, pp. 77, 109-10, 114, 192, 290-1, 306; vol. iv, pp. 104-5, 126-7; vol. vii. pp. 182, 235; *Dictionary of American Biography*, vol. ii, pp. 609-10; vol. iv, p. 119; vol. ix, p. 222; and Boutell, *The Life of Roger Sherman* (Chicago, 1896), pp. 271-3, 275-7, 280.

to Catholicism which he felt was subversive of civil liberty. In 1768, he wrote a series of articles for a Boston newspaper in which he suggested that the New England towns should stamp out " Popery " (this only ten years before the French Alliance!). That the Bible was divinely revealed and that its miracles were valid were accepted by him without question. Later he pleaded with Paine to abandon so unworthy a cause as deism and suggested that the defender of the Rights of Man direct his talents along other lines than those of "unchristianizing" good Americans.[13] Another firm believer in orthodoxy was Patrick Henry who attended church regularly and desired to see religion supported. The Virginian lawyer was a bitter opponent of freethinking; according to his leading biographer,[14] he was among the few who realized " the undermining influence of French infidelity." To check the progress of deism, Henry printed, in 1789, at his own expense, Soame Jenyns' *View of the Internal Evidences of the Christian Religion,* a book reputed to be anti-deistic. This work he circulated free of charge particularly among professional people. Convinced of the truth of Christianity, Henry is said to have written an answer to Paine's *Age of Reason* which, however, he destroyed before his death. Laurens of South Carolina, merchant, planter and President of the Continental Congress in 1777, was an active member of the Anglican Church who entertained distinctly orthodox views. He knew the Bible intimately; believed in its divine origin; and required his children to read it. Yet, Laurens was not a bigot; he was opposed to holding men's consciences in " leading strings." A liberal

[13] S. Adams, *Writings*, ed. Cushing (New York, 1904), vol. i, pp. 202-3, vol. ii, pp. 269, 271, vol. iii, p. 286, vol. iv, p. 238 and T. Paine, *Writings*, ed. Conway (New York, 1898), vol. iv, pp. 201-2.

[14] W. W. Henry, *Patrick Henry, Life, Correspondence and Speeches* (New York, 1891), vol. ii, p. 200.

in the best sense of the word, he even refused to condemn Voltaire on the ground that he knew too little about the Frenchman.[15]

During the Revolutionary War, Americans came in contact with French soldiers and officers who, according to contemporary New England accounts, were responsible for the spread of a militant freethinking movement. The large majority who came to defend the new Republic were not " without faith and morals ", despite the assertions of pious commentators. Outwardly, at least, the French were religious; they were willing to face the possibility of derision rather than renounce the public celebration of the mass. This sacrament was held in many communities where Catholicism was regarded as " a superstitious and idolatrous religion." Moreover, the men who led the French forces in America were, for the most part, more concerned with military than intellectual pursuits; some of them were old soldiers like Rochambeau, a veteran of the Seven Year's War, or young ones like Count Berthier, later to become Napoleon's chief of staff. The youthful Saint-Simon, destined to be the first great socialist theorist of the coming century, the brilliant Marquis de Chastellux, described by Franklin as " a friend of humanity ", and the scholarly Count de Ségur, the historian, were notable exceptions to the general rule. As was to be expected, some skeptics could be found among the French officers; one of these was de Lauzun whose " sage " observations on philosophy, morality, history and religion so delighted Frederick the Great that the Prussian monarch desired him to remain in Berlin as French ambassador. Whether the skeptical Duke " made " a single American doubt the Christian revelation, as von Steuben " caused " Timothy Pickering to question the Trinity, is

[15] D. D. Wallace, *The Life of Henry Laurens* (New York, 1915), pp. 181, 438-40.

problematic and in the absence of evidence is difficult to ascertain.

The rise of a more intense anti-clerical feeling rather than the " influence " of French culture was responsible for the impetus given to deism after 1783. In that year, a number of American states had established churches and religious discriminations of one sort or another. To the advocates of liberalism, it seemed obvious that liberty meant freedom not only from English but from ecclesiastical interference. In order to destroy clerical meddling, they thought it necessary to undermine priestly pretensions to authority. To achieve this purpose, the deists adopted two methods of approach. First, most of them endeavored to show that the real teachings of Christ, said to be essentially deistic, were perverted by his followers who substituted for them rituals, creeds and churches. In turn, these, the deists held, led to bloody struggles within Christendom. To do away with internal strife, it was necessary to destroy the power of the priesthood and restore the simple teachings of Jesus or, in other words, natural religion. The second approach, being motivated by a more intense anti-clerical feeling, was by far more militant and attracted fewer supporters. These men trained their guns of destructive criticism upon the citadel of the Christian revelation upon which rested clerical pretensions to speak authoritatively. They were convinced that once this fortress fell, the power of the clergy would be forever shattered and the new dispensation begun.

The call for a bolder deism was subtly presented in an article entitled " A Disquisition on Rational Christianity " which appeared in *The Boston Magazine* for 1783. Although the name of the author was not given, it has been definitely established that an Englishman, Soame Jenyns, wrote this pretty little piece.[13] Jenyns (1704-1787) acquired

[16] L. N. Richardson, *History of Early American Magazines*, pp. 218-9.

197609

quite a reputation for himself as a literary figure. In 1776, his *View of the Internal Evidences of the Christian Religion,* which went through ten editions and was translated into several foreign languages, appeared. The exacting Dr. Johnson thought that the work was not very "theological" but the pious Hannah More was happy to note that it was responsible for the conversion of a "philosophical infidel". The book itself called forth a great controversy; some rejoiced that Jenyns had discarded his early skepticism, others, questioning his sincerity, thought that he was still poking fun at the Christian religion. This then was the author whose work *The Boston Magazine* thought fit to reprint. Stripping the Englishman's "Disquisition on Rational Christianity" of its cynicism, the work represented a thrust at the Christian religion. To Jenyns, the Christian drama of salvation appeared "so adverse to all the principles of human reason, that, if brought before her tribunal, it must be inevitably condemned. . . ." Moreover, revelation could not be based on reason because it implied something above the rational. Ironically, the writer held that although various denominational churches could be represented as Christian, rationalists did not deserve this designation because they rejected all Christian doctrines "as impious, ridiculous and contradictory to the justice of God and the reason of man. . . ." In conclusion, the author called upon "the religious and moral deist" to assert his faith, since deism could not be considered as disgraceful to a virtuous man's character. This article was hotly resented by the faithful and was answered by Aaron Dexter, Professor of Chemistry and Materia Medica at Harvard, under the pseudonym of a "Rational Christian".

About this time, "a religious and moral deist" proclaimed his faith in no uncertain terms. Convinced that the clergy had subverted the "religion of Reason, Nature and Truth", Ethan Allen published a distinctly anti-Christian work,

Reason the Only Oracle of Man. During his youth, the future leader of the Green Mountain " boys " came into contact with an English physician, Thomas Young, who probably acquainted him with Blount and other deistic writers. It is believed that Allen and Young at first agreed to write a freethinking work together but later decided that the one who outlived the other was to publish the book. Since Allen survived Young, he inherited the latter's notes.[17] In his preface to *Reason, the Only Oracle of Man,* Allen frankly admitted that he was not a Christian and consequently his book was one long diatribe against the religion of his birth. In condemning the Trinitarian doctrine as unreasonable and unintelligible, and in discarding a belief in the original fall of man as irrational and " chimerical ",[18] he repudiated the basic tenets of the Christian creed. Furthermore, he rejected prophecies on the ground that they were often vague, questionable and contradictory. Likewise he discarded miracles since their performance implied that God had created an imperfect machine.[19] Pointing out the possibilities of Biblical fallibility, Allen rejected the divine origin of the Scriptures and assailed particularly the Old Testament accounts of the creation of the world and the death of Moses.[20] Anticipating Paine, the hero of Ticonderoga showed how impossible it was for Moses to have written that portion of Deuteronomy which dealt with an account of his

[17] J. Pell, *Ethan Allen* (Boston, 1929), pp. 16, 226; H. Hall, *Ethan Allen, the Robin Hood of Vermont* (New York, 1892), p. 21; and Koch, *Republican Religion,* pp. 31-2.

[18] Allen, *Reason, the Only Oracle of Man* (New York, 1836), pp. 73, 81-2. In view of his Trinitarian position, Allen rejected the divinity of Jesus (pp. 75-6).

[19] Concerning the arguments against prophecies see *ibid.,* pp. 52-7, 62-6; and those against miracles, pp. 40-6.

[20] *Ibid.,* pp. 13-4, 42, 59.

own death.[21]   In short, the work was a rejection of revealed
religion in general, and Christianity in particular.

Allen's repudiation of Christianity was based on his conviction of the sufficiency of natural religion.   To him,
reason, upon which true religion must be based, would lead
men to exalt God and to practice morality.   Like his
fellow-deists, he accepted the existence of one God and the
human duty of divine worship.   Virtuous living, which
conformed to "right reason", was conducive to happiness
and those practicing it would be rewarded here and hereafter.[22]   Since the religion of nature was rational, it was
"universally promulgated to mankind. . . ."   In brief,
Ethan Allen attempted from a positive viewpoint to substitute
for the particular revelation of the Christian faith the all-
embracing revelation of natural religion.

Although *Reason, the Only Oracle of Man* was later described by one sympathetic observer as "a work valuable
from its own intrinsic merits . . .", it was far from being
either original or intellectually stimulating.   Yet, because it
was among the first anti-Christian works to be produced in
America, its author attracted some attention.   The poetic
Dwight of Yale described Allen in the following lines:

> In vain thro realms of nonsense . . . . . ran
> The great clodhopping oracle of man.
> Yet faithful were his toils: What could he more?
> In Satan's cause he bustled, bruised and swore.

Another staunch defender of the faith pictured Allen
as "an ignorant and profane deist . . . who died with
a mind replete with horror and despair. . . ."   Still a third
believer, not content to have him die in this manner, con-

---

[21] Compare Allen, *ibid.*, p. 59 with Paine, *Age of Reason*, pt. ii, p. 107.

[22] *Ibid.*, pp. 7-9, 20, 29, 97, 100.

signed him to the punishments of the infernal regions. In his diary, Ezra Stiles, President of Yale College, wrote that on February 13, 1789 there " died in Vermont the profane and impious Deist Gen. Ethan Allen, Author of the ' Oracle of Reason ', a book replete with scurrilous Reflexions on Revelation. . . ." The good clergyman piously added " ' And in Hell he lift up his Eyes being in Torments.' " [23]

Because of a fire in the printer's garret almost all of the copies of Allen's work were destroyed. Yet, the few which remained circulated rather widely. William Bentley, a liberal clergyman of Salem, loaned the book to a Colonel C. who promised to keep the transaction a secret. He, in turn, loaned the work to a Mr. Grafton who soon died a " Confirmed Infidel." The relatives of the latter found the book in the dead man's home. Since the treatise was initialed W. B. (William Bentley), Bentley was accused of being its owner and of encouraging skepticism.[24] Another evidence of the circulation of *Reason, the Only Oracle of Man* was an article appearing in *The Country Journal and the Poughkeepsie Advertiser* for September 12, 1787 (no. 110). The writer, describing himself as " Black Beard ", compared Rhode Island with the Barbary States. He thought that the principles of these two commonwealths were similar in every respect " except in religion, and in this they may become nearly so by . . . adopting the ' Oracle of Reason ' for an Alcoran. . . ."

Another Revolutionary War leader, Charles Lee, was accused of being " an enemy of religion ". In a letter to

[23] E. Stiles, *Diary*, ed. Dexter, vol. iii, p. 345; U. Ogden, *Antidote to Deism* (Newark, 1795), vol. ii, p. 270 (footnote) ; T. Dwight, *Triumph of Infidelity* (New York, 1788), pp. 23-4; *Travels in New England and New York* (London, 1823), vol. ii, pp. 387-8; and the *Free Enquirer*, April 8, 1829, vol. i, p. 191.

[24] W. Bentley, *Diary*, November, 1787, vol. i, p. 82.

Dr. Benjamin Rush, dated September 26, 1779, Lee denied the charge and, in the characteristic fashion of an eighteenth-century deist, he pointed out that " no Society [could] exist without religion "; that of all faiths " the most excellent " was that of Christianity provided it was " unincumbered of its sophistications ".   On another occasion, he informed the celebrated Philadelphian physician of his desire to become an orthodox Christian.   With this in mind, he read Dr. Warburton's account of the divine laws of Moses but, as he put it, his choice was " injudicious " for he went away utterly detesting " the God of the Jews."   He consequently asked Dr. Rush to "recommend [him] to some other Apothecary. . . ." [25]   In his will, Lee showed his deistic inclinations; he gave his soul to

the Creator of all worlds and of all creatures; who must from his visible attributes, be indifferent to their modes of worship or creeds, whether Christians, Mahometans or Jews; whether instilled by education, or taken up by reflection; whether more or less absurd; as a weak mortal can no more be answerable for his persuasions, notions, or even skepticism in religion, than for the colour of his skin.[26]

Regarded as "erratic and untrustworthy ", General Lee was at least logical in his refusal to be buried in a church or churchyard on the ground that he did not choose to continue to keep " bad company " when dead.[27]   Less outspoken than Lee, Willie Jones of North Carolina, merchant, planter and member of the Continental Congress, was a freethinker on the style of Jefferson.   Like the Virginian, he hated the

[25] *The Lee Papers*, vol. iii, p. 468 (New York Historical Society *Collections*, 1871-74).

[26] *Ibid.*, vol. iv, pp. 31-2.

[27] *Ibid.*, vol. iv, p. 31.   See also Meade, *Old Churches, etc.*, vol. ii, p. 308 and Fiske, *Essays Historical and Literary* (New York, 1902), vol. i, p. 64.

clergy and consequently directed his heirs not to allow any minister to say anything over his body. Still another prominent Revolutionary figure, Stephen Hopkins, Governor of Rhode Island, was a freethinker or, at least, was so regarded by his contemporaries. Under the date of July 20, 1785, Ezra Stiles, in commenting on the death of the former governor, wrote that he was convinced that the friends of Hopkins were correct in describing him as a deist. The good President of Yale continued: " He was a Man of a Noble fortitude & Resolution. He was a glorious Patriot!—[but Jesus will say unto him *I know you not*]."

In the meantime, a Boston magazine was reproducing the writings of leading European deists. Voltaire's prayer addressed to the " God of all beings, of all worlds and of all ages . . ." was republished from his *Treatise on Toleration.*[28] Another deistic composition appeared in a New York periodical, *The American Magazine*. In 1788, its readers were requested by " Candidus " to explain certain supposed discrepancies in the New Testament accounts as to the genealogy of Jesus, his anointing by a woman, his being reviled on the cross by thieves and the actual hour of his crucifixion. The writer ironically stated that any gentleman who reconciled the different accounts of the Evangelists " would deserve the thanks of his christian friends." He was answered in the very next number by another anonymous writer who not only attempted to resolve his deistic opponent's doubts but also advised " Candidus " to read a few books on the evidences of Christianity.[29] In addition to the magazines, the newspapers served to spread deistic speculation. *The Country Journal and Dutchess and Ulster County Farmer's Register* for January 20, 1789 (no. 181) published upon request an article in which some imaginary Indian chiefs advocated

[28] *The Boston Magazine*, June, 1784 (no. 8), vol. i, pp. 338-9.

[29] *The American Magazine*, May, 1788, pp. 420-1 ; June, 1788, pp. 491-2.

deistic principles. This composition was similar to one published in 1752 by James Parker.[30]

As a result of increased activity, especially after 1783,
deism began to spread among the people some of whom discussed and openly espoused its cause. In 1772, Francis
Asbury, a Methodist-Episcopalian minister, making a trip
from Trenton to Philadelphia, met a group of men whom he
described as "stupidly ignorant, sceptical [and] deistical.
. . ." That deism was a common topic of conversation is
shown in letters addressed to newspapers. One correspondent, in the *New-York Packet* for March 24, 1785 (no. 474),
informed his readers that he, together with a clergyman and
two others, argued the merits of revealed religion. Another
writer, " Pietas ", sent a letter to the same newspaper in
which he denounced all who aired skeptical thoughts without
the least provocation. In this communication, the correspondent related that upon one occasion he was in the company of a rather elderly gentleman and a number of " young
wits ". Without any reason, the young men presented
arguments against Christianity whereupon the older man
impressed upon them the uselessness of their " profanity." [31]

The constituted authorities were aware of the social and
political dynamite frequently hidden in apparently harmless
religious or intellectual heresies, and sometimes intervened
to check the progress of deism. John Dickinson, President
of the State of Delaware, issued, in 1781, a proclamation
against freethinking which was reprinted in *The Pennsylvania Gazette and Weekly Advertiser* for June 23, 1782. In
an introductory article, the editor congratulated Dickinson

[30] See chapter iii, p. 77. It is interesting to note that this same
speech was reproduced in a deistic New York newspaper, *The Correspondent*, January 5, 1828 (No. 24), vol. ii, pp. 372-4.

[31] *New-York Packet*, April 28, 1785 (No. 484). This letter was addressed to the *American Spectator*. For Asbury's observation see his
Journal (New York, 1821), vol. i, p. 120.

upon his advocacy of revealed religion and observed that a pronouncement from so distinguished a personage would do much to check " vice and infidelity ". The Delaware proclamation called upon all rational creatures to submit to the holy laws of God, to attend His worship and to practice true virtue. Moreover, it called upon the magistrates to prosecute and punish all who were guilty of blasphemy or profanity. Dickinson's proclamation was followed by a number of newspaper and magazine articles written by pious Christians to stem the deistic tide. The young were especially warned against the pitfalls of deistic speculation. In *The Providence Gazette and Country Journal* for September 24, 1785 (no. 1134), the work of a noted English Dissenter, Dr. Isaac Watts (1674-1748), on *Advice To a Young Man, upon His Entrance into the World,* was reprinted. The famous hymn writer counselled his readers against gambling their " eternal interests in the world to come, upon the mere light of nature. . . ." Moreover, all those who rejected " the blessings of divine revelation and grace " were conceited and thoughtless. In the same vein, a Boston newspaper, *The Continental Journal and Weekly Advertiser* for January 5, 1786 (no. 515), warned the people that " the cool and deliberate villainy of infidels [could not] be compared with one hour of conscious rectitude, far less than with their felicity, who at their last moments, have witnessed in what peace a Christian [could] die."

The vagueness of the deistic philosophy was further pointed out by William Livingston, Governor of New Jersey, whose article, " Thoughts on Deism," was printed repeatedly in the magazines of the period under the pseudonym of " Hortensius ".[32] In this essay, the writer asserted that

[32] *The New-Haven Gazette, and the Connecticut Magazine*, June 22, 1786; *The American Museum*, November, 1788 and *The Massachusetts Magazine*, January, 1789. For an eulogistic sermon upon Livingston see the *Universal Asylum*, January, 1791, pp. 7-8.

deists were "superficial reasoners" who preached a morality which did not surpass in practice that exercised by a horse. The light of nature, he held, was an insufficient guide in matters concerning salvation. Could any one, he asked, believe that the moral precepts of Christianity had been destroyed by "the unphilosophical philosophy of a Boling-broke, or the wretched pun or threadbare jest of a Voltaire or a Rousseau"? Deism, unlike Christianity, could not account for the entrance of sin into the world, or could not prove the immortality of the soul. In conclusion, "Horten-sius" represented the deists as simple blockheads.

Deism was answered not only with ridicule but also with a reasoned defense of Christian miracles and prophecies. Upon these evidences the validity of the Biblical revelation was believed to rest; consequently the faithful were extremely anxious to popularize their views. In 1785, in a series of newspaper articles, "American Spectator" defended the necessity of a "particular Providence" and the truth of Christianity. In order to vindicate his first position, he held that it would be absurd to imagine that the Deity created worlds only to forget them. From this, he concluded that a miracle-working Providence existed. That Christianity was of divine origin could be attested by its prophecies, miracles, moral excellence, and rapid spread.[33] Similarly, a writer in a New Haven periodical sought to prove the truth of the Christian revelation. To him, miracles were not only possible, since the Deity could suspend or alter natural laws, but also rational since they were as much an evidence of divine power as His natural works. Especially did he defend the miracles of Jesus as both divine and duly attested. Furthermore, he doubted whether the deists would have believed the miracles of Jesus, even if they had actually wit-

[33] *New-York Packet*, August 29, September 19, October 3 and 10, 1785 (Nos. 519, 525, 529, 531).

nessed their performance.[34] A New Jersey magazine also
came to the aid of Christian evidences. The very aim of
The Christian's, Scholar's and Farmer's Magazine was " to
advance the general interests of our holy religion. . . ."
That Jesus actually lived, that he was the Messiah and that
the morality of the New Testament was consistent with divine
goodness were argued by the orthodox within the pages of
this Elizabethtown magazine.[35]

The champions of Christianity attacked deistic speculation
through the medium not only of periodicals but also of
lectures. In 1783, William Hazlitt, an English Unitarian,
came to America and, during that year and the one following,
delivered a series of public discourses in Philadelphia and
Boston. His talks were well attended and favorably
received. In one sermon, he associated American prosperity
with belief in the Christian revelation and pleaded with his
hearers to teach the Scriptures to their children and servants.
He urged, however, the encouragement of free enquiry in
the hope that by such a procedure Christianity would be
purged of its accretions.[36] From a more orthodox stand-
point, Ezra Stiles delivered sermons designed to support the
Christian revelation. In an Election Day address (1783),
he assailed the arguments of Hume, Voltaire, Tindal and
that " amiable Confucius of Deism," Shaftesbury. He also
condemned the deistic procedure of glorifying all religions
but that of Christianity. Stiles took the position that deism
could not be checked " by hiding the Deistical writings "
but by refuting them and consequently, as President of Yale,

[34] *The New-Haven Gazette* and *Connecticut Magazine*, November 30,
December 7, 14 and 21, 1786 (Nos. 42-45). These essays were entitled
"A Dissertation on Miracles ".

[35] *The Christian's, Scholar's, and Farmer's Magazine*, vol. i, pp. 18-22,
149, 153, 286, 408-11.

[36] W. Hazlitt, *A Thanksgiving Discourse*, December 15, 1785 (Boston,
1786), pp. 8-11, 13-17.

he allowed his students to debate such subjects as whether the historical parts of the Bible were of divine inspiration; whether there was anything in the Scriptures which was contradictory to reason; and whether religion had on the whole benefited mankind.   In 1790, the good minister requested the aged Franklin to state his religious views, especially those concerning Jesus of Nazareth.   In his answer, the venerable Doctor affirmed his faith in the deistic creed of his youth. Subscribing to the three basic tenets of natural religion, he refused to say a single word as to the need of supplementing these articles by any revealed religion.   In regard to Jesus, Franklin was convinced that his original system of morality and religion, before it became corrupted, was " the best the World ever saw or is likely to see. . . ."   The skeptical philosopher, however, had some doubts as to the divinity of Christ.   Tactful to the end, the eighty-four year old man thought that it was needless for him to busy himself with the question because he soon expected to have "an Opportunity to know the Truth with less Trouble. . . ." [37]

As the Revolutionary era was drawing to a close, the northern defenders of orthodoxy secured an addition to their ranks in the person of Timothy Dwight whose *Triumph of Infidelity* appeared in 1788.   In the opinion of Stiles, Dwight's poetic work harmed rather than promoted the cause he intended to defend, since the author had not confined himself to a criticism of the deists, but had gone so far as to vilify them with an acrimony decidedly un-Christian.[38]   *The Triumph of Infidelity* was addressed to Voltaire, who had taught that " the chief end of man was to slander his God, and abuse him forever."   In the poem proper, such English deists as Herbert and Bolingbroke were described as leaders

---

[37] Stiles, *Diary*, ed. Dexter, vol. iii, p. 387; Franklin, *Writings*, ed. Smyth, vol. x, p. 84.

[38] E. Stiles, *Diary*, ed. Dexter, vol. iii, p. 326 (August 15, 1788).

in "Satan's cause". Moreover, these thinkers had been aided in their iniquity by such lesser lights as Toland, Tindal, Collins, Chubb, Morgan and Woolston, all of whom "help'd rakes to sin. . . ." [39] If these deists were to win the day, usury and immorality would be widespread, since modern freethinkers were free from all principles and virtues. Roundly abusing the " heathen " ideas of the Chinese, Dwight indirectly assailed those deists who were accustomed to praise all faiths except that of Christianity. In a hopeful note, the satire ended with the prophecy that virtue would triumph over vice, true religion over " infidelity ".

The poem was rather harshly criticized in the July 1788 number of *The American Magazine.* Its editor, Noah Webster, who reviewed the work, was at that time on un-friendly terms with Dwight because the latter had just agreed to contribute to *The American Museum,* a rival periodical published by Carey. While Webster was willing to admit that *The Triumph of Infidelity* had some poetic merit, he felt that it could never pass for true wit or good satire. He severely censured Dwight for his abusive description of the religious ideas of the Chinese. This the critic thought had been written because the Chinese were not Christians. Web-ster further held that Dwight was a "theological dogmatist " who was not destined to achieve a heaven reserved for love and benevolence. This article, however, was not typical of the religious ideas of Noah Webster which were distinctly orthodox. The celebrated lexicographer was brought up in a Calvinistic household and although, according to his own testimony, he at first became a " rational Christian ", he later defended evangelicalism. He even went so far as to con-tribute to the *Panoplist,* an orthodox magazine of the early nineteenth century, and one of his articles was printed in

[39] Dwight, *Triumph of Infidelity,* p. 16. As for Voltaire, Dwight thought him so superficial a reasoner that he could prove anything (p. 18).

pamphlet form under the title of *The Peculiar Doctrines of the Gospel Explained and Defended*. In this work, he defended the Calvinistic doctrines of predestination and election, affirmed his belief in the historic truthfulness of the Bible and accepted the miracles of Jesus as evidences of his divine mission. In conclusion, Webster regretted to see " a large portion of the world so inattentive to religion." [40]

As during the provincial period, so now, deistic speculation was less conspicious in the South than in the North. Yet, in Virginia, it was more prevalent than ever before, chiefly because of an increasing anti-clerical spirit stimulated, in turn, by the struggle for the disestablishment of the Anglican Church. Up to 1776, the fight waged in Virginia by the dissenting denominations was one for religious toleration; after that year, it became a battle for religious liberty. In 1776, a law was passed suspending the salaries of Anglican clergymen with the result that many of them were forced to leave their flocks. Eight years later, the Dissenters won a notable victory by defeating the general assessment bill providing for the support of religious teachers. Though in the same year, the Episcopalians recovered some lost ground through the passage of an incorporation act, their victory was shortlived and the following year brought the passage of the Act for Establishing Religious Freedom.

The Presbyterians and Baptists of Virginia were aided in their struggle to disestablish the Anglican Church by the deistic Jefferson and the liberal Madison. Both of these men, moved by an anti-clerical spirit, objected to grants of public funds for religious support. They were opposed by Patrick Henry whose hostility to deism made him associate that movement with everything vicious and depraved. The

---

[40] Scudder, *Noah Webster* (Boston, 1882), pp. 167-8; and Noah Webster, *The Peculiar Doctrines of the Gospel Explained and Defended* (Poughkeepsie, 1809), pp. 8-9, 13, 15.

fight for disestablishment naturally stimulated an interest in religious questions and made the more advanced thinkers react with such force against Christianity that they were drawn into the deistic camp. During the Revolutionary era a large number of prominent Virginian statesmen were either deists at one time or another or held liberal religious views. Coming under the last category were such notable figures as Washington, Mason and Madison. Washington, because of his great popularity, was and still is claimed alike by the friends of orthodoxy and of freethinking. As early as 1800, Jefferson remarked that, according to Gouverneur Morris, the Father of his Country did not subscribe to the Christian system of religion. Thirty years later, another freethinker, Frances Wright, declared in a speech that " . . . Washington was not a Christian—that is, he believed not in the priest's God, nor in the divine authority of the priest's book." [41] Since then, others have classified him as a deist.[42] The stand taken by this group has been based on the evidence that Washington always mentioned God in deistic rather than Biblical phraseology, that he refused to kneel in prayer or request the presence of a clergyman at his death-bed and that he continually refrained from making any affirmative statement in support of Christianity. In answer to these contentions, the orthodox have presented such counter-proofs as the testimony of his contemporaries, the "high religious motives" actuating his military leadership, his attendance at church and service as vestryman, his reference in 1783 to the "benign influence" of revelation, his response to religious

[41] T. Jefferson, *Writings*, ed. P. L. Ford (New York, 1892), vol. i, p. 284; Wright, *Course of Popular Lectures* (New York, 1831), pp. 10-11.

[42] J. McCabe, "Six Infidel Presidents" (*Haldeman-Julius Quarterly* April, 1927, pp. 37-40) ; J. M. Robertson, *Short History of Free Thought* (London, 1915), vol. ii, pp. 382-3; W. E. Woodward, *George Washington* (New York, 1926), p. 284; and R. Hughes, *George Washington, 1777-1781* (New York, 1930), pp. 270-98 (especially pp. 286-98).

denominations in 1789, and his farewell address.[43]   With such conflicting assertions based equally on well established facts and utterances, the classification of Washington in a definite category is impossible.   To one not interested in furthering causes it is apparent that the Virginian professed to be a Christian, although he showed the deistic tendencies of his age.   His skeptical leanings, however, were never strong enough to make him openly renounce Christianity. If anything, he should have desired it to continue as a vital force in the life of the young Republic because he was firmly convinced that religion and morality were " the essentials pillars of civil society. . . ."

George Mason was even less deistic in tendency than Washington.   Although regarded as a liberal in religion, he was never accused by his contemporaries of being a freethinker or deist.   He was a regular church member, a vestryman and together with Washington supervised the construction of a house of worship.   Mason believed firmly in the doctrine of religious liberty and true to his convictions he took an active part in the disestablishment of the Anglican Church in Virginia.   His course throughout the struggle was a consistent one; as a liberal, he desired to see the Anglican Church placed on an equal footing with others; as a Christian, he wanted the church to continue its functions and therefore fought to secure its property.   His liberal religious views were reflected in the Virginia Bill of Rights and although some claim that Henry was the author of its religious clauses, it appears that Mason composed them.[44]   To Mason, religion

[43] W. Meade, *Old Churches, etc.*, vol. ii, pp. 243-5; G. Washington, *Writings*, ed. J. Sparks (Boston, 1855), vol. xii, pp. 399-403, 411 (Religious Opinions and Habits of Washington); George Washington, *The Christian* (issued by U. S. George Washington Bicentennial Commission, prepared by A. B. Hart), (Washington, 1931), pp. 1-16; and Sears, *George Washington* (New York, 1932), pp. 6-7, 113, 127-8, 254, 322, 409.

[44] The religious provisions of the Virginia Bill of Rights have been

was simply the duty owed by man to his Creator. It was to be discharged by the individual as his reason and conviction dictated. In the exercise of religion, man was to enjoy the fullest toleration. Mason believed that it was " the mutual duty of all to practice Christian forbearance, love and charity towards each other." [45]

Like other Virginians, James Madison, historical, legal and theological scholar, was caught up by the deistic currents of his age and was almost swept into the deistic whirlpool. As an ardent advocate of religious liberty, he viewed with disgust the " diabolical, hell-conceived principles of persecution " which prevailed among Christian sects and to which " business " the clergy were always eager to furnish " their " quota of imps. . . ." During the struggle for disestablishment, Madison made an important speech on the question of the Assessment Bill. Desiring to know upon what basis the courts would decide what constituted Christianity, the future President was led to raise such skeptical questions as: Was the entire Bible or only a few of its parts inspired? What copy, translation or edition of the Scriptures would be used? Unfortunately, Madison did not answer the questions which he raised and therefore the extent of his deistic leanings remains problematic. At least, this seems

ascribed to Henry on the basis of Edmund Randolph's testimony written thirty years after the events took place. Randolph's statement is unsupported by contemporary evidence; nowhere did Henry assert his authorship of these articles nor was such a claim made during his lifetime. Conway, the biographer of Edmund Randolph, thinks that Randolph was mistaken in the entire matter. (M. D. Conway, *Omitted Chapters of History Disclosed in the Life and Papers of Edmund Randolph* [New York, 1889], p. 158). On the other hand, Mason himself declared that he wrote the Bill of Rights. (Rowland, *The Life of George Mason* [New York, 1892], vol. i, pp. 236-8).

[45] J. Madison, *Writings*, ed. Hunt (New York, 1900), vol. i, p. 40; Rowland, *op. cit.*, vol. i, pp. 84, 113, 241, 243-4, 344; and Sherlock, *Tall Timbers* (Boston, 1926), pp. 12-3, 33.

certain: the Virginian never rejected Christianity; on the contrary in a letter written as late as 1832, he described it as " the best and purest religion." [46]

More to the left than Madison, Mason or Washington was Thomas Jefferson, whose position was typical of the American climate of deistic opinion, which desired the reformation and not destruction of Christianity. Convinced that the " real" enemies of the gentle Jesus were the clergy, he proposed to strip them of their power. To accomplish this end, the Sage of Monticello adopted a rather cautious approach; instead of aggressively assailing the Biblical revelation upon which priestly authority rested, he contented himself with drawing a nice distinction between " the religion of the priests and that of the Gospels." The first he desired to overthrow; the second, which he considered to be natural religion, he wished to restore. Interested in the intellectual concerns of the age, the prominent Virginian read Bolingbroke, Shaftesbury, Priestley, Voltaire and Rousseau. [47] In spite of his acquaintance with the writings of Voltaire, Jefferson's deism was not that of the militant French school; rather was it similar to the position of such English deists as Tindal and Chubb who were anxious " to save " Christianity. To the author of the American Declaration of Independence, reason was to be given first place in the task of reforming

[46] Madison, *Writings*, ed. Hunt, vol. i, p. 21, vol. ii, pp. 88-9, vol. ix, p. 485; Meade, *Old Churches, etc.*, vol. ii, pp. 99-100; and Rives, *Life and Times of James Madison* (Boston, 1859), vol. i, p. 603.

[47] Jefferson, *Writings*, ed. Ford (New York, 1892), vol. ii, p. 95; Chinard, *Thomas Jefferson* (Boston, 1929), p. 26; B. Faÿ, *Revolutionary Spirit in France and America* (New York, 1928), p. 78; H. S. Randall, *Life of Thomas Jefferson* (New York, 1858), p. 556 and Riley, *American Philosophy* (New York, 1907), pp. 268-9. Both Riley and Randall contend that Priestley, the English Unitarian, exerted a tremendous influence upon Jefferson's religious views. According to Chinard, Jefferson owed very little to Bolingbroke but a great deal to the Stoic philosophers of Greece with whose ideas he came in contact through Cicero.

the Christian religion which was to be purged of its existing corruptions. To Jefferson, the moral system of Jesus was " the most benevolent and sublime probably that has ever been taught. . . ." The moral precepts of Christ, however, had been corrupted by those pretending to be his disciples. In reality, these false prophets had

disfigured and sophisticated his actions and precepts, from views of personal interest, so as to induce the unthinking part of mankind to throw off the whole system in disgust, and to pass sentence as an impostor on the most innocent, the most benevolent, the most eloquent and sublime character that has ever been exhibited to man. . . .[48]

The Sage of Monticello endeavored to recall Christians to the simple gospel first expounded by Christ. This gospel was in reality a restatement of the religion of nature, since it taught a belief in one God, the practice of virtue and the existence of a future state.[49] For his deistic leanings, Jefferson was bitterly assailed by the New England clergy. Although described in 1784 by the Reverend Dr. Stiles as " a truly scientific and learned Man—and every way excellent . . .", by 1800 he was characterized by the Congregational ministry as " the arch-apostle of the cause of irreligion and freethought." [50] This change in tone was undoubtedly due as much to Jefferson's political as to his religious views.

Unlike the third American President, neither Edmund nor John Randolph remained true to the deistic faith of their youth. While a student at William and Mary, Edmund Randolph was " poisoned " by two of his " preceptors, who,

[48] Jefferson, *Writings*, ed. Ford, vol. viii, p. 225.

[49] *Ibid.*, vol. iii, p. 264; vol. iv, pp. 430, 432; vol. viii, pp. 21-2, 224-5 (footnote), 228.

[50] Stiles, *Diary*, ed. Dexter, vol. iii, p. 125; Stauffer, *New England and the Bavarian Illuminati* (New York, 1918), p. 121.

though of the ministry," encouraged him to read books on
" infidelity ".   In a like fashion, Thomas Jefferson was probably open to the same " pernicious " influences during his
student days at the Williamsburg seat of learning.   Here, in
the early 'sixties, he came in contact with a liberal-minded
professor, William Small, and a deistically-inclined future
professor, George Wythe, both of whom exerted an influence
upon the impressionable young man.   "Infidelity" at
William and Mary was, however, fought by the forces of
orthodoxy which opposed the appointment of any trustee
who was not a Christian.   In fact, John Randolph (1728-
1784), the father of Edmund, was twice rejected as a Visitor
of William and Mary College because he was regarded as a
deist.   Edmund Randolph followed in his father's footsteps;
according to his own testimony given many years later, he
was so confirmed a deist in 1776 that had it not been for
the piety of his wife he might never have forsaken his
" infidel " views.   Her " sacred regard " for the Bible eventually " converted " him to Christianity; in the last years of
his life he found comfort in Wesley's sermons.[51]   Another
Randolph, John of Roanoke, strayed from the fold and
became a champion of an unpopular cause.   Influenced by
Shaftesbury, Bolingbroke, Gibbon, Voltaire and Rousseau,[52]

[51] Conway, *Omitted Chapters of History Disclosed in the Life and
Papers of Edmund Randolph*, pp. 12, 156, 389, 391 and Meade, *Old
Churches, etc.*, vol. i, p. 182 and vol. ii, pp. 292-3.

[52] Garland, *Life of John Randolph of Roanoke* (New York, 1851), vol.
ii, p. 652, H. M. Jones, *America and French Culture* (Durham, 1927),
p. 367.   One of the first books which Randolph read was Voltaire's
Charles XII (Letters of John Randolph to a Young Relative [Phila-
delphia, 1834], p. 190).   In fact, his library contained some seventy
volumes of the works of this French cynic.   In addition to Voltaire, the
deistic works of Gibbon and Rousseau together with the atheistic tracts
of Hume and Diderot were included in his library collection.   (Garland,
ibid., vol. ii, pp. 9-10 and *Letters of John Randolph to a Young Relative*,
p. 41).

he condemned Christianity as vigorously as did Ethan Allen but, unlike the latter, he generally did not take the trouble of putting his deistic thoughts on paper. On one occasion, however, he did so, as his notes approving the position of Gibbon indicate. Although he later repudiated these as " horrible " examples of sophisms, they nevertheless reflected the deistic inclinations of his youth. It was not until 1817 that he made his peace with Christianity. In a letter to Francis Scott Key, composer of the Star-Spangled Banner, he announced in that year that he was reconciled to his God and was assured of His pardon through faith in Christ.[53]

[53] Garland, *ibid.*, vol. ii, pp. 66-9, 97-100, 102, 652-3; Meade, *Old Churches, etc.*, vol. ii, p. 459 (Appendix, No. X) and H. Adams, *John Randolph* (New York, 1898), p. 14.

CHAPTER V

Deism Militant: Early National Period (1789-1805)

From 1789 to 1805, deism assailed more vigorously than ever before the supernatural revelation of Christianity. Paine, Volney and Palmer, though not typical of the American movement, were nevertheless examples of its rising militancy. By means of popularized accounts, they spread the notion that traditional Christianity would disappear before deism as inevitably as the morning mist before the rising sun. The deistic tendency was distinguished not only by its greater aggressiveness but also by its greater appeal. Up to the time of Paine, deism was an aristocratic cult confined almost solely to the " well-to-do classes." With the publication of *The Age of Reason,* the axis about which deistic thought in America rotated, the new ideology reached the rural and urban masses. Volney's *Ruins: or a Survey of the Revolutions of Empires* continued the work of Paine, while Palmer, the outstanding American-born deist, established societies, lectureships and newspapers in order to propagate the " new religion ".

The tendency toward a greater degree of deistic militancy was occasioned by clerical opposition to the principles of the French Revolution. To save republicanism and equalitarianism from ecclesiastical destruction, the advance guard of liberalism, composed of Paine and Palmer, tried to discredit the clergy by showing that the Biblical revelation upon which clerical authority rested was a human and not a divine document. The attack was led by Paine whose *Age of Reason* was the first blast of deistic dynamite to disturb the complacency of the faithful. So profoundly were they

120

shocked by this work that its author, Thomas Paine, was treated with such deep and relentless hatred that his undeserved reputation of "a filthy little atheist" has survived him by more than a century. He was repeatedly described by his opponents as an inveterate drunkard, a superficial reasoner, a malignant blasphemer and an impious atheist.[1] The vilification of Paine was due to the fact that he was guilty of carrying heresy to the people. The popularity of his early pamphlets and his earnestness in attacking dogmas common to all denominations were considered revolutionary. No longer was deism confined to people of education and social prominence; it was now spread among the masses. It was said that *The Age of Reason* could be found in practically every village in America and that it was tending to "unchristianize" nominal believers. Boys engaged in dressing flax, students enrolled in leading colleges, men enjoying the hospitality of convivial taverns were reading or eagerly discussing Paine's tract. Consequently, according to one account, tens of thousands proceeded to desert their faith, while millions were led to applaud—probably an exaggerated estimate.[2] The extensive circulation of Paine's pamphlet was

[1] J. Adams, *Works*, ed. C. F. Adams, vol. ix, p. 627; Levi, *Defence of the Old Testament* (New York, 1797), p. 5; Nelson, *An Investigation of that False, Fabulous, etc.* (Lancaster, 1800), pp. 10-11, 41, 45; Ogden, *Antidote to Deism*, vol. i, pp. 15, 18, 122, vol. ii, p. 297; Gouverneur Morris, *Writings*, ed. Sparks (Boston, 1832), vol. ii, p. 409, vol. iii, p. 46; and Watson, *Apology for the Bible* (Albany, 1796), pp. 3-4. Also consult Conway, *Life of Thomas Paine* (New York, 1892), vol. ii, pp. 181-190. For the characterization quoted above see T. Roosevelt, *Gouverneur Morris* (Boston, 1891), p. 289.

[2] D. Nelson, *Cause and Cure for Infidelity* (New York, 1841), p. 258. Consult also *Theological Magazine*, March, April and May, 1798, vol. iii, p. 187; Priestly, *Observations on the Increase of Infidelity* (Philadelphia, 1797), p. 53; Beecher, *Autobiography*, ed. C. Beecher (New York, 1864), vol. i, pp. 48-9; Francis, *New York during the last Half a Century* (New York, 1857), p. 89 and the Massachusetts Historical Society *Collections*, vol. iv, 6th series (Boston, 1891), pp. 585, 614 (Letters written by Brown to Belknap, February 6 and 25, 1797).

due to the fact that it was brought to the attention of people through newspaper advertisements [3] and orthodox replies; [4] that it was distributed free of charge by deistic organizations; [5] and that it was written in a style likely to be understood by the average man.

If left to himself, Paine might have continued indefinitely his life-long resolution of not wishing to discredit openly the Christian religion; circumstances, however, intervened.[6] During the French Revolution, most of the higher clergy of the Catholic Church allied themselves with the monarchy and thus were associated with the forces of reaction.   In order to overthrow the alliance of throne and altar and thereby save republican and equilitarian principles, Paine determined to destroy the priesthood by putting an end to the source of their authority—the Biblical revelation.   The growth of atheism, which was endangering the existence of the only true religion—deism, was another consideration motivating the Anglo-American to attack the divine origin of the Scriptures. To him, disbelief in God and a future state was occasioned by the disgust men felt for the fanatical and reactionary tendencies of the clergy.   To save deism and republicanism, Paine published the first part of his *Age of Reason* (1794). This was devoted to a generalized attack upon revealed religion.   The author argued that the word of God was not to be found in any written or spoken expression but in the Creation itself.   Moreover, the Biblical account was not

[3] Thomas' *Massachusetts Spy or the Worcester Gazette*, November 19, 1794 (no. 1128), August 13, 1796 (no. 1220), September 7, 1796 (no. 1221) ; *The American Mercury*, July 21, 1794 (vol. ix, no. 524) and *The Mercury*, October 28-31, 1794 (no. 216).

[4] For these replies see chapter vi, pp. 164-7.

[5] Riley, *American Philosophy*, p. 305 and Ruttenber, *History of the Town of Newburgh* (Newburgh, 1859), pp. 87-8.

[6] H. H. Clark, *Toward a Reinterpretation of Thomas Paine* (in American Literature, vol. v, no. 2, May, 1933, pp. 135-6).

binding upon future generations because it could not be regarded as a revelation, which, according to Paine, was a direct message communicated by God to man. Its stories of miracles and prophecies were false because the former were invented by impostors and were derogatory to the Deity and nature and because the latter were vague and indefinite. These "evidences", having been added to "fabulous religion", were not necessary to true faith.[7] The genuine creed consisted in a belief in the existence of one God and the practice of virtue. Although not greatly concerned with the problem of immortality, Paine accepted the idea of a future state.

Whereas the first part of *The Age of Reason* dealt with revelation in general, the second discussed the Judaic-Christian account in particular. One by one, Paine submitted the books of the Old Testament to the dictates of reason—only to find them wanting. Asserting that their authenticity depended upon the certainty of their authorship and upon the credit to be given to their testimony, he attempted to prove that Moses, Joshua, Samuel, David and Solomon did not compose the books bearing their names. In fact, the Pentateuch was written "by some very ignorant and stupid pretenders to authorship, several hundred years after the death of Moses. . . ."[8] Moreover, the Hebrew prophets were unimportant figures in their day and Isaiah, who was reputed to have predicted the coming of Jesus, was actually an impostor. Paine held also that the Gospels were not written by the apostles and that they appeared centuries after the death of Christ. He admitted the greatness of Jesus as a

[7] Paine, *Age of Reason* (New York, no date), pp. 8, 21-2, 38, 40, 82, 84-7, 89-90.

[8] For a discussion of the books of Moses consult *ibid.*, pp. 105-20; for those of Joshua, pp. 124-9; for Samuel, p. 134; for the Psalms of David, pp. 155-6 and the Proverbs of Solomon, pp. 156-7.

man but denied that Jesus was God. The life of Christ was a " fable . . . blasphemously obscene ", his ancestry a piece of fiction, his immaculate conception an impossible imposture and his resurrection doubtful.[9] Consequently, Paine repudiated the divine origin of Christianity on the ground that it was too " absurd for belief, too impossible to convince and too inconsistent for practice. . . ." Furthermore, the Christian religion was " an engine of power " serving the purpose of despotism as well as " a species of Atheism " denying God by introducing the necessity of a Redeemer.[10] Therefore, Paine suggested the introduction of deism which was unfavorable to tyranny and avarice and which taught all that was necessary.[11] A deistic David had arisen to slay the Goliath of Christendom.

Satisfied that his *Age of Reason* had intellectually disposed of one enemy to natural religion, Paine turned to its second foe, atheism. In 1797, in an address before the Paris Society of Theophilanthropists, an organization denying the divine origin of the Bible but accepting the existence of God and a future state, he assailed the atheistic concept of a universe which came into being without the aid of an efficient Agent. Since the cosmos consisted of matter which did not possess the property of motion, the rotation of the planets would be impossible without the assistance of an external Cause. Paine held that the prevalence of atheism was due to the introduction of orthodox religion which created atheists by its persecutions. The days of persecution over, atheism would disappear.[12] This speech was circulated in America

[9] *Ibid.*, pp. 194, 196-8, 200, 213-5.

[10] *Ibid.*, pp. 248-9. See also pp. 33, 45, 57.

[11] *Ibid.*, pp. 247, 249. For a definition of Deism see p. 216 and for other references consult pp. 66, 92.

[12] Paine, *A Letter to the Honorable Thomas Erskine . . . with his Discourse to the Society of the Theophilanthropists* (Paris, 1797), pp. 28-31.

and was reprinted in *The Temple of Reason* for January 3, 1801.

When, in 1802, Paine returned to the United States upon the request of Jefferson, deistic newspapers hailed his arrival, while conservative sheets bitterly lamented it.[13] In the same year, Samuel Adams sent a letter to the visitor urging him to publish no further work on " infidelity ".   In his answer, Paine cleverly pointed out that if " infidelity " consisted in accepting the existence of God. he was an " infidel." [14]   If Adams had written in the hope of dissuading the champion of natural religion from writing deistic tracts during his American residence, he was destined to disappointment.   In the deistic newspaper, *The Prospect, or View of the Moral World* for February 18, 1804 (no. 11), there appeared an article by Paine which stated that the chief difference between a deist and a Christian was a matter of fact and that fact was the evidence of revelation.   He described Christianity as " the strangest system of religion ever set up " because it committed a murder upon Jesus in order to redeem mankind for the sin of having eaten an apple.[15]

Although the State of New York presented Paine with a farm at New Rochelle, he spent his last years in poverty. Broken in health and reduced in finances, he was forced to move to a miserable lodging house on Fulton Street in New York City.   Just before he died in 1809, two clergymen

[13] Contrast the jubilant article in *The Temple of Reason*, November 6, 1802, vol. ii, p. 287 with several articles published in the *Balance and Columbian Repository*, November 30, December 7 and 14, 1802 (nos. 48-50), vol. i, pp. 377, 385, 393-4.

[14] Paine, *Writings*, ed. Conway (New York, 1894-1896), vol. iv, pp. 201-2, 205.

[15] In subsequent issues a correspondent describing himself as T. P. (probably Thomas Paine) wrote a number of articles attacking Christianity and various Biblical stories.   See the *Prospect or View of the Moral World*, March 3, 10, 24 and April 7, 1804 (nos. 13, 14, 16, 18).

gained access to his room. To their questions concerning
his religious opinions, Paine simply said: " Let me alone;
good morning." In his will, he mentioned having in manuscript Part III of *The Age of Reason* and also an *Answer to
the Bishop of Llandaff*. Only some fragments of these
works remain, although, as early as 1802, Paine attempted to
find a publisher for them. His friend, Jefferson, however,
cautiously " advised and requested him " not to have them
printed.[16] Yet, in 1807, most of the work did appear in
pamphlet form under the title of *An Examination of the
Passages in the New Testament, quoted from the Old and
called Prophecies concerning Jesus Christ*.[17] Three years
latter, *The Theophilanthropist,* a New York magazine,
designed to promote the " mild, tolerant religion of virtue,
which the Creator has wisely revealed to the conscience of
all mankind . . .", printed Paine's *Answer to Bishop Watson's ' Apology for the Bible '*. In this tract, the deist maintained that the Englishman was wrong in his contention that
the Book of Genesis was the oldest work in the world. Paine
held that its story of the creation was taken from other
peoples and that it was the last book of the Pentateuch to
be written. He argued that Job, a Gentile work, was composed before Genesis.[18]

Like Paine's *Age of Reason,* Volney's *Ruins: or a Survey
of the Revolutions of Empires* (1791) achieved such popularity that it was spoken of as late as the mid-nineteenth century.[19] Although concerned chiefly with the causes for the

[16] Paine, *Works,* ed. Van der Weyde (New Rochelle, 1925), vol. i,
p. 425, Letter from Congressman Eben Elmer to David Moore, December
11, 1802).

[17] This was the last work that Paine ever published. It can be found
in Paine, *Works*, ed. Van der Weyde, vol. ix, pp. 205-292.

[18] *The Theophilanthropist*, June (?) and July, 1810 (nos. 6, 7), pp.
220-28, 263-72.

[19] D. Nelson, *Cause and Cure of Infidelity*, p. 238 and R. Owen and A.

fall of ancient empires,[20] the work incidentally touched upon the question of divine revelation. The French savant rejected all supernatural accounts because it was impossible to determine which religion possessed the true evidences. Through the medium of Mohammedan, Indian and Jewish speakers, the former delegate to the French National Assembly ridiculed such Christian doctrines as the divinity of Jesus and original sin. He also derided the gospel precept of turning one's cheek because it degraded the good by making them servile. Furthermore, many passages in the New Testament were derogatory to the character of God.[21] The treatise was likewise characterized by its anti-clerical spirit. The priesthood " had universally found the secret of living in tranquility amidst the anarchy they occasioned; secure under the despotism they sanctioned; in indolence amidst the industry they recommended; and in abundance in the very bosom of scarcity; and all this, by . . . selling words and gestures to the credulous. . . ." [22]

In his *Observations on the Increase of Infidelity* (1797), the English chemist, Priestley, then residing in America, upbraided Volney for his " inaccuracy " in dealing with the ancient Hebrew religion and with Jesus.[23] Charging that the Frenchman was either ignorant of the truth or misrepresenting it, the English Unitarian demanded an answer to

---

Campbell, *Evidence of Christianity; A Debate* (Cincinnati, 1852), p. viii (Introduction). *The New Harmony Gazette* printed the significant deistic passages of Volney's work (December 26, 1827, January 9, 16, 23 and 30, 1828 and February 6, 1828 [nos. 12-17 inclusive]).

[20] Volney attributed the ruin of these great states to the desire for gain which led to tyranny and slavery. As a result of these two abuses, the natural rights of man were infringed upon and the ancient empires disappeared.

[21] Volney, *Ruins, etc.* (New York, 1796), pp. 152-6, 163-6, 288-9.

[22] *Ibid.*, pp. 295-6. See also pp. 81, 293-4.

[23] Priestley, *Observations, etc.*, pp. 111-4, 118-20.

his accusations. Upon his arrival in Philadelphia (1797), Volney refused to enter into any serious discussion with Priestley because he felt that the Englishman had not assailed the *Ruins* but had merely attacked him. Persuaded that a controversy would be futile, the deist asked only to be left alone.[24]

In the meantime, another deist attempted to destroy traditional Christianity. Elihu Palmer was one of the most important deists produced in America. Forced to resign from a Baptist Church in Philadelphia because of his heterodox views and prevented from holding meetings because of the hostility of the clergy, the blind preacher was ready to accept the challenge of the French Revolution. He proposed to save liberalism from despotism by destroying that powerful ally of the throne—the clergy. Like Paine, he set out to accomplish this purpose by doing away with revealed religion. In 1793, Palmer, announcing the dawn of " the age of reason and philosophy ", thought that the time had arrived for the advent of a " pure and unadulterated morality " stripped of all " mysteries and external trappings. . . ."[25] Some years later, in his *Principles of Nature,* he endeavored to offer such a system of ethics. While his friends enthusiastically acclaimed this pamphlet as a certain guide to " the path of Truth and Virtue ", his enemies bitterly condemned it as an excellent example of how wretched and comfortless a thing deism was.[26]

In his *Principles of Nature,* Palmer sought to divorce

[24] Volney, *Answer to Dr. Priestley* (Philadelphia, 1797), pp. 4-9, 12-3.

[25] *Political Miscellany, etc.* (New York, 1793), pp. 22, 26. For Palmer's life see *Posthumous Pieces ... To which are Prefixed a Memoir ... by his friend John Fellows, etc.* (London, 1824).

[26] Contrast *The Temple of Reason,* February 19, 1803, vol. ii, p. 407 with the *American Review and Literary Journal,* October, November and December, 1801 (no. 4), vol. i, pp. 448-59.

morality from theology and consequently was led to assail the dogmas and divine revelation of Christianity. The doctrines of the Trinity, the immaculate conception, and original sin were discarded as absurd and immoral. Christian miracles were also rejected because many of them were not accepted by those living at the time of Jesus. Since some of the prophecies of Christianity had not been fulfilled, they likewise were repudiated. Naturally Palmer denied the divine authority of the Bible and therefore looked to "the nature of man" for the basis of his ethical system. Although such a system could not be categorically set forth, it was best exemplified in the "pure and holy religion" of "Theism" or deism. This "faith" declared "the existence of one perfect God . . . [and] the practice of a pure, natural, uncorrupted virtue. . . ." Built upon this creed, deism would flourish long after "Christian superstition and fanaticism" were forgotten.[27]

The deism of Paine, Volney and Palmer, presented in a popular form, was designed to reach the masses in order to destroy their faith in traditional Christianity with its priesthood, dogmas and supernatural revelation. Its ultimate end was to replace the Christian religion by the religion of nature with its three-fold creed—God, virtue and immortality, a creed believed in even by devout Christians. To popularize the teachings of "the new faith", societies, lectureships and newspapers were established to supplement the writings of

[27] Palmer, *Principles of Nature* (London, 1823), pp. 8, 10-16, 30-3, 35-7, 42, 67-8, 85. Although Palmer looked upon theism and deism as synonymous terms, they are not necessarily so regarded to-day. After showing how theism is different from atheism, polytheism, pantheism and how it is similar to deism, *The Shorter Oxford English Dictionary* (Oxford, 1933) states, "Belief in one God as creator and supreme ruler of the universe, without denial of revelation; in this use distinct from *deism*." (See also Funk and Wagnalls, *New Standard Dictionary of the English Language* [New York, 1933], p. 2497).

Paine, Palmer and Volney. The first of these agencies was the most important cog in the deistic missionary machine because it was used to distribute skeptical treatises, to initiate discussions and to raise funds. The collection of money was, however, a difficult matter because these organizations were largely supported by the poorer classes—artisans, booksellers and printers—whose financial resources were limited. Of the learned professions, physicians alone were represented.[28]

In 1790, a deistic club, the Universal Society, was founded in Philadelphia under the guidance of John Fitch, one of the early inventors of a steamboat. Feeling that Christians were not adhering to their professed beliefs, Fitch drifted into the deistic current. He was especially disgusted with the Methodist denomination of which he was a member. During the Revolutionary War, his Trenton brethren censured him because he worked on Sundays to supply the American forces with arms. His repugnance reached a climax when leading Methodists refused to see him upon his arrival at New York in 1782. Fitch became an avowed disbeliever and, under his guidance, the Universal Society adopted a series of skeptical questions for its weekly discussions. Was there any religion which could be framed useful to society? If so, what were its principles? Was there a Providence? Did a future state exist? A strict moral code was instituted to guide the lives of the organization's thirty members. In 1791, the Universal Society joined Elihu Palmer who was then holding his religious services in the Church Alley meeting-house. In his sermons, the minister denied the divinity of Christ with such force that the Episcopal Bishop of Philadelphia, White, used his influence to prevent the owner of the building from allowing Palmer and his congregation to continue their assemblies. In view

[28] Koch, *Republican Religion*, pp. 290-1.

of this situation, the society came to an end after a year's activity.[29]

Philadelphia soon had another deistic organization in the form of a Theophilanthropic Society. The militant skepticism of this club was reflected in a discourse delivered before it and reprinted in *The Temple of Reason* for May 27 and June 3, 1801. In this speech, the lecturer urged the formation of more deistic societies where skeptical Christians might rally in order to save their neighbors from the chains of superstition. He encouraged his hearers to promote deism and at the same time launch a movement to revise the system of property holdings. Property was to be acquired on the basis of natural justice which left no room for greed. Without realizing it, the speaker was a prophet of the future because succeeding deists formed freethinking organizations and associated themselves with Owenite socialism.

Meanwhile, Palmer, with the aid of some members of a local democratic club established a deistic society in New York. In 1794, a group of New Yorkers founded an organization devoted to the spread of French revolutionary principles. This body was soon joined by the members of an older democratic order, Tammany. In the same year (1794), the newly organized radical society asked Palmer, who was then visiting the city, to deliver a speech before its members. Some of the latter were deeply impressed and proposed to aid the blind clergyman. For this purpose, a Deistical Society was founded during the winter of 1796-7. The name was suggested by the militant Palmer who desired to advocate frankly deistic principles and consequently refused to hide behind the harmless appellation of theophilanthropy. Moreover, Palmer himself drew up its consti-

---

[29] T. Westcott, *Life of John Fitch* (Philadelphia, 1878), pp. 302, 308-9; and Scharf and Westcott, *History of Philadelphia* (Philadelphia, 1884), vol. ii, pp. 1404-5 (note).

tution which consisted of a number of principles proclaiming the existence of God, the moral and intellectual sufficiency of man, the necessity of political and religious liberty and the universality of natural religion.   Since the association sought to promote " moral science " and the religion of nature, its members were urged to oppose " all schemes of superstition and fanaticism, claiming divine origin." [30]   The organization was divided into a number of grades and since secrecy was prescribed, the members of one grade did not know those of another.   The meetings were closed; at these gatherings Christianity was ridiculed and Palmer's *Principles of Nature* read.   On the whole, the society was far from being successful; it was unable to attract the " sober and substantial " elements of the community.   From a financial viewpoint, it was forever in difficulties; one of its chief sources of revenue was the payment of membership dues. In 1802, these amounted to six cents payable at each meeting, a rather modest contribution which was probably fitted to the financial status of these " ' scattered dregs of . . . Jacobin Infidels.' "   Yet, in spite of its monetary embarrassments, the association was for a time able to support the publication of *The Temple of Reason* under the editorship of Dennis Driscol, a recent Irish immigrant and ex-priest. Besides financial difficulties, there were political ones; at the turn of the century, the society became involved in New York politics on the ground that members of the Clintonian faction were at the same time members of the association. The exact connection of De Witt Clinton, later vice-president of the American Bible Society, with Palmer's deistical organization is not clear but it has been established that David Denniston, his cousin, was one of its members.[31]   With the

[30] E. Palmer, *Posthumous Pieces . . . To which are prefixed . . . Mr. Palmer's Principles of the Deistical Society of New York*, pp. 8-9, 12.

[31] Koch, *Republican Religion*, pp. 76-7, 80, 84-5, 98, 100, 103.

death of Palmer in 1805, the deistic club languished; a few years later the remnants of the Old Guard formed a Society of Theophilanthropy in whose official organ, *The Theophilanthropist,* the posthumous works of Paine appeared.

Unlike the New York deistic society, the Newburgh organization drew its membership from the more " respectable " elements of the community; for example, doctors of medicine, like Dr. Hedges, were connected with it.   The Druidical Society of Newburgh was an offshoot of an earlier and more conservative organization.   In 1788, a Masonic lodge was founded which developed along radical lines during the course of the French Revolution.   From its membership the Druidical Society was formed.   The new body continued to use not only the ceremonies of the Masonic order but its former meeting place.   In adopting the name Druid, these apostate Masons believed that they were returning to the pure worship of the sun from which both Christianity and Freemasonry were derived.   At their weekly meetings, the Bible was openly ridiculed.   Like the New York deists, the Druids fell under the influence of Palmer who lectured before them and was offered a salary by them.   The society reprinted Paine's *Age of Reason* and Tindal's *Christianity as Old as the Creation* both of which it diligently circulated. After 1800, it declined in importance; the last notice of its activities appeared in the Newburgh *Rights of Man* for September 17, 1804.[32]   Like Newburgh, Baltimore possessed a deistic club in the form of a Theophilanthropic Society, while the newly settled region west of the Genesee River in New York State also boasted of a freethinking association with a circulating library containing the writings of Voltaire, Volney, Hume and Paine.[33]

[32] *Ibid.,* pp. 118-9, 122-3, 129; Ruttenber, *History of the Town of Newburgh,* pp. 87-9.

[33] *The Temple of Reason,* October 2, 1802, vol. ii, p. 251; Gillett, *His-*

Just as Palmer was connected with the activities of deistic societies, so was he associated with deistic lectures. From Newburgh to Atlanta, this apostle of missionary deism addressed enthusiastic audiences, the size of which varied in direct ratio to the sympathies of the reporter. Colonel John Fellows, editor of the New York *Beacon* and a friend of Palmer, Jefferson and Paine, stated that the former minister's addresses were well attended, while an unfavorable newspaper critic asserted that upon one occasion only fifty-four were to be found at a well-advertised lecture in New York.[34] Palmer was so superb a speaker that, according to a New York historian of the period, " none could be weary within the sound of his voice. . . ." Even an unfriendly contemporary, Hargrove, conceded the oratorical brilliance of the former clergyman.

His lectures were characterized by their poignant hostility toward traditional Christianity. On December 25, 1796, in a New York speech, Palmer rejected the divinity of Jesus as an event which was " very singular and unnatural. . . ." He also discarded the doctrines of original sin, atonement, faith and regeneration as immoral and incomprehensible. In subsequent addresses, Palmer showed New Yorkers that a miracle-working Providence was inconsistent with the nature of God and that " Christian superstition " was one of the worst banes in the history of mankind. He even had the audacity to censure Jesus for having cried on the cross that God had deserted him. The speaker claimed that this action showed a lack of philosophical firmness in the hour of death and an inability to work miracles when needed. Having

tory of the Presbyterian Church (Philadelphia, 1864), vol. ii, p. 109 and J. H. Hotchkin, *A History of the Purchase and Settlement of Western New York* (New York, 1848), p. 26.

[34] Palmer, *Posthumous Pieces*, etc., p. 8 and the *Balance and Columbian Repository*, November 22, 1803 (no. 47), vol. ii, p. 372.

been invited by the deists of Baltimore to address them, Palmer continued to hurl his shafts of criticism at revealed religion in general and Christianity in particular.[35] So distinctly anti-Christian were his speeches that upon one occasion he was temporarily prevented from delivering one of them. In July 1801, he was asked to address the Universalist Church in Philadelphia on the subject of morality. A large audience gathered at the meeting-house but Palmer was not allowed to speak. A month later, however, he addressed a large and attentive assembly in the same city upon the same subject.[36] Another deistic orator aided Palmer in an endeavor to spread the gospel of natural religion. The speeches of John Foster were even more daring than those of his blind co-worker whom he addressed as brother. Foster, who probably taught Palmer theology at Pittsfield in 1787, was hailed in New York during the years 1803-06 as a brilliant orator and keen thinker. His speeches were especially well received by the skeptically inclined.

An attempt was made to propagate deism not only by lectures designed to reach the masses but also by newspapers aimed to popularize freethinking arguments. On November 8, 1800, *The Temple of Reason* appeared with the announcement that it proposed to show the purity and soundness of deistic doctrines by " exposing . . . the corruption of those of our adversaries. . . ." For more than two years, it sought to fulfill its aim by vigorously assailing Christian dogmas and evidences.[37] Adopting such a position, the

[35] These speeches were reported and refuted by Hargrove, editor of *The Temple of Truth*, an orthodox Baltimore periodical. See *ibid.*, September 5 and 12, 1801 (nos. 5 and 6), pp. 65-8, 81-91. Consult also *Temple of Reason*, August 26 and September 9, 1801, vol. i, pp. 263, 278-9.

[36] *Temple of Reason*, July 18, August 12 and 26, 1801, vol. i, pp. 207, 247, 262-3.

[37] *Temple of Reason*, December 3, 1800, vol. i, pp. 45-6, January 7, 1802,

newspaper urged all deists to cast prudence aside and boldly proclaim their support of deism. It also advised them to join theophilanthropic societies in order to revive "true morality". In view of the fact that the appearance of *The Temple of Reason* coincided with the election of Jefferson to the presidency, religious and political conservatives had the opportunity of circulating the rumor of a carefully arranged plot to stamp out religion. Making as much of the opportunity as possible, they spread the report that *The Temple of Reason* was seeking the patronage and protection of the "atheistic President." In its issue of May 3, 1801, the accused newspaper felt called upon to deny the rumor by asserting that deism differed from "a religion of dreams and fables, of whales and asses, [and] of pigeons and strumpets" in that it was not dependent on state aid for success.

In the meantime, a Baltimore clergyman, John Hargrove, published *The Temple of Truth* to serve as an antidote to the influence of the deistic newspaper. Since *The Temple of Reason* refused to print some of his articles, Hargrove established a journal which would circulate his views and those of other orthodox believers.[38] The new periodical appeared in August 1801 and naturally defended the cause of Christianity. Its articles pointed out the advantages of the Christian religion in contrast to the disadvantages of deism. Besides, they sought to uphold the divine origin of the Old Testament and the utility of the Christian doctrine of patience.[39] The latter was defended because the more patient the man the better the reasoner; the better the reasoner the

vol. i, p. 409 and July 24, 1802, vol. ii, pp. 201-3. For the newspaper's deistic profession of faith see *ibid.*, November 8, 1800, vol. i, pp. 1-2 and July 31, 1802, vol. ii, pp. 213-4.

[38] See *The Temple of Truth*, August 1 and 15, 1801 (nos. 1 and 2) and *The Temple of Reason*, July 1 and 15, 1801, vol. i, pp. 199, 214-5.

[39] *The Temple of Truth*, August 15 and 29, October 31, 1801 (nos. 2, 4, 13), pp. 25-6, 58-60, 205-6.

more virtuous the man. Popular support of the newspaper, however, waned to such an extent that it ceased publication after October 31, 1801. To console himself, its editor assigned its failure to the fact that its truths were too rational for the fanatic and too spiritual for the deist. Its rival, *The Temple of Reason,* commenting upon the fate of the orthodox newspaper, remarked jubilantly, " We fear that faith has fled the land, and that infidelity is going to take her place! "

Less than two years later, *The Temple of Reason* discontinued its activities because subscriptions were not paid promptly enough. In its last number, it informed its readers that Elihu Palmer intended to revive the newspaper and, on December 10, 1803, the first issue of the *Prospect, or View of the Moral World* appeared with the expressed purpose of investigating fully the divine nature of Christianity. Consequently, its editor, Palmer, wrote a series of articles which commented upon every chapter in the Old and New Testaments. Beginning with the first section of Genesis, he continued his work with such extreme minuteness that some forty-four subsequent editions of the *Prospect* were issued before he completed the thirty-fifth chapter of Exodus.[40] Palmer announced a plan to erect a Temple of Nature where one God would be worshipped. In order to facilitate the matter, a meeting was held at 89 Broadway, in New York, where $600 was subscribed. To secure more money another meeting was proposed,[41] and soon with the help of Paine a " Theistic Church " was founded. The expectations of an

---

[40] *Prospect, or View of the Moral World,* January 14 to November 17, 1804 inclusive (nos. 6 to 50). It is interesting to note that after his publication of *The Principles of Nature,* Palmer desired to publish in pamphlet form his views on every chapter of the Bible (Palmer, *Posthumous Pieces, etc.,* p. 9).

[41] *Ibid.,* August 18 and 25, 1804 (nos. 37 and 38), pp. 296, 304.

organized deistic movement were given a temporary setback
when the *Prospect* was discontinued on March 30, 1805
because of financial difficulties.   The extent of its circulation
is somewhat revealed by the fact that its subscribers were
requested to pay their money to Dr. Hedges in Newburgh,
to Mr. Spalding in Rhinebeck, to Mr. Miles in Philadelphia
and to Mr. Palmer in New York.

While this organized deistic movement was being launched,
a deistic liberal, Jefferson, was elected to the presidency.
Throughout the campaign of 1800, the Republican candidate
was vilified by political and religious conservatives who
charged him and his party with the desire to overthrow
Christianity.   That this accusation was groundless is seen
in the fact that the leadership of the Republican group represented all shades of religious opinion.   On the left, were
Jefferson, Willie Jones and Freneau whose approach to the
question of the Christian revelation was most prudent.   For
instance, Philip Freneau, editor of *The National Gazette,* felt
called upon as a good republican to defend the principles of
the French Revolution from clerical destruction.   Although
bitterly condemning the clergy, especially the Congregational
order of New England, he nevertheless did not, like Palmer,
reject explicitly the Biblical basis of ecclesiastical pretensions to authority.   In his *Letters on Various Interesting and Important Subjects* (1799), Jefferson's friend
assailed religious dogmas on the ground that they promoted
discord.   Moreover, he argued that the practice of orthodoxy
was impossible because ministers were constantly changing
their positions.   To illustrate his contention, he pointed out
that for two hundred years the American ministry had been
praying for the downfall of the Pope but now seemed anxious
to see his power restored in France.   Cynically he advised
Calvinistic clergymen to sail to that " unfortunate country "
and there preach gospel sermons to unhappy Frenchmen.   In

the same sarcastic vein, Freneau told how a school boy once misread the New Testament text to the effect that there would be "whipping and slashing to death" instead of the original "weeping and gnashing of teeth". Commenting upon this, he asserted that the boy had nearly preserved the sense of the passage and even if he had not, it did not matter.[42]

More to the right, were Sullivan and Barlow whose position was that of religious liberals. James Sullivan, a member of Brattle Street Church, Boston, used his influence in 1802 to secure the appointment of a Unitarian clergyman, Joseph Buckminister, whose religious opinions coincided with his own. Sullivan believed in the divine authenticity of the Bible but repudiated the Trinitarian doctrine. Moreover, he was persuaded that what the various churches held in common was more important than their disagreements. Although charged with being a deist and atheist, Joel Barlow, according to his own testimony, was neither. The famous American poet was made a citizen of France because of the active part which he played in the French Revolution. While in Europe, he was on intimate terms with Paine whose *Age of Reason* he helped to publish and with Volney whose *Ruins* he translated. His epic poem, *The Columbiad,* appeared in 1807, two years after his return to America. Two of his friends, Noah Webster and the Abbé Gregoire immediately assailed him as an atheist. When the orthodox joined in the attack, Barlow was forced to state explicitly his religious views. In a letter, written in 1809, he emphasized the point that at no time during the Revolution had he embraced either deism or atheism. He denied that his *Columbiad* was designed to ridicule or insult "the Christian system, as inculcated in the Gospels and explained by the Apostles. . . ." Furthermore, since the religious views of men depended upon the place of their birth, he, being born and educated among

<hr>

[42] Freneau, *Letters, etc.* (Philadelphia, 1799), pp. 35-6, 72-5, 79.

Puritans, was still a Presbyterian.   Had he been reared in
Constantinople, the probability would be that he would adhere
to the Moslem faith.[43]   To the right of Barlow and Sullivan,
were such religious conservatives as Samuel Adams of
Massachusetts and William Findley of Pennsylvania whose
orthodoxy and political liberalism were beyond question.

In a similar fashion, the Federalist leadership represented
diverse religious views.   John Jay, Fisher Ames and Alexander Hamilton were all sincerely attached to the Christian
religion and vigorously opposed to deistic innovations.   Jay
scrupulously observed the customs of the Episcopalian
church.   The New York governor attended services regularly, was responsible for the erection of a house of worship,
and felt that the support of the clergy was a duty obligatory
upon all Christians.   When the American Bible Society was
formed, he became its president.   This organization was
responsible in no small measure for the decline of deism.
To Jay, " mere human reason " was incapable of acquiring
sufficient knowledge to inform men either of their actual or
future state.   Again, Biblical mysteries were to be accepted,
since they could never be understood by the " light of
reason ".   That the Hebraic revelations were carefully preserved, that Jesus fulfilled the prophecies of the Old Testament and that he performed miracles which were faithfully
recorded—these tenets were accepted by Jay without question.
According to him, deism failed to accomplish its sinister
designs because the people were shocked by the tactics of its
disciples.   Like Jay, Ames was a firm believer in the divine
origin of the Christian religion and upon one occasion made
a public profession of faith.   The Christian system being
" excellent and benign . . .", the Massachusetts Federalist

[43] Todd, *Life and Letters of Joel Barlow* (New York, 1886), pp. 222-
232; Hazen, *Contemporary American Opinion of the French Revolution*
(Baltimore, 1897), p. 224 and the *Dictionary of American Biography*, vol.
i, pp. 611-2 (Article on Joel Barlow).

never troubled himself with subtle theological difficulties. Moreover, he was persuaded that these related to insignificant and uncertain points. Similarly, Alexander Hamilton strongly supported the cause of religion which appeared to him to be essential to stability in government. Deism was an " hideous " monster which had to be crushed.[44]

Yet, among the leaders of Federalism there were at least three distinguished religious liberals, Timothy Pickering, John Adams and Josiah Quincy. At Harvard, Pickering came in contact with the latitudinarian views of Tillotson whose works he was urged to read but was cautioned against their " heresies ". He soon began to doubt his Puritan theology going even so far as to question the Trinitarian doctrine. This he did during the Revolutionary War when he heard von Steuben say that he would sooner believe in an absurdity than in the Trinity. In time, Pickering became a Unitarian who accepted the existence of one God, Governor of the World, and of one Mediator, Jesus, who " ' gave himself as a ransom for all ' ". Every Christian was to do those things which he believed the Deity enjoined. Persons who espoused the Christian religion could not be said to be credulous, since Boyle, Locke and Newton were among its sincere believers. Furthermore, the Old and New Testaments were divinely inspired.[45]

On the question of the validity of the Christian revelation, John Adams was a trifle more skeptical than Timothy Pickering. To the second President of the United States, the disclosures of nature were to be trusted to a greater degree

[44] Hazen, *Contemporary American Opinion of the French Revolution,* p. 266; F. Ames, *Works,* ed. S. Ames (Boston, 1854), vol. i, pp. 25-6; and W. Jay, *Life of John Jay* (New York, 1833), vol. i, pp. 13, 253, 434, 461, 463, 495-505 (Appendix, no. iv).

[45] Pickering and Upham, *Life of Timothy Pickering* (Boston, 1867), vol. i, pp. 11 (note), 35-6, vol. ii, p. 283, vol. iv, pp. 325-6 and Schneider, *Puritan Mind,* pp. 203-4.

than the Biblical testimony of miracles and prophecies. Although accounts of supernatural predictions and events could be used to frighten men, they could never make them believe that " two and two [are] five. . . ." Yet, in spite of his skeptical tendencies, Adams did not reject Christianity but actually supported it as an indispensable aid to stability in government. Therefore, as far as he was concerned, the deism of Paine was to be fought, since it promoted " the cause of revolution. . . ." [46] In short, the conservatism of Adams overcame his intellectual radicalism and forced him to remain within the limits of religious propriety.

Like Adams and Pickering, Josiah Quincy was a native of Massachusetts, a prominent Federalist leader and a religious liberal with distinct Unitarian inclinations. The President of Harvard opposed all theological controversies because they tended to divide rather than unite Christians. To him, it was of little consequence what a man thought so long as he acted according to the principles and sanctions of Christianity. These were essential to knowledge which in turn was basic to virtue. Virtue led to freedom; freedom to happiness. Moreover, Quincy held that religion had no reference to place and that true goodness would always conform to nature.[47]

Probably more of a freethinker than any of these three New Englanders was Charles Cotesworth Pinckney who was charged with being a deist during the campaign of 1800.

[46] Although these observations of Adams were taken from letters written after 1805, they represent to all intents and purposes his position on religion during the last decade of the eighteenth century. J. Adams, *Works*, ed. C. F. Adams, vol. ix, p. 627 (Letter to Benjamin Rush, January 21, 1810) and P. Wilstach, *Correspondence of John Adams and Thomas Jefferson* (New York, 1925), pp. 80-5 (Letter of September 14, 1813).

[47] J. Walker, *Memoir of Josiah Quincy* (Massachusetts Historical Society *Proceedings* [Boston, 1867], vol. ix, pp. 155-6).

This accusation was based upon a statement made by Dwight in his *Triumph of Infidelity*. Besides this " proof ", another one was presented by the anonymous author of *Serious Facts, Opposed to ' Serious Considerations '*, etc. This proof consisted of the testimony of Dr. William Linn to the effect that Pinckney was a deist. It is interesting to note that Linn was the author of *Serious Considerations,* a pamphlet directed against Jefferson's " open profession of Deism ".[48] Like Pinckney, William Davie was a southerner and a prominent Federalist. Born in England, he was taken to America in 1763 where he was adopted by a Presbyterian clergyman who saw to it that he received a collegiate education. During the Revolution, he rendered distinguished military services and after the struggle, settled in the borough of Halifax which he represented in the North Carolina legislature almost continuously from 1786 to 1798. As a recognized leader of the state's Federalist forces, Davie bitterly fought " that man " Jefferson as well as all Republican principles. In spite of his conservative politics, he was, as one of his biographers puts it, " infected with the infidelity of his times, [and] was never in any sense a religious man ",[49] although his actions were highly moral and his character unassailable. Thoroughly distrusting clergymen, he opposed the selection of a Scotch-Irish Presbyterian McCorkle as President of the University of North Carolina because nothing went well so long as " these men of God " had a " hand in it ". In place of McCorkle, David Ker, who later became an avowed skeptic, was chosen. Moreover, Davie did not hold the Bible in

---

[48] Marcus Brutus, *Serious Facts, Opposed to ' Serious Considerations ':
Or the Voice of Warning to Religious Republicans* (New York [?]ₐ
1800), pp. 10-11, 14; Linn, *Serious Considerations on the Election of a
President* (New York, 1800), p. 4.

[49] J. G. de R. Hamilton, *William Richardson Davie, A Memoir, etc.*
(in U. of N. C. James Sprunt Historical Monograph, No. 7, p. 22).

high esteem.   When the wife of one of his friends died, he did not try to console the bereft husband with texts taken from Christian origins but, in characteristic deistic fashion, quoted Mohammedan sources.

The leaders of Republicanism and Federalism represented all shades of religious thought but the contemporary belief, especially of New England, was that all Jeffersonians were champions of deism and all Federalists defenders of orthodoxy.   In the words of one New England newspaper, Jefferson and his associates were " philosophical infidels " who were plotting to usher in " the heretic ' Age of Reason '. . . ."   Yet, these sinister men were being supported by stern Presbyterians, Baptists and Methodists!   In Connecticut and Massachusetts, the Republican Party drew its main support from members of these last two denominations who assailed the Federalist Congregational order on the ground that a state church maintained by forced contributions led to the rise of freethinking.   Elder John Leland, a Baptist clergyman who played an important role in the evangelical movement, made this quite clear in a sermon delivered in 1801. This ardent adherent of Jeffersonianism held that the only way to prevent the spread of deism was for religion to renounce state aid and convince the world it could stand alone. In a like fashion, the Scotch-Irish of western Pennsylvania, though radical in politics, were conservatives in religion. Representing their position were such popular Republican leaders as William Findley and John Smilie.   Findley was distinctly orthodox in his views; he was brought up with the Bible as his companion, was for many years an elder of the Presbyterian Church and, at the turn of the century, was willing to bolt the Jeffersonian Party rather than accept a gubernatorial candidate, Ross, reputed to be a deist.   Likewise, his friend, Smilie supported the Presbyterian Church and, according to his biographers, was in the " truest sense a Christian." [50] In view of the religious conservatism of these supporters of the Republican Party, it is not surprising to note that after 1800 good Jeffersonians pointed with pride to the spread of revivalism as an ample refutation of the Federalist charge that a Republican victory would mean the advent of deism. In spite of contemporary accounts, Liberalism, not Religion, was at stake in 1800. Abraham Bishop, a New England leader of Jeffersonian democracy, was quite right in stating that at the turn of the century deists were to be found in both the Republican and Federalist parties. [51]

Contemporary public opinion in New England associated deism not only with the Republican movement but also with French influence. In his *Discourse on Some Events of the Last Century* (1801), Dwight pointed out that " infidelity " was accorded " an extensive reception " in America due chiefly to enthusiasm for the leaders of the French Revolution. Another New Englander, Seth Payson, wrote in 1802 that the " principles of infidelity have attended the progress of French influence. . . ." [52] Yet, in spite of these observations, the deistic movement in America was scarcely influenced by that of France. An interest in things French was greatly stimulated by the French Revolution and a Francophile spirit characterized the followers of Jefferson. A

---

[50] McMaster and Stone, *Pennsylvania and the Federal Constitution* (Lancaster, 1888), pp. 727-9, 753; Albert, *History of the County of Westmoreland, Pa.* (Philadelphia, 1882), pp. 208-11; *Dictionary of American Biography*, vol. vi, pp. 385-6; Lewis and Veech, *The Monongahela of Old* (Pittsburgh, 1892), p. 148; Robinson, *Jeffersonian Democracy in New England* (New Haven, 1916), pp. 41, 129-34, 136; Purcell, *Connecticut in Transition* (Washington, 1918), p. 31 and J. Leland, *Blow at the Roots* (New London, 1801), p. 29.

[51] Koch, *Republican Religion*, pp. 127-8, 262, 275.

[52] Dwight, *Discourse on Some Events of the Last Century* (New Haven, 1801), pp. 19, 32; Payson, *Proofs of the Real Existence, etc.*, p. 214.

majority of Republicans, however, were not pleased with the religious experiments of the Revolution and consequently apologized for or condemned them.   Some sympathizers with France attempted to explain away the irreligious tendency of her leaders.   The *National Gazette* for March 27, 1793 held that aristocracy was more dangerous than deism or atheism because it oppressed the moral and physical faculties of men. Moreover, the article pointed out that deists or atheists did not request the aid of rich and cruel priests.

Other supporters of France, instead of approving the activities of the revolutionaries, endeavored to show that the charge of irreligion was unfounded because the French constitution allowed peaceful assemblies for religious worship. Hard-pressed, these sympathizers seized upon the speeches of Godineau and Robespierre as evidences of the religious spirit of the French leaders.   On November 20, 1793, Godineau, a tribune of the National Club of Bordeaux, delivered an address on the subject of religious worship.   Taking his cue from Rousseau, he asserted that although the simple teachings of Jesus surpassed all others, they were distorted by mysteries and miracles.   He urged all Frenchmen to spread the true gospel of Christ which appeared to him to be the gospel of the " sans-culotte." [53]   In the same vein, in April 1794, Robespierre addressed the National Convention on the necessity of instituting the Worship of the Supreme Being.[54] In order to save France from " stupid " and " perverse " atheists and money-mad priests, the Incorruptible advised the

[53] That the basis of this speech is to be found in the teachings of Rousseau may be seen if one compares the *Social Contract*, tr. Cole (London, 1913), book iv, chapter viii, pp. 113-22 with Godineau's address reprinted in *The Temple of Reason*, September 16 and 23, 1801, vol. i, pp. 286-9, 296.

[54] Mathiez in his *Fall of Roberspierre* shows that this speech was based on a report made by Mathieu, a deputy of Oise, who first proposed such a worship. Mathiez, pp. 93-5.

initiation of public festivals dedicated to the Deity. These celebrations were designed to inculcate respect for laws, enthusiasm for liberty and love for one's country. On June 8, 1794, Robespierre himself officiated at the Parisian festival and in a brilliant speech informed his audience that republicans were alone worthy of adoring "the Being of Beings, Author of Nature . . ." who created men to love one another and attain happiness. After bitterly denouncing fanaticism and atheism, he called upon the French sans-culottes to free the world from tyranny. These speeches were reported in American newspapers [55] and as far as the *Independent Chronicle* for July 24, 1794 was concerned, it was impossible to believe that after Robespierre's speech anyone could accuse France of being atheistic or irreligious. While some Republicans were defending the religious policy of the revolutionaries, others felt that France had gone astray in this particular. Most conspicuous among these was Governor Samuel Adams of Massachusetts who, in his Fast Day proclamation of 1794, implored God to inspire France with a spirit of wisdom and true religion.

Unlike Adams, a small group of Republicans, headed by Paine and Palmer, was pleased with the attacks of French leaders upon religion. Capitalizing the interest stimulated by the Revolution for things French, this faction sought to promote the cause of deism by using the writings of French freethinkers. Consequently, the works of Voltaire, Rousseau and Volney [56] were reprinted in deistic newspapers

[55] For Godineau's speech see *Salem Gazette*, June 22, 1794 (no. 406) and *Temple of Reason*, September 16 and 23, 1801. For those of Robespierre consult the *American Mercury*, August 4 and 11, 1794 (vol. xi, nos. 526-7) and *The Pennsylvania Gazette*, August 27, 1794 (no. 3345).

[56] For a reprint of Voltaire's writings see *Temple of Reason*, May 6 and June 24, 1801, vol. i, pp. 136, 189, May 1 and August 14, 1802, vol. ii, pp. 111, 227; for Rousseau's *Prospect, or View of the Moral World*, May 5 to November 17, 1804 (nos. 22-50); and for Volney *Temple of Reason*, January 31 to June 3, 1801.

and were distributed through deistic societies. To what extent these French authors, who were read in America, "caused" Americans to assume a more aggressive stand is problematic. Voltaire and Volney were undoubtedly sources of inspiration for exceedingly radical deists who felt called upon to discredit clerical pretensions to authority in order to preserve the principles of the French Revolution. They used an approach similar to that adopted by the Sage of Ferney, an approach whose explicit negations were not at all to the liking of most American deists, not to say of most Americans. In short, although French deists exerted some "influence" upon a relatively small section of the American public, their "influence" was greatly exaggerated by Dwight and Payson, who, because of their Federalist affiliations, viewed with alarm the rise of Jeffersonianism which they sought to check by using the French bugaboo.

Likewise, New Englanders saw in Freemasonry a powerful force stimulating the growth of a militant deistic movement and again their observations were far-fetched. Masonic lodges appeared in America during the early eighteenth century and gradually attracted quite a following. Their members greatly increased after the Revolution on account of the infiltration of many French societies and the enrollment of prominent war heroes. The names of Washington, Franklin, Warren, Madison and Lafayette unquestionably attracted members and with increased membership came increased influence.[57] The growing importance of Freemasonry was reflected in articles and poems appearing in the periodical press after 1783.[58] During

---

[57] Jones, *America and French Culture* (Durham, 1927), p. 398; Tatsch, *Freemasonry in the Thirteen Colonies* (New York, 1929), pp. 140-1; and Fosdick, *French Blood in America* (New York, 1906), pp. 386-7.

[58] Laudatory articles appeared in *The Gazette of the State of South Carolina*, May 27, 1784 (no. 2204); *Maryland Gazette or Baltimore*

the last quarter of the eighteenth century, French lodges were also established in America. Among these were the Perfect Union Lodge, Boston (1781), Lodge Wisdom, Portsmouth, Virginia (1786), *L'Amenité*, Philadelphia (1797) and the Grand Orient and Union Lodges in New York. Likewise, the Harmonic and Friendship societies, founded in Boston in 1792 and 1793 respectively, were composed of a considerable French element.[59]

The formation of these French Masonic orders at first caused little alarm. At the turn of the century, however, the self-appointed guardians of American institutions sounded the tocsin and informed the people that Freemasonry in America was being corrupted by "illuminism" in the guise of French lodges. On August 25, 1798, a Connecticut periodical *The Religious Monitor, or Theological Scales* announced "a secret conspiracy of the Illuminati in league with corrupted Masons . . ." which proposed to root out religion in Europe and America. In the meantime, the Reverend Jedidiah Morse showed the German origin of Illuminism and spoke of its spread to the new Republic. Its rapid progress, he held, was due to the popularity of such "an unprincipled author" as Thomas Paine.[61] To the aid of

---

Advertiser, March 30, 1787 (no. 259) ; *American Museum or Repository*, June, 1787, vol. i, pp. 546-8; and *Providence Gazette, etc.*, February 21, 1795 (no. 1625). Extracts from Masonic books and addresses appeared in the *Christian's, Scholar's and Farmer's Magazine*, April and May, 1789, vol. i, pp. 84-5 and *American Museum or Repository*, June, 1789, vol. ii, 597-600; poems were published in *The American Universal Magazine*, January 9, 1797, vol. i, p. 65 and the *Literary Museum or Monthly Magazine*, March, 1797, p. 160.

[59] Fosdick, *French Blood in America*, pp. 389, 393, 395-6; Morse, *A Sermon, Exhibiting the Present Dangers, etc.* (Charlestown, 1799), pp. 34-7; S. Payson, *Proofs, etc.*, pp. 197-8; and V. Stauffer, *New England and the Bavarian Illuminati*, pp. 321-2.

[60] J. Morse, *ibid.*, pp. 12-3, 27, 34-7 and Stauffer, *ibid.*, pp. 229-239, 264-71, 288-303.

Morse came such redoubtable warriors as Dwight and Payson who assiduously damned Illuminism, Infidelity and political radicalism. In his *Proofs of the Real Existence and Dangerous Tendency of Illuminism* (1802), Payson asserted that Voltaire, D'Alembert, Frederick II and Diderot were the principal actors in a plot to overthrow " the adorable religion " of Christ. Especially did he warn the young against the dangers of Illuminism and he urged parents to teach their children " the fear of God . . . and the evidences of the Christian faith. . . ." Stating that there were 1700 agents of the Illuminati in America, he suggested the temporary suspension of Masonic lodges.[61]

Although American Freemasonry was not as anti-Christian as these statements would indicate, it nevertheless showed distinct deistic tendencies. By referring to God as " the Great Architect " and by alluding to natural religion, Masonic prayers and addresses familiarized Masons with deistic phraseology. Moreover, the Masonic charge that members were to comply with " the essentials of religion " rather than with Christian usages gave Masons an opportunity to embrace deism. Some of them, like those in Newburgh, went so far as to form deistic societies,[62] but these were the exceptions to the rule. On the whole, the American Masonic movement was far from being anti-Christian, in fact, Masons were requested to shun deism. *The Ahiman Rezon* of 1783, edited by William Smith upon the request of the Pennsylvania Grand Lodge, stated that good Masons could never " tread in the irreligious paths of the unhappy libertine, the deist or the stupid atheist." Although fifteen years later the Reverend Mr. Harris, chaplain of the Grand Lodge of Massachusetts, qualified the statement quoted by excluding

[61] Payson, *Proofs, etc.*, pp. 31-36, 55-6, 155-8, 198, 254, 275.
[62] See chapter v, p. 133.

the name deist,[63] he pointed out that both Christianity and Freemasonry desired the encouragement of charity and benevolence as well as of moral and social duties. In order to protect themselves against the suspicion of being deistic, some grand lodges, like that of Maryland, went so far as to propose that no member be initiated within its jurisdiction who refused to believe that the Ten Commandments were divinely revealed. This proposition was suggested in 1804. Some seven years before, the Reverend Mr. Harris challenged " the most severe critic, the most precise moralist, the most perfect christian to point out anything in [Masonic ideals] inconsistent with . . . pure religion. . . ." [64] Moreover, many respectable religious and political leaders were connected with the Masonic movement so that eventually the bubble of Illuminated Freemasonry burst.

Although these New Englanders were wrong in their belief that Masonry was scheming to overthrow Christianity, they were correct in their assumption that deism was spreading. Doctors, teachers, artisans, farmers and social leaders were embracing the deistic philosophy of Paine and Palmer. According to one report, a young physician of Hadley, New York, " was personally acquainted with Thomas Paine [and] had embraced his infidel sentiments . . .", while another statement spoke of a teacher, described as D. R., who secured for himself the reputation of being " a zealous opposer of the gospel and a universal seducer of unwary " youth. The clergyman Lyman Beecher, who as a young man dressed flax, told how boys around him read Paine and believed in him. In a similar manner, in the seats of the mighty, the leaders

---

[63] Compare the *Ahiman Rezon* (Philadelphia, 1783), p. 14 with T. M. Harris, ed., *Constitution of the Ancient and Honorable Fraternity of Free and Accepted Masons* (Worcester, 1798), p. 34.

[64] Harris, *Ignorance and Prejudice shewn to be the Only Enemies of Freemasonry* (Leominister, Massachusetts, 1797), p. 23.

of fashionable society openly ridiculed Christianity. In 1793, the artist Trumbull was asked to dine at Jefferson's home. Here he met a group of freethinkers who proceeded to poke fun at the doctrines and character of Jesus. Much to his exasperation and astonishment, the only one at the table besides himself who was willing to defend the Christian religion was a Jew named Franks.[65]   At another party, held some four years later, James Kent, a Federalist in politics and future Chancellor of the State of New York, remarked that well-informed men were free from the " vulgar super-stitions " of the Christian religion. This information was apparently approved by those present among whom were William Dunlap, a playwright, William Johnson, a lawyer and Elihu Hubbard Smith, a physician. It is interesting to note that when Smith died one year later, his parents anxiously asked Dunlap and his friends whether their son had died a deist or not. Those to whom the question was put were happy to evade it by pointing out that Smith had passed away so suddenly that even had he desired to recant, he would have been physically unable to do so.[66]   Besides the professional classes, army officers were stung by the deistic bumble-bee. In 1798, John Davis, a British traveler, met and spoke to Major Howe, a Revolutionary veteran and a member of the Order of Cincinnati. According to Davis, Howe, while a commanding officer at West Point, borrowed Gibbon's *Decline and Fall of the Roman Empire*. He read the work diligently and soon rejected the Christian revelation. So thorough was his repudiation of the Bible that Howe became a follower of Palmer.[67]

[65] Griswold, *The Republican Court* (New York, 1855), p. 312.

[66] Koch, *Republican Religion*, pp. 82-3.

[67] J. Davis, *Travels of Four Years and a Half in the United States of America during 1798, 1799, 1800, 1801 and 1802* (New York, 1909), pp. 22-3.

Yet, in spite of the alarmist accounts of the faithful and the exultant reports of the heterodox, the deism of the Paine school was far from being popular. That it did attract some attention was due to the noisy aggressiveness of a small band of militant deists and to the attention bestowed upon them by the clergy. The deistic Freneau hit the nail on the head when he remarked that *The Age of Reason* might not have achieved the popularity it did, had not the clergy written tracts answering it. These, he continued, were read by people, who, on turning to Paine, would realize how badly the Christian cause was handled by its " weak, yet conceited friends. . . ." [68] Like Communism in 1919, deism in late eighteenth-century America attracted an attention which was out of proportion to its actual influence. With this in mind, let us turn to our sources of information and use these as an index to, rather than an exact account of, the extent of skepticism.

From 1794, deism, aided by the popular pamphlets of Paine and Volney, made its way throughout the country. At Lebanon, New York, in 1795, few would profess Christianity; those who did believe in the divine origin of the Bible felt that the " fundamental doctrines of religion were disgustful." Again it was said that in Windham County, Connecticut, the majority of people were deists while no more than six individuals in Marlborough, Vermont, would make a public profession of faith; at one time, not a single person was even willing to declare himself a Christian. [69] Philadelphia was regarded as a center of " infidelity "; one traveler observed that the services of learned apologists were

[68] Freneau, *Letters on various Interesting and Important Subjects*, pp. 37-8.

[69] Larned, *History of Windham County, Connecticut* (Worcester, 1894), vol. ii, p. 221; *Connecticut Evangelical Magazine*, September and November, 1803, vol. iv, pp. 111, 179. See also Dwight, *Travels in New-England and New-York* (London, 1823), *passim*, for skepticism in Vermont.

needed. there in order to check the progress of skepticism. In New York, the "astonishing growth of infidelity" was given as the cause of the death of several hundred people during the yellow fever epidemic. In 1796, the Methodist Episcopal Church recommended a day of fasting and prayer in order to turn back the swelling tide of deism.

From 1797 to 1800, according to contemporary opinion, the skeptical current swept forward so rapidly that Christianity itself seemed about to be engulfed in a sea of deistic oblivion. Although Dwight cheerfully estimated that "the friends of Revelation" outnumbered its enemies, Priestley felt called upon to publish a work designed to prevent the spread of freethinking. His *Observations on the Increase of Infidelity* (1797) assigned two penetrating reasons for the ultimate defeat of deism—the absence of an established church in America and the inertia of the masses. Yet the immediate danger of deistic success was apparently so great that the General Assembly of the Presbyterian Church issued a solemn warning to the American people. In its Philadelphia meeting of 1798, the assembly predicted that unless Americans turned away from deism, the wrath of God would be visited upon them. To avert the impending day of doom, it was suggested that a day of humiliation, prayer and fasting be set aside. In the same vein, a writer in an orthodox magazine warned the people against "infidelity" which was raising "her presumptuous voice among both sexes and [leveling] her artillery against divine revelation. . . ." [70] These dire admonitions evidently had little effect, for during the following year such diverse observers as Morse and

[70] T. Dwight, *Nature and Danger of Infidel Philosophy*, p. 64; Priestley, *Observations, etc.*, pp. xv (Preface), 143-4; *Religious Monitor or Theological Scales*, June 30 and August 25, 1798, pp. 50, 81-3; *The Theological Magazine*, March, April and May, 1798, vol. iii, pp. 186-90; and E. H. Gillett, *History of the Presbyterian Church* (Philadelphia, 1864), vol. i, pp. 296-8.

Freneau reported an increase in the number of freethinkers. To check " the awful prevalence of speculative and practical infidelity ", the Congregational clergy of Massachusetts urged the initiation of positive and vigorous action.[71]

As in Massachusetts, so in North Carolina, freethinking was causing great anxiety among the faithful. Joseph Caldwell, President of the University of North Carolina, found religion " ' little in vogue ' " and noted that in the region east of Chapel Hill, politicians, in order to secure votes, had to disavow publicly the doctrines of the Bible. Surveying the scene with the same Federalist bias, Caldwell's predecessor, Harris, held that only around Salisbury could " true religion " be found (whatever the good Professor, who was a Unitarian, might mean by the phrase " true religion "). When the *Minerva,* in August 1800, described Jefferson as " a second-handed varnished Deist ", the " Hermit of Wake " defended the deism of the Republican standard-bearer in the *Raleigh Register.* The deistic philosophy was adopted so extensively by the professional classes of the South that the General Assembly of the Presbyterian Church viewed with satisfaction the conversion of many of these people to the " doctrines of Christianity ".[72]

While deism was spreading, the orthodox were setting in motion an evangelical movement. Their efforts in this direction were recorded in letters sent to magazines, communications which indicated the triumph of Christianity over deism. From Caldwell, New Jersey, came the consoling news that some " chiefs of the devil's kingdom " had em-

[71] *The Panoplist,* February, 1809, vol. i, pp. 402-5; Morse, *A Sermon, Exhibiting the Present Dangers, etc.,* p. 8 and Freneau, *Letters, etc.,* p. 36.

[72] *The Panoplist,* August, 1810, vol. iii, pp. 145-7; and Gilpatrick, *Jeffersonian Democracy in North Carolina* (New York, 1931), pp. 121-2. See also Williams, *Memoirs of the late Rev. Thomas Belsham* (London, 1833), p. 593.

braced the gospel, while Ontario County, New York, reported the conversion of a deist of long standing. "Infidelity" also stopped "its brayings" in Milton, New York, where "many of its hearers, (or rather its dupes) fell prostrate at the feet of the Redeemer whom they had impiously denied and blasphemed!" A similar, although decidedly less graphic, report arrived from Middletown, Vermont, where skeptics were said to be again embracing the doctrines of Jesus. In Providence, Rhode Island, the "Deist [was bowing] to our King, and [was hailing] Jesus as his rightful Lord, and divine lawgiver. . . ." While these "glad tidings" were circulating, Dwight announced that New England had escaped "the dreadful bondage of Infidelity, corruption and moral ruin . . ." thanks to the activities of her leaders and of her God.[73] In the face of these orthodox reports, the deistic *Temple of Reason* for October 16, 1802 asserted that there were more deists than Christians in America. Two years later, Palmer's *Prospect, or View of the Moral World* for June 16, 1804 declared more modestly, albeit more accurately, that there were "thousands and tens of thousands of deists in the United States and Europe. . . ."

Deism was prevalent not only along the Atlantic seaboard but also in the region west of the Alleghanies. Here, as in the case of most frontier settlements, a general indifference to religion flourished. In 1800, in the Ohio Valley country, one missionary observed that "only a small number of people openly professed an attachment to religion. . . ." Shellyville, Kentucky, was "destitute of the gospel . . .", while Blount County, Tennessee, was "cold and indifferent" to

---

[73] Dwight, *A Discourse on Some Events of the Last Century*, p. 34; *The Theological Magazine*, January, 1797, vol. ii, p. 233; *The New-York Missionary Magazine*, 1800, vol. i, p. 37; and *The Massachusetts Baptist Missionary Magazine*, September, 1803, May, 1804 and January, 1806, vol. i, pp. 17-8, 50-1, 180.

religion. People in the vicinity of Pittsburgh also showed little interest in "spiritual matters." [74]

This indifference to religion, however, did not necessarily mean that the people of the West were deists or skeptics. There were among them deeply religious men and women drawn from the ranks of God-fearing Presbyterians, Baptists and Methodists. Into the trans-Appalachian country they carried their Bibles and attempted to establish their own churches. In their log schoolhouses, their children used the Scriptures as a textbook and were taught to sing hymns and answer questions taken from religious catechisms. Moreover, sermons, church histories and Bibles were the books most commonly read in the new region.[75] Their apparent indifference toward religion often signified merely that they did not have the same opportunity of worshipping as did their eastern neighbors. Lacking a sufficient number of ministers and widely scattered throughout the countryside, they found it difficult to conduct religious exercises. That the majority did desire to do so was evidenced by the success of the evangelical movement in Kentucky, Tennessee and Ohio. Addressed as it was to their hearts, revivalism appealed more easily to the frontiersmen than did deism.

The capital of Kentucky, Lexington, was reputed to be a center of deistic speculation. Here John Bradford, publisher of the *Kentucky Gazette,* helped organize democratic clubs and Harry Toulmin, "a sycophantic satellite of Thomas Jefferson" and a member "of the Priestly [sic] lineage", presided over Transylvania Seminary.[76] Founded

---

[74] *The New-York Missionary Magazine* for 1800, vol. i, pp. 120-2 and *ibid.,* for 1801, vol. ii, p. 238.

[75] C. Cleveland, *The Great Revival in the West, 1797-1805* (Chicago, 1916), pp. 10-1, 17, 28-9.

[76] D. C. Troxel, "French Deism in Kentucky, 1800" (see summary in American Society of Church History, *Bulletin 5,* July, 1929, pp. 4-5).

in 1783, this institution was at first dominated by Presbyterians.   By 1794, their influence waned to such an extent that Toulmin, who was popular with the deistic element of Lexington, was appointed head of the seminary.   In view of this situation, the Presbytery of Transylvania established the Kentucky Academy in 1797.   The following year, the state legislature authorized the two rival institutions to unite under the name of the Transylvania University.   The board of trustees, created by the Act of 1798, was soon divided into two groups, the Presbyterian faction favoring the practices of evangelicalism and the deistic supporting the cause of rationalism.   As time passed, the number of Presbyterians serving on the board was so reduced that the freethinking groups secured control of the university's policies.[77]

As early as 1793, the Kentucky legislature dispensed with the services of a chaplain.   Two years later, the Presbyterians set aside a day for fasting, prayer and humiliation in order to check the growth of freethinking.   Yet, this remedy appeared to be of little avail since it was asserted that a majority of the people of Kentucky were " infidels " at the turn of the century.[78]   Freethinking was likewise prevalent in western New York where the Bible was openly ridiculed and where deistic societies were established.   In 1798, one traveler observed that this newly settled region was seriously infected with deism.

[77] The struggle between these two forces continued into the early nineteenth century and broke with full fury during the presidency of Horace Holley. Holley, a deist of the Jeffersonian type, was naturally assailed by the orthodox. Because of the agitation of the faithful he was forced to resign in 1827.

[78] Gillett, *History of the Presbyterian Church in the United States,* vol. i, p. 421.

CHAPTER VI

CHRISTIANITY DEFENDED: EARLY NATIONAL PERIOD
(1789-1805)

To one contemporary clergyman, it seemed that during the last decade of the eighteenth century " every appearance of religion [would] vanish, yea that our Zion must die without an helper and that infidels would laugh at her dying groans. . . ." To avert such a catastrophe, another advocate of religion urged " the real friends of Zion " to check " the spreading frenzy of [the] Infidel Philosophy. . . ."[1] Among those who sought to " save " Christianity none were more zealous than the college authorities whose tranquility was deeply disturbed by the skeptical drafts of the deistic whirlwind. At Rhode Island (Brown) College, Queen's (Rutgers) College and Union College, baccalaureate addresses were delivered to impress the graduating classes with the superiority of Christianity over " mere philosophy ". At the Rhode Island College commencement of 1795, the presidential discourse dealt exclusively with the necessity of the Biblical revelation as a guide to the good life, while the student oration of Amos Hopkins sought to minimize the importance of deism by indicating that it was merely a prelude to the universal establishment of Christianity. Eliphalet Nott of Union College delivered a graduation address in 1805 in which he endeavored to show most vividly the advantages of the Christian religion over deism.[2]

[1] *The Connecticut Evangelical Journal*, October, 1800, vol. i, p. 137 and *The Religious Monitor*, August 25, 1798, p. 25.

[2] *The Providence Gazette and Country Journal*, September 12, 1795 (no. 1654) ; *The Independent Chronicle and Universal Advertiser*, September 17, 1795 (xxvii, no. 1515) ; and Schmidt, *The Old Time College President* (New York, 1930), pp. 195, 202-3.

The authorities at Yale also attempted to save the souls of their students. During the years 1794-5, a young sophomore at the New Haven college, Lyman Beecher, declared that the majority of the members of the class entering before his were skeptics. These students addressed each other by the names of Voltaire, Rousseau and D'Alembert. The evidences of Christianity were debated not only outside of the institution but also within its walls, since the " Deistic controversy was an existing thing, and the battle was hot, the crisis exciting. . . ." In the Divinity class, conducted by the President of the College, the following questions were discussed: Was Revelation necessary? Was Moses the author of the Pentateuch?

Although Yale students doubted the courage of their faculty to assail deism openly, Timothy Dwight advanced to the attack in his baccalaureate address of 1797. Warning the undergraduate body to avoid the deistic philosophy, the President described it as vain, deceitful and contradictory; its doctrines " gross and monstrous "; its authors vicious and depraved. Voltaire was an atheist, Rousseau a thief, perjurer, fornicator and Tindal " infamous for vice in general, and the total want of principle. . . ." In a sudden burst of magnanimity, Dwight conceded that some deists were ingenious and learned fellows but could not be compared with such " sober " Christians as Bacon, Erasmus, Locke and Newton. Even though the contemporary world was favorably disposed towards freethinking, Christianity would triumph because the " weight of virtue has been wholly on [her] side. . . ." [3]

Although Dwight was extremely orthodox, the same could not be said for his faculty. Tutor Silliman, though not parading heterodox views, was regarded as a deist and did

[3] T. Dwight, *Nature and Danger, of the Infidel Philosophy* (New Haven, 1798), pp. 20-37, 39-42, 45-7, 58, 63, 82.

not profess himself to be a Christian until 1803 during which year a revival took place at Yale. Another member of the staff whose religious complacency had been broken by Hume was "converted" through the efforts of Dwight. The benign influence of the ubiquitous college President was further seen in the changing attitude of the student body. Students organized a Moral Society which sought to reclaim "lost souls" by debating such topics as the necessity of divine revelation and the truth of Biblical stories. The salutary effects of these discussions were probably responsible for a student poem delivered at the commencement exercises of 1797. The poem consisted of a rejection of Volney's contentions concerning the providence of God.

A deistic spirit prevailed in other colleges besides Yale. In 1794, William E. Channing, a student at Harvard, observed a decided tendency toward skepticism at the Cambridge seat of learning.[4] Here the deism of Paine was making such rapid progress that the authorities felt it necessary to present each student with a copy of Watson's *Apology for the Bible*.[5] At the same time, a Dudleian lecturer, Nathan Fiske, warned all undergraduates to avoid reading *The Age of Reason* because its author was a "daring insurgent" who was ever ready to disturb peace and order. Fairness of treatment and learned research were not to be expected of him. These were characteristic only of the work of Christian apologists. Deism was not only partisan and superficial but also foreign and futile. Its doctrines were imported into the United States and in spite of their apparent popularity they would not achieve their end since Christianity has "been, and ever will be, under the patronage

[4] W. H. Channing, *Life of William Ellery Channing* (Boston, 1880), p. 30.

[5] In 1791, the college authorities publicly banned Gibbon's *Decline and Fall of the Roman Empire*.

of the Almighty. . . ." [6]   It was said that at Dartmouth
only one member of the class of 1799 was willing to admit
publicly that he was a Christian.   It was not until 1801 that
a permanent student's Religious Society was established at
the college.   The same state of affairs existed at Bowdoin;
here only one student was ready to state openly his belief
in Christianity.   At Princeton, in 1799, there were, according to report, only three or four " pious " youths.[7]   Although
these accounts were undoubtedly exaggerated, they nevertheless indicated the spread of deistic influence.   The authorities at Princeton attempted to fight the hydra of deism.   In
1802, its trustees, appealing for funds, informed all friends
of religion that they intended to make the college " an asylum
for pious youth, so that in this day of general and lament-
able depravity, parents [might] send their children to it
with every reasonable expectation of safety and advantage.
. . ."   The trustees significantly added that this purpose
would make the college many enemies.[8]   Provost John
Mason of Columbia also endeavored to preserve his institution against the inroads of deistic attacks.   He had no
patience with the sophistries of those rationalists who relied
on " the light of nature."   A living faith in the merits of
Christ was the only consolation of a troubled conscience.[9]

Down in the Southland, conditions at the University of
North Carolina were such as to cause uneasiness among the
faithful.   Opened in 1795, the college was presided over by

[6] Fiske, *A Sermon Preached, etc.*, September 7, 1796 (Boston, 1796),
pp. 16-18.

[7] Koch, *Republican Religion*, pp. 243, 281; Dorchester, *The Problems
of Religious Progress* (New York, 1881), p. 99.

[8] *Address of the Trustees of the College of New-Jersey, etc.* (Philadelphia, 1802), p. 4.

[9] Schmidt, *The Old Time College President* (New York, 1930), pp.
118, 189-90.

a well-read Presbyterian clergyman, David Ker, who proved himself to be such an " outspoken infidel " that he was forced to resign within a year. His wife, a steadfast Christian, burnt all his writings for fear that they would contaminate others. Ker was succeeded by Charles W. Harris, Tutor of Mathematics, who, though not a deist, was heterodox enough to reject the Trinitarian creed. In turn, he made way for another man—a young Princeton graduate, Joseph Caldwell. A firm believer in the evidences of Christianity, the new acting President found upon his arrival that his faculty included so many " infidels " that he was unable to converse with his own staff. He openly charged one of the instructors, Samuel A. Holmes, with believing in nothing and even questioning the existence of virtue. Holmes was originally a Baptist preacher who was probably at this time a Republican and who " indulged in the Voltairean, Tom Paine cant of the times . . ."; consequently he was assailed by the Federalist president of the college. Like the faculty, the student body was skeptical; one boy wrote home that the favorite book of his fellow students was Paine's *Age of Reason.* Student clubs purchased Locke's *Essay on Human Understanding,* Gibbon's *Decline and Fall of the Roman Empire,* and Helvetius' *On the Human Mind;* they also held debates on various religious subjects. Upon one occasion, a club voted that it was inconsistent with reason to love one's enemy as taught by Christianity.[10]

Deism was assailed not only in the colleges but also in the outside world where some of the faithful endeavored to show the irrationality of the deistic position. Among the first to feel the fury of the orthodox blast was Paine whose *Age of Reason* was inspired by a deep feeling of devotion for humanity. So profound was his love for mankind that his

---

[10] Battle, *History of the University of North Carolina* (Raleigh, 1907), vol. i, pp. 61, 66, 68-9, 80-1, 85, 91, 101, 105, 107, 114-5, 157.

work assumed a religious flavor and consequently it is not surprising to note that it was first published in America by a religious house as a religious book and was sold in Virginia along with the Bible by Parson Weems, Washington's old friend and biographer.[11]   Although time has reduced *The Age of Reason* to a comparatively moderate treatise, so far as its negations are concerned, in its own day it was the acme of radicalism.   Naturally the gauntlet which this deistic knight threw down was quickly taken up by an array of Christian pamphleteers who ran the gamut from the vituperative and bigoted Ogden to the moderate and scholarly Watson.   Most of the works written against *The Age of Reason,* though masquerading under the pretentious titles of Answers, were nothing but emotional diatribes directed against its author.   On the whole, Uzal Ogden and David Nelson added nothing new to the deistic controversy with the possible exception of a more extensive list of abusive terms which the orthodox could fling at Paine.   To Ogden, the deistic champion was a sot devoid of reason, " grossly ignorant " and totally unoriginal.   This last remark might well have been used against the good Ogden himself.   Believing in the depravity of man, he held that natural religion needed the aid of revelation.   Since many things existed which were beyond human comprehension, men were fortunate to have special messengers sent by the Supreme Being to disclose these " mysteries ".   Like Ogden, Nelson, who adopted the pseudonym of " A Delaware Waggoner ", vented his spleen upon Paine whom he pictured as deceitful, degenerate and wanting in knowledge.   Describing *The Age of Reason* as an impious and erroneous book, he was satisfied that his own work completely refuted all of its arguments.[12]

[11] Paine, *Works,* ed. Van der Weyde, *With a Life of Thomas Paine,* vol. i, pp. 401-2.

[12] U. Ogden, *Antidote to Deism,* vol. i, pp. 15, 18-9, 121-2, 124-6, 150-72,

The works of Thomas Williams and James Muir were in the same general category as those of Ogden and Nelson. In his *Age of Infidelity*, Williams defended the truth of Christian evidences on the ground that Jesus fulfilled in his life the prophecies of the Old Testament and confirmed his mission by miracles. After examining the specific objections of Paine, Williams was convinced that deistic principles would spread only among " the young, the gay and the voluptuous . . .", and that Christian truth would prevail. The Reverend Mr. Muir of Alexandria was likewise certain that Christianity would be victorious; but, in order to make its triumph surer, he wrote an *Examination of the Principles Contained in the Age of Reason*. Believing that Paine's work was a specimen of effrontery and ignorance, he gently admonished the deist to mend his ways. After defending vigorously revealed religion, the Presbyterian clergyman concluded that unbelief led inevitably to crime and pestilence.

On a higher rational and scholarly plane was Priestley's *Answer to Mr. Paine's Age of Reason*. To the English chemist, the deistic knight-errant seemed to know as little about " the writings of Voltaire and other better informed unbelievers . . ." as he did about the circumstances surrounding the resurrection of Christ and the influence of Christianity upon the Middle Ages. Moreover, the Englishman reminded Paine that " intelligent Christians " no longer believed such doctrines as the Trinity and that he was therefore unfair in loading Christianity with these " absurdities." [13] As indicated by this work, Priestley and other

184, 192-8, 201-5, 308-14, 319; vol. ii, pp. 112-3, 171, 259, 297; and D. Nelson, *Investigation of that False, and Fabuluous, and Blasphemous Misrepresentation of Truth, set forth by Thomas Paine*, pp. 10-1, 14, 17, 41, 45, 47.

[13] Priestley, *Answer to Mr. Paine's Age of Reason* (Northumberland, 1794), pp. v. (Preface), 59-61, 66, 69-70, 77-9; Muir, *Examination of*

eighteenth-century Unitarians agreed in many respects with the deists. Like the latter, they accepted the notion that religion must be rational, simple, tolerant and broad. Yet, the Unitarians differed from the deists on the two-fold question of revelation and Jesus. Whereas the champions of deism rejected implicity or explicitly the divine origin and truth of the Biblical accounts, the Unitarians of the eighteenth century accepted them. Hence Priestly, like Hazlitt before him,[14] was able to pity " unbelievers " and to deliver lectures on the evidences of revelation. Moreover, deists and Unitarians were unable to agree on the person of Jesus. Whereas the former looked upon Christ as a superb philosopher, the latter regarded him as more than a man, even though he was not a member of the Godhead. To Priestly and his associates, Jesus was able to perform miracles, a supernatural power which was undoubtedly given to him by God. In short, Unitarianism and deism, although having a great deal in common, developed more or less independently and along different lines.

Probably the most scholarly work written against Paine was by the English Bishop of Llandaff, Richard Watson. His *Apology for the Bible* was extremely popular in America and though designed for mass consumption, it did not descend to ridicule and scurrility. Watson seemed impressed by *The Age of Reason* for, in his reply, he spoke of the " philosophical sublimity " which he found in certain portions of the work. His many quotations from the deistic book greatly stimulated its circulation—hardly what the good Bishop expected or desired. Proceeding in a manner similar to that of Paine, Watson discussed the Old Testament

the Principles, etc. (Baltimore, 1795), pp. 116, 139-40, 145; and Williams, *Age of Infidelity: In Answer to Thomas Paine's Age of Reason* (London, 1794), pp. 11-3, 17-20, 37-40, 42, 49.

[14] See chapter iv, pp. 86, 109.

book by book and pointed out that many Hebrew scholars during the Middle Ages were cognizant of Paine's contentions. Although admitting the validity of his opponent's arguments in respect to Genesis, Watson accepted the divine origin of the Hebraic accounts and declared that if he were not a Christian, he would become a Jew. He also defended the New Testament narratives concerning the miraculous conception, the genealogy of Jesus and the resurrection. In conclusion, the Anglican clergyman pleaded with God to forgive Paine for his " infidelity ".[15] A Jew, David Levi, agreed with Watson that Hebrew scholars were quite familiar with Paine's exceptions to certain Old Testament texts. The writer especially assailed the deistic representation of the Jews as an ignorant and barbarous people [16] and in his *Defence of the Old Testament,* he showed that their religious and moral principles were superior to those of other ancient peoples. Although Levi did not expect to convert Paine, he did desire " to save " people from Paine's disbelief in revelation, a disbelief which, if circulated among Jews, might prove as destructive to Judaism as it was to Christianity.[17]

Meanwhile Paine's critics were themselves being criticized in an anonymous pamphlet attributed to Palmer and entitled *The Examiners Examined: Being a Defence of the Age of Reason* (1794). The author desired to vindicate " the undaunted champion of reason, and the resolute and unconquerable enemy of tyranny, bigotry, and prejudice. . . ."

[15] R. Watson, *Apology for the Bible, in a Series of Letters to Thomas Paine's Age of Reason* (Albany, 1796), pp. 27-36, 46, 58-61, 68-83, 87, 141, 144-5, 177, 186-7.

[16] In spite of their professed tolerance, some deists, like Morgan and Voltaire, were anti-Semites.

[17] D. Levi, *Defence of the Old Testament* (New York, 1797), pp. 5, 7, 45-9, 67-71, 119-20. It is interesting to note that copies of *The Age of Reason* have been translated into Yiddish. In 1922, one appeared in New York.

To the writer, Christianity was a monument of "ignorance and credulity, which the wisdom of the present generation probably [was] destined to overthrow. . . ." The "Examiner" not only took Williams to task for condemning Mohammedanism but even went so far as to assert that the religion of the Prophet was superior to Christianity and Judaism. He likewise condemned Ogden for his attempt to slur the character of Paine. In conclusion, the writer predicted the triumph of deism over Christianity and the substitution of "Temples of reason . . . [for] temples of superstition. . . ."[18] *The Examiners Examined* was immediately answered by a Newport clergyman, William Patten. Representing his opponent as a "Deluded worm", the preacher foretold the victory of Christianity over its enemies because its case was defended by "the perpetual care and irresistible power of God. . . ." Patten assailed the position of his deistic rival on such matters as the sufficiency of reason, the doctrine of original sin and the superiority of Mohammedanism.[19] *The Age of Reason* was assailed not only in pamphlets but also in periodicals. Paine was described in the newspapers as vain, ignorant, bold, superficial and unoriginal,[20] while his opponents received favorable consideration.[21] Magazines likewise ridiculed the advocate

[18] *Examiners Examined, etc.* (New York, 1794), pp. 6, 16, 53-60, 81, 83.

[19] W. Patten, *Christianity the True Theology . . . With an Appendix in Answer to the 'Examiners Examined'* (Warren, 1795), pp. 132-174.

[20] *Western Star*, September 9, 1794 (no. 250) ; *Massachusetts Spy*, October 8, 1794 (no. 1122) ; *The Independent Chronicle and Universal Advertiser*, December 15, 1794 (xxvi, no. 1436) ; *The Salem Gazette*, September 6, 1796 (no. 531) ; and *The Columbian Sentinel*, December 23, 1797 (no. 1436).

[21] *Massachusetts Spy*, November 19, 1794 (no. 1128), August 31, 1796 (no. 1220) ; *The Mercury*, December 30, 1794–January 12, 1795 (no. 235) ; *The Independent Chronicle*, January 12, 1795 (xxvii, no. 1445) ; *The Salem Gazette*, February 3 and 10, 1795 (nos. 434 and 435), August 12, 1796 (no. 524) ; and the *Federal Gazette and Baltimore Advertiser*, October 14, 1796 (v, no. 918).

of deism [22] and warned their readers not to peruse his work.

In the meantime, monthly publications were assailing Paine's deistic associates. In *The American Museum: or Repository* for September 1792, " Philagathos " took his skeptical adversaries to task for abusing the clergy. If unbelievers desired to popularize their views, they should republish " a new edition of Tindal-Toland-Chubb or some other of the fraternity . . ." whose works were " now out of print as well as out of credit. . . ." The writer concluded by taunting the deists with their lack of courage. Other magazine contributors defended Christianity by showing the insufficiency of deism. One author asserted that whereas natural religion was unable to explain the creation of the world and the origin of sin, the Christian revelation was capable of doing so.[23] Another writer, in *The South-Carolina Weekly Museum* for January 1, 1797, asserted the inability of deism to establish solidly the idea of immortality because such a principle could not be proved by " natural deductions and unassisted reason. . . ." Unable to offer any definite hope of salvation, deism was worthless in the hour of death. For the edification of those deists who still hoped to achieve heaven, *The Connecticut Evangelical Magazine* for March 1801 told how a freethinker, steeped in the militant deistic teachings of Allen, Paine and Voltaire, was forced to renounce his shallow views when faced with death. Maintaining that deism was essentially superficial, two authors, one in *The Theological Magazine* for October, November and December 1797, and the other in *The Connecticut Evangelical Magazine* for October 1800, urged that

---

[22] *American Monthly Review*, January, 1795, vol. i, pp. 17-21; *The Theological Magazine*, January and February, 1796, vol. i, pp. 285-7; and the *Connecticut Evangelical Magazine*, July, 1801, vol. ii, p. 29.

[23] *The Rural Magazine: or Vermont Repository*, June, 1795, p. 295.

it be replaced by the divine revelation of Christianity.　The young were especially advised to shun vice and infidelity in order to live happily and temperately.[24]　One correspondent, in *The Baltimore Weekly Magazine* for February 16, 1801, went so far as to assert that " every man who endeavors to invalidate the truth of the everlasting Gospel is a liar. . . ." Less hot-headed than this last contributor were others who sought to vindicate their belief in Christianity by proving the validity of its doctrines and evidences.　In 1797, a New York periodical upheld the Trinitarian creed and severely condemned Paine for his unenthusiastic acceptance of immortality.[25]

During the same year, *The American Universal Magazine* reprinted an extract from one of Dr. Price's dissertations in which the noted Englishman requested people to judge Christianity solely by the good it had done.　In 1800, *The Monthly Magazine and American Review* published a very favorable criticism of Dobson's *Letters on the Existence and Character of the Deity*.　Dobson was a Philadelphia printer and bookseller who sought to impress upon the youth of the land the truth of Christian dogmas and testimonies.　Consequently, his *Letters* defended the authenticity of the Old Testament and the need of such theological doctrines as original sin and election.　He was described by the reviewer as a " public-spirited and useful citizen . . ." who wrote like " a serious, well-informed and sensible man. . . ."[26]

The defenders of the faith also used the newspapers to

---

[24] *The Connecticut Evangelical Magazine*, November, 1800, vol. i, p. 197.

[25] *The Theological Magazine*, August and September, 1797, vol. ii, pp. 422-4, 429-35.

[26] For a criticism of the first part of Dobson's pamphlet consult *The Monthly Magazine and American Review*, September, 1800, vol. iii, pp. 197-200. See also *The American Review and Literary Journal*, April, May and June, 1802, vol. ii, pp. 216-9.

spread anti-deistic arguments. Under the pretentious title, "Moral and Divine Philosophy", an anonymous writer for a Boston journal showed that Christianity consisted not only of the religion of nature but also of "matters of pure revelation." The miracles of Jesus proved the divine origin of the Christian religion which was destined to stand the test of time in spite of "all the artful, unfair and flattering opposition that has been made to it by Deists. . . ." [27] Another newspaper correspondent, "Common Sense", wrote a series of articles for *The Virginia Gazette and Richmond Chronicle* in which he defended the miracles attributed to Moses and Jesus, though he denied those credited to Mohammed. During the course of his work, the orthodox advocate was assailed by a deist who contended that the books ascribed to Moses were once lost and that Ezra had actually altered them. The skeptic was soon answered by another defender of the faith who was surprised that the remarks of "Common Sense" "should have raised the bristles of one of your Richmond Deists. . . ." Apparently "the bristles" of more than one Richmond deist had been raised as was evidenced by the fact that another freethinker severely censured "Common Sense" for misrepresenting the position of his deistic rival.[28] A Hudson newspaper likewise published a series of articles designed to prove the validity of the Biblical revelation, especially its story of the Deluge. The existing marks made by the flood upon the earth's surface and the prevalence of pagan traditions and fables were presented as

[27] *The Boston Gazette and Weekly Republican Journal* from June 30, 1794 (no. 2074) to October 27, 1794 (no. 2091) inclusive.

[28] The first essay of "Common Sense" appeared in *The Virginia Gazette and Richmond Chronicle* for March 10, 1795 (no. 213), while the ninth and last article was published on May 5, 1795 (no. 229). See especially the issues of April 4, May 5 and 9, 1795 (nos. 223, 229, 230).

proofs of the narrative's truth.   Jefferson's rejection of the story was especially objected to.[29]

To check the spread of deism, the champions of Christianity used not only press but also pulpit.   Particularly prominent in this crusade were the Congregational clergy of New England who endeavored to show that freethinking was subversive of a belief in the existence of God and of a continuation of organized government.   With such lofty watchwords as " For God and Country! " they sought to entangle men on the barbed wires of prejudice.   The effort to identify deism with atheism was reflected in a sermon, delivered in 1798, by James Dana of New Haven.   After condemning the deists for their attack upon Christianity, the clergyman asserted that too many concessions were being made to these " atheists ". The divine origin of the Bible ought to be accepted by the clergy without any more ado.[30]   Some three years later, Timothy Dwight also linked deism and atheism under the general head of " infidelity ".   Besides he injected into the deistic controversy, the anti-French political issue.   Asserting that freethinking was characteristic of the eighteenth century, he stated that its success in America was " totally unprecedented . . ." and was undoubtedly due to enthusiasm for the French revolutionaries.   Yet, he modestly reassured his hearers that New England had escaped the " dreadful bondage " of deism through the untiring work of her leaders among whom was that inconspicuous servant of the Lord, Timothy Dwight.[31]   The Yale President was vigorously condemned by a deistic newspaper, *The Temple of*

[29] *The Balance and Columbian Repository*, February 1 to March 1, 1803 (nos. 5 to 9).

[30] J. Dana, *A Sermon: Preached October 17, 1798 at the Ordination of the Rev. Mr. Dan Huntington* (Lichtfield, 1799), pp. 18, 22-3.

[31] T. Dwight, *A Discourse on Some Events of the Last Century*. Delivered January 7, 1801, pp. 19, 21-2, 32, 34.

Reason for April 29, 1801, which described his sermon as a bigoted and unlearned discourse. Another New England clergyman, John Foster, attempted to check deism by showing that the movement was un-American. In his sermon, *Infidelity Exposed, and Christianity Recommended* (1802), Foster held that freethinking was characteristically European and consequently the nations across the Atlantic had more to fear from the forces of darkness than our own " favored land, happily disjoined from those degenerate and luxurious regions. . . ." Yet, the danger was even present in America where Paine was being eulogized; therefore the ever vigilant minister urged all, regardless of age or sex, to be on the watch to detect and avoid the snares of deism.[32]

The more or less rational defense of Christianity necessarily appealed to a limited minority, the educated few. Most of the people were neither capable of following antideistic arguments nor were they especially interested in them. Weary of endless disputation and desiring a consoling faith, the masses were ready to listen to revivalist preachers who urged them to heed the promptings of their hearts which would lead them to accept without question the divine origin of the Bible and the Messiahship of Jesus. Beginning in 1792, evangelicalism made its way from New England to western New York and Pennsylvania and, by 1801, reached its peak in Kentucky and Tennessee. Although free from " abnormal excitement" in New England, the movement was characterized by " excesses " in the region west of the Alleghanies where open meetings were conducted by ignorant and unlearned preachers who reënforced their messages by dire observations on the depravity of man. At these " ingatherings ", some " sinners " would lie on the ground, suddenly arise and begin to shriek, groan and pray, while

[32] J. Foster, *Infidelity Exposed, etc.* (Cambridge, 1802), pp. 19-20, 27, 33 (Appendix, note, iv).

others, falling into trances, would unexpectedly throw themselves down and roll about like a ball. Sometimes these
neurotic activities were indulged in by as many as twenty
thousand people and continued for many days. It was felt
that at these meetings the Spirit of God descended upon converted sinners and disclosed to them "the glorious mysteries
of the Gospel." [33]

From our viewpoint, the most significant result of the
Awakening of the late eighteenth and early nineteenth centuries was the advent of a more vigorous orthodox movement designed to check the progress of deism. Missionary
societies, religious periodicals, Bible associations and educational institutions rendered effective service. At the turn of
the century, Connecticut, New York, Massachusetts, New
Hampshire and Vermont established missions in order to
spread the Gospel in the West and South. Aided financially
by Female Cent Institutions, these bodies possessed well
filled treasuries; by 1807, the Missionary Society of Connecticut reported a permanent fund of $15,000. In 1816, a
Board of Home Missions was organized to send better informed ministers westward and thereby check indifference
to religion.[34] Connected with these organizations were
periodicals founded for the double purpose of reporting the
successful work of missionaries and of defending revelation.
The Connecticut Evangelical Magazine and the *New-York*

[33] L. W. Bacon, *History of American Christianity* (New York, 1897),
pp. 233-45; F. G. Beardsley, *A History of American Revivals* (New
York, 1904), pp. 85-107; J. M. Buckley, *A History of Methodism in the
U. S.* (New York, 1896), p. 298; H. M. Jones, *America and French
Culture*, pp. 388, 411-2; and R. E. Thompson, *A History of the Pres-
byterian Churches in the U. S.* (New York, 1895), pp. 73-4.

[34] Bacon, *op. cit.*, pp. 246-7; Sweet, *Story of Religions in America*
(New York, 1930), p. 352; Newman, *History of the Baptist Churches in
the U. S.* (New York, 1894), p. 385; Thompson, *op. cit.*, p. 81; and
Walker, *History of the Congregational Churches in the U. S.* (New
York, 1884), p. 313.

Missionary Magazine and Repository appeared in 1800. These were followed by others, the most popular of which was *The Panoplist, and Missionary Magazine United*. This periodical was conducted by a society called the Friends to Evangelical Truth which, in turn, was under the patronage of the Massachusetts, Hampshire, Maine, Berkshire and Rhode Island Missionary Societies. Attaining a circulation of seven thousand readers by 1809, *The Panoplist* assailed those who desired to sap the foundation of Christian faith and consequently its sheets were filled with articles praising Christianity and vindicating the divinity of Jesus and the authenticity of the Mosaic account in Genesis.[35] Moreover, Massachusetts Baptists had their own magazine (1803 to 1807), while the Presbyterian General Assembly issued a journal containing articles which showed the absurdities of deism and the superiority of revelation.[36]

Bible and Tract Societies were also formed to fight the deistic " legions of darkness ". Securing eager volunteers from the laity and clergy of all denominations, these organizations, " convinced of the great value of the revealed will of God ", were established in Pennsylvania, Vermont, Connecticut and Massachusetts. In 1816, a national organization, The American Bible Society, appeared which immediately published copies of the Scriptures and distributed them free of charge to the farmers of the South and West. In addition to these agencies, educational institutions were founded. From 1808 to 1827, Congregationalists, Presbyterians and Episcopalians established divinity schools designed to pro-

[35] *Panopolist, and Missionary Magazine United*, June, 1808, vol. i, pp. 24-8 and October, 1808 to August, 1809, vol. i, pp. 211 *et seq.* and 391 *et seq.*

[36] *The General Assembly's Missionary Magazine; or Evangelical Intelligencer*, March, 1805 (no. 3), vol. i, pp. 133-5 and May, 1805 (no. 5), vol. i, p. 228.

duce an educated ministry which would be better prepared to meet skeptical contentions. The faithful concerned themselves not only with higher but also with lower branches of education. In order to impress upon young minds the need of the Christian religion, infant schools were founded where simple Biblical questions were answered, Scriptural scenes shown and the Ten Commandments taught. In addition, there were Sunday schools where catechisms were used. These categorically praised the truth and excellence of Christianity and condemned the falsity and absurdity of Mohammedanism.[37]

Thus, during the early nineteenth century, the forces of deism were compelled to give way before the advancing columns of evangelical Christianity. The deistic army, though eventually defeated, was far from routed. In the ' twenties and early 'thirties, it reformed its wavering ranks and renewed its attack under the banners of Utopian socialism. Frances Wright and the Owens endeavored to liberate the proletariat from " the opium of religion " but all to no avail. In the end, " the foot of the spoiler " was unable to " trample down the cross of the redeemer ". Even though militant deism was unable to accomplish this objective, it nevertheless profoundly affected American intellectuals. The Higher Criticism, which sought to determine after careful investigation the authorship and dates of Scriptural books and passages, was influenced by it. This tendency, which originated in Germany, made its way to America during the early nineteenth century [38] and was popularized here by Thomas Cooper, President of the College of

[37] See *A Missionary Catechism for the Use of Children* published by the Yale College Society of Inquiry concerning Missions (New Haven, 1821), pp. 6, 8-12.

[38] John Adams mentioned it in a letter to Jefferson ,July 18, 1813. Wilstach, *Correspondence of John Adams and Thomas Jefferson*, p. 69.

South Carolina and Theodore Parker, Unitarian minister.[39] Although many deistic observations on the Bible were superficial and biased, some, especially on the Pentateuch, were penetrating and later verified.

The New England Unitarian movement of the nineteenth century had something in common with the deistic tendency; both agreed as to the attributes of God, the aim of religion and the character of Jesus. William Channing, a leading Unitarian, accepted the deistic notion that the Supreme Being was so benevolent and just that He would not damn the greater part of mankind for the sake of a chosen few. Moreover, as with most deists, so with Channing, the end of religion was the love of God and the practice of the good life. Furthermore, the New England clergyman in describing Christ as a tender, humble and philanthropic soul distinct from and inferior to God was merely stating what the disciples of deism were saying all along.[40] Yet, a wide gulf separated Channing and the deists and that gulf was revelation and miracles. Unlike the deistic champions, he argued that Christian "disclosures" were needed to make "the voice of nature" more audible and that supernatural acts in general and those of Jesus in particular were of divine origin.[44] In short, the Unitarianism of Channing was more than a diluted form of deism purged of its anti-Christian ingredients. Developing along different lines the Unitarian

---

[39] See Cooper, *A Letter to Prof. Silliman On the Connection between Geology and the Pentateuch* (Boston, 1833), pp. 21-2, 31-2, 39-40, 47-8 and Parker, *A Discourse on the Transient and Permanent in Christianity* (Boston, 1841), pp. 21-2. Consult also Parrington, *Main Currents in American Thought*, vol. ii, pp. 417-8 and Robertson, *Short History of Free Thought*, vol. ii, p. 438.

[40] Channing, *A Sermon, Delivered at the Ordination of the Rev. Jared Sparks* (Liverpool, 1821), pp. 18-9, 23, 25, 31 and *Works* (Boston, 1875), pp. 228-9, 385.

[41] Channing, *Works*, pp. 221, 223-4, 230, 232, 384.

movement was essentially hostile to it. Uncompromising in the eighteenth century, it remained so in the nineteenth when "infidelity" was only a hollow shell. Proposing to stamp it out by discarding traditional Calvinistic doctrines and by interpreting the Bible along "reasonable" lines, Channing employed arguments reminiscent of the liberal and dignified apologists of the eighteenth century. It is interesting to note that long after deism had died out as an independent movement, a transcendental Unitarian. Theodore Parker went beyond Channing's position by rejecting the Biblical revelation and the miracles of Christianity and substituting for them "the absolute Religion of Nature" consisting of "normal feelings toward God and man, of the correct thoughts about God and man, and the relation between them, and of actions corresponding to the natural conscience. . . ." [42]

[42] T. Parker, *A Discourse on the Transient and Permanent in Christianity*, p. 19 and Weiss, *The Life and Correspondence of Theodore Parker* (New York, 1864), vol. ii, pp. 451-2, 464, 474 (Appendix).

LIST OF AUTHORITIES

The works cited below are arranged under the various chapter headings

EUROPEAN BACKGROUND

PRIMARY SOURCES

Blount, C., *Oracles of Reason* (London, 1693).

Bolingbroke, H. St. John, *Works*, ed. D. Mallet (London, 1754).

Cheyne, G., *Philosophical Principles of Religion: Natural and Revealed* (London, 1715).

Chubb, T., *True Gospel of Jesus Christ Asserted. To which is added a Short Dissertation on Providence* (London, 1738).

Clarke, S., *A Discourse concerning the unchangeable Obligations of Natural Religion, and the Truth and Certainty of the Christian Revelation* (in Watson, R., *A Collection of Theological Tracts* [London, 1791], vol. iv, pp. 109-295).

——, *Discourse on Natural Religion* (in Selby-Bigge, L. A. [ed.], *British Moralists, Being Selections from Writers Principally of the Eighteenth Century* [Oxford, 1897], vol. ii, pp. 3-56).

Collins, A., *A Discourse of Free-thinking occasioned by the rise and growth of a sect called Free-thinkers* (London, 1713).

——, *Discourse of the Grounds and Reasons of the Christian Religion* (London, 1724).

Herbert of Cherbury, *Religion of the Gentiles with the Causes of their Errors* (London, 1705).

d'Holbach, P. H., *The System of Nature; or the Laws of the Moral and Physical World* (London, 1836).

Locke, J., *Essay Concerning Human Understanding*, ed. A. S. Fraser (Oxford, 1894).

——, *Reasonableness of Christianity. To which is added A Discourse on Miracles* (One of a volume of nine pamphlets in the Columbia University Library, no title page).

Newton, I., *Mathematical Principles of Natural Philosophy*, translated by Motte (London, 1803).

Pope, A., *Essay on Man* (in Richards, J. A. [ed.], *Outline of Knowledge* [New York, 1924], vol. xi, pp. 289-318).

Rousseau, J. J., *Confessions*, Hedouin Edition (London, no date).

——, *Emilius and Sophia; or A New System of Education* (London, 1783).

——, *Profession of Faith of A Savoyard Vicar* (New York, 1889).

Shaftesbury, A., *Characteristics of Men, Manners, Opinions, Times, etc.*, ed. J. M. Robertson (London, 1900).

Tillotson, J., *Works* (London, 1717).

Toland, J., *Christianity not Mysterious: or A Treatise Shewing, That there is nothing in the Gospel Contrary to Reason, Nor Above it: And that no Christian Doctrine can be properly call'd A Mystery* (London, 1696).

Voltaire, F. M. A. de, *Letters on the Christian Religion* (New York, no date).

——, *Philosophical Dictionary . . . with Notes, containing A Refutation of such Passages as are in any way exceptionable in regard to Religion* (London, 1765).

——, *Romances*, ed. Komroff (New York, 1928).

——, *Toleration and Other Essays*, tr. with an introduction by J. McCabe (New York, 1912).

Wollaston, W., *The Religion of Nature Delineated* (London, 1738).

Woolston, T., *A Discourse on the Miracles of our Saviour, in view of the Present Controversy Between Infidels and Apostates* (London, 1727).

CATALOGUES OF BOOKS

(See also citations under *Rise of Deism in Colonial America, Primary Sources, Catalogues of Books*)

Berrian, S., *A Catalogue* (New York, 1803).

Blake, W. P., *Catalogue of Books* (Boston, 1796).

Carey, Stewart and Company, *Catalogue of Books, etc.* (Philadelphia, 1791).

Caritat, H., *Catalogue Livres Français* (New York, 1799).

Catalogue of the Books Belonging to the Loganian Library (Philadelphia, 1795).

Catalogue of Books in the Massachusetts Historical Library (Boston, 1796).

The Charter, Bye-Laws, and Names of the Members of the New York Society Library: With A Catalogue of Books Belonging to the said Library (New York, 1789, 1792, 1793).

Cox and Berry, *A Catalogue of A very large Assortment of the most esteemed Books, etc.* (Boston, 1776 [?]).

Gaine, H., *Catalogue of Books* (New York, 1792).

Knox, H., *Catalogue* (Boston, 1773).

Prichard, W., *A Catalogue of a Scarce and Valuable Collection of Books* (Philadelphia, 1785).

Thomas, Andrews and Penniman, *Catalogue of Books* (Albany, 1798[?]).

PERIODICALS

(Consult citations under *Rise of Deism in Colonial America, Deism in Revolutionary America, Deism Militant* and *Christianity Defended, Primary Sources, Periodicals*)

SECONDARY AUTHORITIES

Abbey, C. J. and Overton, J. H., *The English Church in the Eighteenth Century* (London, 1878).

Benn, A. W., *History of English Rationalism in the Nineteenth Century* (London, 1906), vol. i.

Burtt, E. A., *Metaphysical Foundations of Modern Physical Science* (London, 1925).

Bury, J. B., *History of Freedom of Thought* (New York, 1913).

Farrar, A. S., *A Critical History of Free Thought in Reference to the Christian Religion* (New York, 1863).

Hunt, J., *Religious Thought in England* (London, 1870), 3 vols.

Lecky, W. E. H., *History of the Rise and Influence of the Spirit of Rationalism in Europe* (New York, 1919), vol. i.

Life of George Cheyne, M. D., with Extracts from his Works and Correspondence (Oxford, 1846).

Lodge, O., *Pioneers of Science* (London, 1893).

McGiffert, A. C., *Protestant Thought Before Kant* (New York, 1911).

Morley, J., *Rousseau* (London, 1891), vol. ii.

——, *Voltaire* (London, 1919).

Overton, J. H. and Relton, F., *English Church from the Accession of George I to the End of the Eighteenth Century* (London, 1906).

Pattison, M., *Essays*, collected and arranged by H. Nettleship (Oxford, 1889).

Randall, J. H, *The Making of the Modern Mind* (Boston, 1926).

Robertson, J. M., *Short History of Free Thought* (New York, 1906), vol. ii.

Sedgwick, W. T. and Tyler, H. W., *Short History of Science* (New York, 1923).

Shields, C. W., *The Final Philosophy* (New York, 1877).

Stephen, L., *English Thought in the Eighteenth Century* (New York, 1902), vol. i.

Whitehead, A. N., *Science and the Modern World* (New York, 1925).

RISE OF DEISM IN COLONIAL AMERICA (1713-1763)

PRIMARY SOURCES

Adams, J., *Works*, ed. C. F. Adams (Boston, 1850).

Briant, L., *The Absurdity and Blasphemy of Depretiating Moral Virtue* (Boston, 1749).

Byrd, W., *Writings*, ed. Bassett (New York, 1901).

Chauncy, C., *Benevolence of the Deity, Fairly and Impartially Considered* (Boston, 1784).

——, *Seasonable Thoughts on the State of Religion in New England* (Boston, 1743).

Clap, T., *An Essay on the Nature and Foundations of Moral Virtue and Obligations; being a Short Introduction to the Study of Ethics* (New Haven, 1765).

Colden, C., *An Explication of the First Causes of Action in Matter, and the Cause of Gravitation* (New York, 1746).

Dickinson, J., *Familiar Letters Upon A Variety of Religious Subjects* (Glasgow, 1775).

——, *The Reasonableness of Christianity, in Four Sermons* (Boston, 1732).

Edwards, J., *Works*, ed. S. L. Dwight (New York, 1830), vols. ii, iii, iv, xi.

Franklin, B., *A Dissertation on Liberty and Necessity, Pleasure and Pain* (in I. W. Riley, *American Philosophy—Early Schools* [New York, 1907], pp. 571-80).

——, *Memoirs* (New York, 1839), vol. ii.

——, *Writings*, ed. A. H. Smyth (New York, 1905-07).

——, *Works*, ed. J. Sparks (Boston, 1836).

Gay, E., *Natural Religion, As Distinguish'd From Revealed* (Boston, 1759).

Johnson, S., *An Introduction to the Study of Philosophy* (New London, 1743).

——, *His Career and Writings*, ed. H. and C. Schneider (New York, 1929).

——, *A Letter from Aristocles to Authades Concerning the Sovereignty and the Promises of God* (Boston, 1745).

Livingston, W., *Philosophic Solitude: or, The Choice of a Rural Life, A Poem* (New York, 1747).

Mather, C., *Student and Preacher; or Directions for a Candidate of the Ministry* (London, 1789).

——, *Christian Philosopher* (London, 1721).

——, *Reasonable Religion: or, the Truths of the Christian Religion Demonstrated* (London, 1713).

Mayhew, J., *Two Sermons on the Nature, Extent and Perfection of the Divine Goodness. Delivered December 9, 1762* (Boston, 1763).

Smith, W., *Discourses on Public Occasions in America* (London, 1762), Appendix, pp. 39-103, 147-60.

Wesley, J., *An Extract of the Reverend Mr. John Wesley's Journal, etc.* (Bristol, 1739 [?]).

Whitefield, G., *A Continuation of the Reverend Mr. Whitefield's Journal, etc.* (London, 1744).

Wigglesworth, E., *A Letter to the Reverend Mr. George Whitefield, by Way of A Reply to his Answer to the College Testimony against him and his Conduct* (Boston, 1745).

MANUSCRIPT MATERIAL

Hawley, J., *Confession of His Belief in Arminianism* (New York Public Library).

Johnson, S., *The Necessity of Reveal'd Religion. A Sermon . . . delivered September 7, 1727 at Stratford* (Columbia University Library).

PERIODICALS

(In these citations and in those following under *Periodicals*, dates of magazines are only given)

The American Magazine (Boston, 1743-46). Also called *The American Magazine and Historical Chronicle; for all the British Plantations.*

The American Magazine and Monthly Chronicle for the British Colonies (Philadelphia, 1757-8).

The American Weekly Mercury.

The General Magazine, and Historical Chronicle, For all the British Plantations in America (Philadelphia, 1741).

The Maryland Gazette.

The New American Magazine (Woodbridge, 1758-60).

The New-York Gazette.

The New-York Gazette Revived in the Weekly Post-Boy.

ALMANACS

Ames, N., *An Astronomical Diary, or, an Almanack for the Year of Our Lord Christ 1733* (Boston, 1733).

More, T., *The American Country Almanack, For the Year of Christian Account 1748* (New York, 1748).

Nadir, W., *Mercurius Nov-Anglicanus, or An Almanack Anno Domini 1743* (Boston, 1743).

Taylor, J., *Pennsilvania, 1743, An Almanack, or Ephemeris* (Philadelphia, 1743).

CATALOGUES OF BOOKS

Byrd, W., *Writings*, ed. J. S. Bassett (New York, 1901), pp. 413-44.

A Catalogue of Books, Imported and to be Sold by Henry Knox (Boston, 1773).

The Charter, Laws, and Catalogue of Books of the Library Company of Philadelphia (Philadelphia, 1764).

Clap, T., *A Catalogue of the Library of Yale College in New Haven* (New London, 1743).

Collections of the New York Historical Society for the Year 1880 (New York, 1881), pp. 339-63.

Johnson, S., *A Catalogue of my Library with the value* (sic) *of each Book.* August 15, 1726 (MS.), Columbia University Library.

The Library of the Late Reverend and Learned Mr. Samuel Lee, etc. (Boston, 1693).

SECONDARY AUTHORITIES

Adams, J. T., *Provincial Society, 1690-1763* (New York, 1927).

Brown, E. F., *Joseph Hawley, Colonial Radical* (New York, 1931).

Burton, J. H., *Life and Correspondence of David Hume* (Edinburgh, 1846).

Cambridge History of American Literature (New York, 1917), vol. i, chapter v.

Christie, F. A., *The Beginnings of Arminianism in New England* (Papers of American Society of Church History, 2nd Series, vol. iii).

Cook, E. C., *Literary Influences in Colonial Newspapers, 1704-1750* (New York, 1912).

Cooke, G. W., *Unitarianism in America* (Boston, 1902).

Curtis, M. M., *Outline of Philosophy in America* (in the Western Reserve University *Bulletin*, March, 1896).

Dexter, F. B., *A Selection from the Miscellaneous Historical Papers of Fifty Years* (New Haven, 1918).

Eggleston, E., *The Transit of Civilization* (New York, 1901).

Faÿ, B., *Franklin, the Apostle of Modern Times* (Boston, 1929).

Foster, F. H., *A Genetic History of the New England Theology* (Chicago, 1907).

Gewehr, W. M., *The Great Awakening in Virginia, 1740-1790* (Durham, 1930).

Greene, M. L., *Rise of Religious Liberty in Connecticut* (Boston, 1905).

History of the College of William and Mary from its Foundation, 1660, to 1874 (Richmond, 1874).

Ingraham, C. A., *A Great Colonial Executive and Scholar—Cadwallader Colden* (in *Americana*, vol. xix, Jan., 1925 to Dec., 1925, pp. 295-314).

Keep, A. B., *History of the New York Society Library, with an Introductory chapter on libraries in colonial New York, 1698-1776* (Devinne Press, 1908), pp. 3-122.

Lamberton, E. V., *Colonial Libraries of Pennsylvania* (in the *Pennsylvania Magazine of History and Biography*, vol. xlii, no. 3, pp. 193-234).

Massachusetts Historical Society, *Proceedings*, Second Series (Boston, 1896), vol. x, pp. 542-4.

Mott, F. L., *A History of American Magazines, 1741-1850* (New York, 1930).

Palfrey, J. G., *History of New England* (Boston, 1897).

Parrington, V. L., *Main Currents in American Thought* (New York, 1927), vol. i, *The Colonial Mind.*

Quincy, J., *The History of Harvard University* (Boston, 1860).

Reed, S. M., *Church and State in Massachusetts, 1691-1740* (U. of Illinois Studies in Social Sciences, vol. iii, no. 4, Dec., 1914).

Richardson, L. N., *A History of Early American Magazines, 1741-1789* (New York, 1931).

Riley, I. W., *American Philosophy—Early Schools* (New York, 1907).

Schneider, H. W., *The Puritan Mind* (New York, 1930).

Sedgwick, T., *A Memoir of the Life of William Livingston* (New York, 1833).

Sprague, W. B., *Annals of the American Pulpit* (New York, 1859).

Tiffany, C. C., *History of the Protestant Episcopal Church in the United States of America* (New York, 1895).

Trumbull, J. R., *History of Northampton, Massachusetts* (Northampton, 1902).

Walker, W., *History of the Congregational Churches in the United States* (New York, 1884).

Winsor, J. (ed.), *The Memorial History of Boston, including Suffolk County, Massachusetts, 1630-1880* (Boston, 1881), vol. ii, pp. 387-436.

Wright, T. G., *Literary Culture in Early New England, 1620-1730* (New Haven, 1920).

DEISM IN REVOLUTIONARY AMERICA (1763-1789)

PRIMARY SOURCES

Adams, S., *Writings*, ed. H. A. Cushing (New York, 1904-08), 4 vols.

Allen, E., *A Narrative of Colonel Ethan Allen's Captivity, etc.* (Philadelphia, 1779).

——, *Reason, the Only Oracle of Man; Or A Compendious System of Natural Religion* (New York, 1836).

Ames, N., *Essays, Humor, and Poems, with Notes and Comments* by S. Briggs (Cleveland, 1891).

Asbury, F., *Journal* (New York, 1831).

Bentley, W., *A Sermon, Preached at the Stone Chapel in Boston* (Boston, 1790).

——, *Diary* (Salem, 1905).

Dwight, T., *The Triumph of Infidelity: A Poem* (New York, 1788).

Hazlitt, W., *A Thanksgiving Discourse, preached at Hallowell, 15 December, 1785* (Boston, 1786).

Jefferson, T., *Writings*, ed. P. L. Ford (New York, 1892).

The Lee Papers (1754-1811), 4 vols. (New York Historical Society *Collections*, 1871-74).

Leland, J., *Writings*, ed. L. F. Greene (New York, 1845).

Madison, J., *Writings*, ed. G. Hunt (New York, 1900).

Massachusetts Historical Society, *Proceedings* (Boston, 1928), vol. lxi, pp. 250-1, 259-60.

Morris, G., *Life, with Selections from his Correspondence and Miscellaneous Papers*, ed. J. Sparks (Boston, 1832).

The Proceedings Relative to Calling the Conventions of 1776 and 1790 . . . The (Pennsylvania) Constitutions of 1776 and 1790 and A View of the Proceedings of the Convention of 1776, etc. (Harrisburg, 1825).

Randolph, J., *Letters to A Young Relative* (Philadelphia, 1834).

Stiles, E., *Literary Diary*, ed. F. B. Dexter (New York, 1901), 3 vols.

Washington, G., *Writings*, ed. J. Sparks (Boston, 1855).

——, *Writings*, ed. W. C. Ford (New York, 1889-92).

Webster, N., *The Peculiar Doctrines of the Gospel, Explained and Defended* (Poughkeepsie, 1809).

Winchester, E., *The Universal Restoration, etc.* (Bellows Falls, 1819).

PERIODICALS

The American Magazine (New York, 1787-8).

The American Magazine or General Repository (Philadelphia, 1769).

The American Museum, or Repository (Philadelphia, 1787-8).

The Boston Gazette and the Country Journal.

Boston Magazine (Boston, 1783-4).

The Christian's, Scholar's and Farmer's Magazine (Elizabeth-Town, 1789).

Columbian Magazine (Philadelphia, 1788).

The Connecticut Journal.

Continental Journal; and Weekly Advertiser.

The Country Journal and The Poughkeepsie Advertiser.

The Country Journal and Dutchess and Ulster County Farmer's Register.

The Gazette of the State of South Carolina.

Maryland Gazette; or the Baltimore Advertiser.

The New-Haven Gazette.

The New-Haven Gazette, and the Connecticut Magazine (New Haven, 1786).

The New-Jersey Magazine, and Monthly Advertiser (New Brunswick, 1787).

The New-York Journal or, The General Advertiser.

New-York Packet.

The Pennsylvania Gazette.

The Pennsylvania Journal; and the Weekly Advertiser.

The Pennsylvania Magazine: or American Monthly Museum (Philadelphia, 1775-6).

The Providence Gazette and Country Journal.
The South-Carolina Gazette and Country Journal.
The Worcester Magazine (Worcester, 1787).

SECONDARY AUTHORITIES

Adams, H., *John Randolph* (New York, 1899).

Adams, H. B., *College of William and Mary: A Contribution to Higher Education* (Washington, 1887).

Allen, J. H. and Eddy, R., *A History of the Unitarians and Universalists in the United States* (New York, 1894).

Bacon, L. W., *A History of American Christianity* (New York, 1901).

Beard, C. A., *An Economic Interpretation of the Constitution of the United States* (New York, 1925).

Boutell, L. H., *The Life of Roger Sherman* (Chicago, 1896).

Bruce, W. C., *John Randolph of Roanoke, 1773-1833* (New York, 1922).

Channing, E., *A History of the United States* (New York, 1924), vol. iii.

Chinard, G., *Thomas Jefferson, The Apostle of Americanism* (Boston, 1929).

Conway, M. D., *Ethan Allen's Oracles of Reason* (in the *Open Court Magazine*, January 28, 1892, vol. vi).

——, *Omitted Chapters of History Disclosed in the Life and Papers of Edmund Randolph* (New York, 1889).

Faÿ, B., *The Revolutionary Spirit in France and America*, tr. by R. Guthrie (New York, 1928).

Fiske, J., *Essays Historical and Literary* (New York, 1902), vol. i.

Foster, W. E., *Stephen Hopkins* (in the Rhode Island Historical Tracts, no. 19), [Providence, 1884]).

Garland, H. A., *Life of John Randolph of Roanoke* (New York, 1851), vol. ii.

Haroutunian, J., *Piety versus Moralism: The Passing of the New England Theology* (New York, 1932).

Henry, W. W., *Patrick Henry, Life, Correspondence and Speeches* (New York, 1891).

Jones, H. M., *America and French Culture, 1750-1848* (Durham, 1927).

Kraus, M., *Intercolonial Aspects of American Culture* (New York, 1928).

Meade, W., *Old Churches, Ministers and Families of Virginia* (Philadelphia, 1861).

Maugras, G., *La Fin d'Une Societié, Le Duc de Lauzun et La Cour de Marie-Antoinette* (Paris, 1895).

McCabe, J., *Six Infidel Presidents* (in the *Haldeman-Julius Quarterly*, April, 1927, vol. i, no. 3, pp. 33-51).

Pell, J., *Ethan Allen* (New York, 1929).

Purcell, R. J., *Connecticut in Transition, 1775-1818* (Washington, 1918).

Randall, H. S., *The Life of Thomas Jefferson* (New York, 1858).

Rives, W. C., *History of the Life and Times of James Madison* (Boston, 1859).

Rowland, K. M., *Life of George Mason* (New York, 1892).

Sanderson, J. and Waln, R. (ed.), *Biography of the Signers To the Declaration of Independence* (Philadelphia, 1823-4, 1827).

Scudder, H. E., *Noah Webster* (Boston, 1882).

Sears, L. M., *George Washington* (New York, 1932).

Sherlock, C. C., *Tall Timbers* (Boston, 1926).

Thompson, R. E., *A History of the Presbyterian Churches in the United States* (New York, 1895).

Wallace, D. D., *Life of Henry Laurens* (New York, 1915).

George Washington, The Christian (Issued by the United States George Washington Bicentennial Commission, A. B. Hart, historian, Washington, 1931).

DEISM MILITANT: EARLY NATIONAL PERIOD (1789-1805)

PRIMARY SOURCES

Ames, F., *Works*, ed. S. Ames (Boston, 1851), vol. i.

Dwight, T., *A Discourse on Some Events of the Last Century* (New Haven, 1801).

Freneau, P., *Letters on Various Interesting and Important Subjects* (Philadelphia, 1799).

Hamilton, A., *Works*, ed. H. C. Lodge (New York, 1904).

Harris, T. M., *Constitutions of the Ancient and Honorable Fraternity of Free and Accepted Masons . . . together with a History and General Regulations of the Grand Lodge of Mass.* (Worcester, 1798).

——, *Ignorance and Prejudice shewn to be the Only Enemies To Free Masonry . . . in A Sermon* (Leominister, 1797).

Leland, J., *A Blow at the Roots: Being a Fashionable Fast Day Sermon delivered at Cheshire, April 9, 1801* (New London, 1801).

Linn, W., *Serious Considerations on the Election of a President: Addressed to the Citizens of the United States* (New York, 1800).

Marcus Brutus (pseud.), *Serious Facts, Opposed to 'Serious Considerations': or, The Voice of Warning to Religious Republicans* (New York [?] 1800).

Massachusetts Historical Society, *Collections* (Boston, 1891), 6th Series, vol. iv.

Morris, G., *Writings*, ed. J. Sparks (Boston, 1832), 3 vols.

Morse, J., *A Sermon, Exhibiting The Present Dangers, and Consequent Duties of the Citizens of the United States of America* (Charlestown, 1799).

Nelson, D., *The Cause and Cure of Infidelity, etc.* (New York, 1841).

Payson, S., *Proofs of the Real Existence, and Dangerous Tendency of Illuminism* (Charlestown, 1802).

Owen, R. and Campbell, A., *The Evidences of Christianity; A Debate* (Cincinnati, 1852).

Paine, T., *The Age of Reason, Being An Investigation of True and Fabulous Theology* (New York, no date). Willey Book Co.

——, *A Letter to the Hon. Thomas Erskine . . . with His Discourse At The Society of the Theophilanthropists* (Paris, 1797).

——, *Works*, ed. W. M. Van der Weyde (New Rochelle, 1925).

——, *Writings*, ed. M. Conway (New York, 1894-1896).

Palmer, E., *Principles of Nature; or A Development of the Moral Causes of Happiness, and Misery among the Human Species* (London, 1823).

Political Miscellany Containing . . . Extracts from an Oration, delivered by Elihu Palmer, 4 of July, 1793 (New York, 1793).

Posthumous Pieces of Elihu Palmer . . . To which are prefixed A Memoir of Mr. Palmer, by his friend John Fellows of New York, and Mr. Palmer's Principles of the Deistical Society of New York (London, 1824).

Priestley, J., *Observations on the Increase of Infidelity. To which are added Animadversions on the Writings of several Unbelievers, especially The Ruins of Mr. Volney* (Philadelphia, 1797).

Smith, W. (ed.), *Ahiman Rezon Abridged and Digested: As A Help to all that are, or would be Free and Accepted Masons* (Philadelphia, 1783).

Volney, C. F. C. de, *Answer to Doctor Priestley* (Philadelphia, 1797).

——, *The Ruins: A Survey of the Revolutions of Empires* (New York, 1796).

Williams, J., *Memoirs of the late Reverend Mr. Thomas Belsham* (London, 1833).

PERIODICALS

(See citations under *Christianity Defended* [1789-1805], *Periodicals*)

The American Mercury.

The American Review, and Literary Journal (New York, 1801-2).

The Balance and Columbian Repository.

Massachusetts Spy: or The Worcester Gazette.

The New-Harmony Gazette.

The Panoplist, and Missionary Magazine United, New Series.

The Pennsylvania Gazette.

Prospect, or View of the Moral World.

The Temple of Reason.

The Temple of Truth.

The Theological Magazine, or Synopsis of Modern Religious Sentiment (New York, 1796-9).

The Theophilanthropist; Containing Critical, Moral, Theological and Literary Essays (New York, 1810).

SECONDARY AUTHORITIES

Albert, G. D., *History of the County of Westmoreland, Pennsylvania* (Philadelphia, 1882).

Amory, T. C., *Life of James Sullivan* (Boston, 1859).

Austin, J. T., *The Life of Elbridge Gerry* (Boston, 1828).

Beard, C. A., *Economic Origins of Jeffersonian Democracy* (New York, 1915).

Clark, H. H., *Toward A Reinterpretation of Thomas Paine* (in *American Literature*, vol. v, no. 2, May, 1933, pp. 133-45).

Cleveland, G., *The Great Revival in the West, 1797-1805* (Chicago, 1916).

Fosdick, L. J., *French Blood in America* (New York, 1906).

Francis, J. W., *New York during the Last Half Century* (New York, 1857).

Gillett, E. H., *History of the Presbyterian Church in the United States of America* (Philadelphia, 1864).

Gilpatrick, D. H., *Jeffersonian Democracy in North Carolina* (New York, 1931).

Griswold, R. W., *The Republican Court* (New York, 1855).

Hamilton, J. G. de R., *William Richardson Davie: A Memoir followed by his Letters with Notes by K. P. Battle* (University of North Carolina, James Sprunt Historical Monograph, no. 7) (Chapel Hill, 1907).

Hazen, C. D., *Contemporary American Opinion of the French Revolution* (Baltimore, 1897).

Jay, W., *The Life of John Jay* (New York, 1833), 2 vols.

Koch, G. A., *Republican Religion. The American Revolution and The Cult of Reason* (New York, 1933).

Larned, E. D., *History of Windham County, Connecticut* (Worcester, 1894).

Lewis, F. and Veech, J., *The Monongahela of Old* (Pittsburgh, 1892).

McMaster, J. B. and Stone, F. D., *Pennsylvania and the Federal Constitution* (Lancaster, 1888).

Myers, E. M., *A History of the Introduction of Freemasonry and its Progress in the United States since 1732* (New York, 1900).

Nash, J. V., *Thomas Paine, Pioneer Freethinker* (in the *Haldeman-Julius Quarterly*, October, 1926, vol. i, no. 1, pp. 31-8).

Pickering, O. and Upham, C. W., *Life of Timothy Pickering* (Boston, 1867).

Robinson, W. A., *Jeffersonian Democracy in New England* (New Haven, 1916).

Ruttenber, E. M., *History of the Town of Newburgh* (Newburgh, 1859).

Scharf, J. T. and Westcott, T., *History of Philadelphia* (Philadelphia, 1884).

Stauffer, V., *New England and the Bavarian Illuminati* (New York, 1918).

Tatsch, H., *Freemasonry in the Thirteen Colonies* (New York, 1929).

Todd, C. B., *Life and Letters of Joel Barlow* (New York, 1886).

Walker, J., *Memoir of Josiah Quincy* (Massachusetts Historical Society, *Proceedings*, vol. ix [Boston, 1867]).

Westcott, T., *Life of John Fitch* (Philadelphia, 1878).

CHRISTIANITY DEFENDED: EARLY NATIONAL PERIOD (1789-1805)

PRIMARY SOURCES

Address of the Trustees of the College of New-Jersey, to the Inhabitants of the United States (Philadelphia, 1802).

Beecher, L., *Autobiography, Correspondence, etc.*, ed. C. Beecher (New York, 1864).

Channing, W. E., *A Sermon, Delivered at the Ordination of the Rev. Jared Sparks* (Liverpool, 1821).

——, *Works* (Boston, 1875).

Cooper, T., *A Letter to Prof. Silliman On the Connection Between Geology and the Pentateuch* (Boston, 1833).

Dana, J., *A Sermon, Preached October 17, 1798, at the Ordination of the Rev. Mr. Dan Huntington* (Litchfield, 1799).

Dwight, T., *The Nature, and Danger, of the Infidel Philosophy exhibited in Two Discourses* (New Haven, 1798).

——, *Travels in New-England and New-York* (London, 1823).

The Examiners Examined: Being A Defence of The Age of Reason (New York, 1794).

Fiske, N., *A Sermon Preached At The Dudleian Lecture in the Chapel of Harvard College, September 7, 1796* (Boston, 1796).

Foster, J., *Infidelity Exposed, and Christianity Recommended in A Sermon* (Cambridge, 1802).

Levi, D., *A Defence of the Old Testament, in a Series of Letters, Addressed to Thomas Paine* (New York, 1797).

A Missionary Catechism, For the Use of Children (New Haven, 1821).

Muir, J., *An Examination of the Principles contained in The Age of Reason* (Baltimore, 1795).

Nelson, D., *An Investigation of that False, Fabulous and Blasphemous Misrepresentation of Truth, Set Forth by Thomas Paine* (Lancaster, 1800).

Ogden, U., *Antidote to Deism: The Deist Unmasked; or An Ample Refutation of all the Objections of Thomas Paine* (Newark, 1795).

Parker, T., *A Discourse on the Transient and Permanent in Christianity* (Boston, 1841).

Patten, W., *Christianity The True Theology . . . With An Appendix in Answer to The Examiners Examined* (Warren, 1795).

Priestley, J., *An Answer to Mr. Paine's Age of Reason, Being a Continuation of Letters to the Philosophers and Politicians of France on the Subject of Religion; and of the Letters to a Philosophical Unbeliever* (Northumberland, 1794).

Stillman, S., *Thoughts on the French Revolution. A Sermon* (Boston, 1795).

Watson, R., *Apology for the Bible, in a Series of Letters addressed to Thomas Paine* (Albany, 1796).

Williams, T., *The Age of Infidelity: In Answer To Thomas Paine's Age of Reason* (London, 1794).

Wilstach, P. (ed.), *Correspondence of John Adams and Thomas Jefferson* (New York, 1925).

PERIODICALS

(See citations under *Deism Militant: Early National Period, Periodicals*)

The American Apollo (Boston, 1792).

American Minerva; an Evening Advertiser.

American Monthly Review (Philadelphia, 1795).

The American Moral and Sentimental Magazine (New York, 1797).

The American Museum: or Repository (Philadelphia, 1789, 1790, 1792).

The American Universal Magazine (Philadelphia, 1797).

Augusta Herald.

The Baltimore Weekly Magazine (Baltimore, 1800-1).

The Boston Gazette and Weekly Republican Journal.

The Christian's Pocket Library (New York, 1796).

The Columbian Centinel.

The Columbian Phenix and Boston Review (Boston, 1800).

The Connecticut Evangelical Magazine (Hartford, 1800-4).

Federal Gazette and Baltimore Daily Advertiser.

The General Assembly's Missionary Magazine; Or Evangelical Intelligencer (Philadelphia, 1806).

The General Magazine, and Impartial Review (Baltimore, 1798).

The Independent Chronicle and Universal Advertiser.

The Literary Museum, or Monthly Magazine (Westchester, 1797).

The Massachusetts Baptist Missionary Magazine (Boston, 1803-7).

The Mercury.

Missionary Intelligence; Being Parts of Two Reports . . . to the General Assembly of the Presbyterian Church, etc. (Philadelphia, 1813).

The Monthly Magazine, and American Review (New York, 1800).

The New Star (Concord, 1797).

The New-York Missionary Magazine, and Repository (New York, 1800-1).

The Providence Gazette and Country Journal.

The Religious Monitor, or Theological Scales (Danbury, 1798).
The Rural Magazine: or Vermont Repository (Rutland, 1795).
The Salem Gazette.
South-Carolina Weekly Museum (Charleston, 1797).
The Universal Asylum, and Columbian Magazine (Philadelphia, 1790-2).
Virginia Gazette and Richmond Chronicle.
Western Star.

Secondary Authorities

Bacon, L. W., *History of American Christianity* (New York, 1897).
Bangs, N., *A History of the Methodist Episcopal Church* (New York, 1892).
Battle, K. P., *History of the University of North Carolina* (Raleigh, 1907).
Beardsley, F. G., *A History of American Revivals* (New York, 1904).
Bruce, P. A., *History of the University of Virginia* (New York, 1920).
Buckley, J. M., *A History of Methodism in the United States* (New York, 1896).
Carpenter, J. E., *The Bible in the Nineteenth Century* (London, 1903).
Channing, W. H., *The Life of William Ellery Channing* (Boston, 1880).
Cooke, G. W., *Unitarianism in America* (Boston, 1902).
Davidson, R., *History of the Presbyterian Church in the State of Kentucky* (New York, 1847).
Dorchester, D., *The Problems of Religious Progress* (New York, 1881).
Goodenough, A., *The Clergy of Litchfield County* (Litchfield, 1909).
Hotchkin, J. H., *A History of the Purchase and Settlement of Western New York* (New York, 1848).
Jeyes, S. H., *The Russels of Birmingham in the French Revolution and in America 1791-1814* (London, 1911).
McGiffert, A. C., *The Rise of Modern Religious Ideas* (New York, 1921).
Newman, A. H., *A History of the Baptist Churches in the United States* (New York, 1894).
Schmidt, G. P., *The Old Time College President* (New York, 1930).
Sweet, W. W., *The Story of Religions in America* (New York, 1930).
Thompson, R. E., *History of the Presbyterian Churches in the United States* (New York, 1895).
Walker, W., *History of the Congregational Churches in the United States* (New York, 1884).
Weiss, J., *Life and Correspondence of Theodore Parker* (New York, 1864).

INDEX

For Rick.

Thank you for always believing

There is a way that seems right to a man, but in the end it leads to death.

Proverbs 14:12

CHAPTER ONE

Jack Logan had ditched his Catholic upbringing but kept the guilt. He hadn't planned on blowing his entire afternoon listening to the woman he was interviewing talk about her dead daughter, but he didn't have the heart to tell the grieving mother that he already had enough for the story. So instead, he bought her lunch *and* dinner, listening as she painted a picture of the girl she had loved and had failed to save. Now he was behind schedule and would have to work all night. Man, he hated the pieces involving kids. The parents got to him every time, and his attempts at comforting them were as effective as a Band-Aid on a gunshot wound.

His phone was ringing as he approached the door to his apartment, and he jammed the key in the lock. Pushing the door open, he rushed over and snatched it, upsetting the bottle of Bass Ale and spilling the dregs on the table.

"Great." He clicked the green button. "Yes?"

"Could you sound any more annoyed?" It was his editor.

"Sorry, Max. What's up?" He sunk into the worn leather sofa and ran a hand through his hair.

"Tried your cell. Went right to voice mail."

"I was interviewing one of the mothers."

The sound of papers rustling came over the phone. "You already did your piece on the decision. What's the angle on the follow-up?"

"The fall out, the casualties left in the wake of the decision to let the show go on."

A sharp intake of breath. "You're not saying they should have censored it?"

"No, no. Of course not. But their voices deserve to be heard." This had been a particularly difficult assignment for him. He wasn't much of a television watcher, but when the class action suit involving the production company behind *Teenage Wasted* reached the Supreme Court, he'd tuned in. At first it looked just like another of the ubiquitous reality shows jamming the airwaves—an eclectic group of teenagers allowing the cameras behind the scenes into their world. Within the first five minutes of the show, Jack had sat open-mouthed while a young man retrieved paraphernalia from under his bed, pulled up a porn site on his computer, and began doing what your average adolescent boy did behind closed doors. Cheap shock value but not much in the way of entertainment. It wasn't until he put the noose around his neck that Jack's shock turned to horror. So, that was what erotic asphyxiation looked like up close and personal.

The blogosphere went nuts the following day, and YouTube videos of other kids demonstrating their own secret hobbies began to appear. When kids started turning up dead, that's when it hit the fan. A class action suit was filed against Omega Inc., the entertainment giant responsible for the new show. The Supreme Court decision had been handed down a few weeks ago, and the parents were still in shock that they'd lost. The show went on—more popular than ever. Omega won under freedom of speech protection, which Jack couldn't argue with, but still, what they were doing was disgusting— perverting the first amendment for their own profit. He was happy to do his part to help tarnish their reputation.

"All right, email it when you're finished. You still coming tonight?" Max asked.

Jack grimaced. Sally Goldman's retirement party. He had forgotten.

"Wish I could, but I'm too jammed up with this." Sally was a great gal. He was sorry he'd have to miss it. He'd send her some flowers tomorrow.

He'd better get to it. He opened his laptop and began to organize

2

his notes. He was starving; he'd barely touched his dinner earlier. He picked up the phone to order a pizza when the doorbell rang. He made no move to answer it. It rang a second, third, and fourth time. He slammed the phone down, jumped up and strode to the door, ready to tell whoever it was to beat it. The words died on his lips when he opened the door. Probably best not to piss off a United States senator.

From the first time he'd met Senator Malcolm Phillips, something about him struck Jack as off. He couldn't put his finger on it exactly: the guy's manners were impeccable, his background impressive. Phillips was perfect. A little too perfect. Everything about him was so well rehearsed that Jack could almost believe an invisible teleprompter fed him his lines. What surprised Jack most was how Phillips's wife, Taylor, failed to see he was all wrong for her. Of course, he kept this to himself. His opinion didn't mean anything to Taylor anymore.

He opened the door, and Phillips walked in.

Going no farther than the hallway, he began. "I won't waste time with pleasantries. I need your help." His voice shook, and his face was ashen.

"What is it?"

"I scuttled the vote. It was supposed to be a good thing. But he added a gateway. He has to be stopped."

"Whoa, what's going on?"

He handed Jack an envelope as he spoke in an uncharacteristically nervous rush. "Take this. You'll need it to convince Taylor. I didn't believe it. He told me he would do it. I didn't believe him but…they'll kill me."

This was insane. He hadn't seen Phillips in years—and now here he was, rambling like a crazy person.

"What are you talking about? Slow down and tell me what's going on," Jack said.

"No time. You're the only one I trust. You've got to find Jeremy. Get Taylor to him. They won't hurt her now, but later…I was so stupid…"

Phillips was pacing now, and sweat had broken out on his forehead.

"Who's Jeremy? You're not making any sense," Jack said.

"Go to Taylor and show it to her." He pointed to the envelope. "It's a sealed letter, so she'll know it's real. Get Taylor and take her to the cabin."

How did he know about the cabin?

"I'm the last person Taylor wants to see. She's not going to go anywhere with me."

Phillips grabbed his arm.

"They own me. And Brody Hamilton too. You'll see when they kill me. Then you'll know."

"When who kills you?"

Phillips backed away.

"Promise me you'll get her to Jeremy." He handed Jack a remote control. "This will get you into the garage. I've taped our address to the bottom." He wiped his forehead with the back of his hand. "Remember, Jack, no matter what it looks like, I'm not suicidal nor prone to accidents."

He was gone before a flabbergasted Jack could respond.

Jack shut the door, began to walk away, then turned back and engaged the extra deadbolt. His eyes narrowed as he looked around, half expecting a phantom to appear.

What was Phillips talking about? Did someone really want him dead—someone powerful enough to own two senators? His head began to pound, and he leaned forward to massage his temples. What had Phillips done? Maybe he was nuts, early onset dementia. Jack could only hope. And now he expected Jack to play the hero to Taylor? He wouldn't blame her if she slammed the door in his face.

He would do some digging. Try and make sense of what had just landed in his lap. He threw the envelope on the table, opened his laptop, and set a Google alert for Senator Malcolm Phillips.

CHAPTER TWO

Senator Malcolm Phillips was 110 feet underwater. He checked the metrics on his dive computer—five more minutes before he was in danger of getting the bends. He had spent too much time in one room of the wreck and now would have to forgo exploring the rest of it. Scuba diving was the only time he truly relaxed. Wreck diving was his favorite. He loved the history and mystery associated with these old Japanese ships. Part of the appeal of this remote Micronesian island was his ability to blend in—nobody knew who he was or paid him any extra attention. After he had landed in Guam, he had called his old friend and borrowed his private plane. He wanted to disappear for a little while. After what he pulled with the vote, he knew it was only a matter of time. He wanted to be as far away from Taylor as possible—to be sure she wasn't caught in the crossfire. It was easy to get away; she'd never shown an interest in diving, and was used to him taking these trips alone. Knowing he was on borrowed time, he was all the more determined to make the most of this trip. Who would have thought that he would be willing to make such a sacrifice? Before Taylor, he had never done a single thing out of concern for another person. As some would say, miracles never cease.

He began ascending, making a concentrated effort to exhale as he rose. The water caressed his skin, and he surveyed the visual feast surrounding him. Angelfish painted in vibrant blues and yellows swooshed by, oblivious to their glory. The soft whooshing of his regulator filled his ears, and the lack of conversation added to his pleasure—no lobbyists hounding him to push a bill. Closing his eyes, he relished the feeling of floating through the ocean. His relaxation was interrupted by the sound of his dive computer. *Beep…beep…beep. What was wrong?* He looked at his wrist—the ascent warning. He was going up too fast. Swimming back towards the wreck, he grabbed the rope dangling from the boat above. Now he would need to hang for at least ten minutes. He continued checking his gauge while he held on to the rope, then began a slow ascent when enough time had elapsed. At last, he broke the surface and felt the warmth of the morning sun on his face. After climbing aboard the boat, he slipped the heavy tanks off his back and discarded his wet suit. He was looking forward to a well-earned lunch.

When he reached the outdoor restaurant, a young man showed him to a table overlooking the sea. He inhaled deeply. Salt and diesel combined to make a surprisingly pleasant aroma. He ordered a Yap and made notes in his diving log. His waiter returned with the beer and smiled at Malcolm.

"We have nice fresh fish mister. You want same as yesterday?"

Malcolm nodded. "Let the chef know it's for me. He knows how I need things prepared."

"Yes, sir." He bobbed his head and left.

The buttery fish was delicious and he devoured it. Leaning back with a satisfied sigh, he debated whether to order another beer. Deciding a nap would be even better, he paid the bill and walked the quarter mile to the small hut he was staying in. His throat felt funny. He tapped his pant's pocket to see if it was there. *Deep breath, don't worry.* Maybe he was coming down with a cold. When he reached the hut, he had to steady himself, and he leaned against the door. The scratchiness in his throat intensified, and he became dizzy. The realization that he was having an allergic reaction hit him, and he pulled the EpiPen® from his pocket. He snapped open the case, removed the safety, and plunged the pen into his right thigh. *Relax. It'll kick in soon.*

But it didn't. The tightening around his neck increased, and he managed to croak out a dry, wheezing cough. Staggering to the dresser, he felt around for another Epi and stabbed it into his other leg. The face looking back at him in the mirror wasn't his, the swelling so exaggerated it rendered him unrecognizable. This couldn't be happening. Not yet. Dread filled him. Someone had tampered with the food—and his medicine. His shellfish allergy was in his medical file. Grasping the dresser, he pulled the phone toward him as he fell to the ground. When he lifted the receiver to his ear, there was only silence.

CHAPTER THREE

Jack had really thought Phillips was off his nut—on drugs, anything but serious. But when he got the Google alert that morning, he realized with a sinking feeling that Phillips *had* been telling the truth.

Dead. Phillips had been standing in this apartment less than a week ago. A chill ran through Jack as he grasped the full implications of this news. Phillips had made a powerful enemy, and if Jack decided to get involved, he would be turning himself into a target.

He'd done some quick research on the bill Phillips had been ranting about. It was innocuous, just broadening the range of vaccines that received federal funding to help those who couldn't afford them. Sure, maybe someone didn't want to allocate the money, but to kill over it? That was a few days ago and he'd chalked up the bizarre visit to some medical thing that must be going on with Phillips. But as soon as he got the alert, he knew he had to get to Taylor right away. It was too coincidental. Phillips *was* dead—reportedly, some kind of accidental death while on a diving trip. He remembered Phillips's warning about not being accident prone.

Throwing a few things into a duffel, he opened his safe and took out his SIG. He made sure to pack extra ammo too. He went to the hall closet and grabbed his go bag. That would take care of Taylor and him for a couple of weeks. Now all he had to do was figure out how to get Taylor to leave with him. He had a few hours to think about it on the drive from the city to her house in McLean, Virginia. He took the 66 Mustang—no GPS.

Why would Phillips have been murdered? Maybe Taylor would know more; Phillips must have discussed it with her. And what was Hamilton's connection?

The sun was setting when he pulled up to the house. The massive, black iron gates were closed, and he had to get out of the car to swipe the card reader to open them. He had never been to the house Taylor shared with Phillips, and when he pulled up to the enormous, French colonial estate, his eyes widened. There were five exterior stone arches illuminated by large, round light fixtures above them. A second-story balcony above the first level ran across the entire front of the house. This place cost serious money—more money then senators made. He remembered reading about it a while ago in *Town and Country*; it had its own basketball court, indoor pool, and home theater. Suited Phillips perfectly, but Taylor? Maybe she had changed over the years. What had happened to the little girl he had grown up with who hated ostentation?

He followed the circular driveway past the front door and around to the four-car garage, per Phillips's instructions. Using the remote, he opened the garage door. Once inside, he pressed the intercom and waited. Jack had the code to get into the house, but he didn't want to spook her.

A wary voice answered. "Who's there?"

Hearing the strain and grief in her voice broke his heart. "It's Jack." He heard a dog growling in the background.

A click and then the door opened. She was standing on the other side, a ghost. They looked at each other.

He pulled something from his pocket. "Gummy bear?"

A forlorn smile appeared then vanished just as quickly. He crossed the threshold, and she fell into his arms. Her shoulders shook, and he held her while she sobbed. A golden retriever lay on the floor at her feet, strangely quiet now, looking back and forth at the two of them.

Finally, she pulled away and wiped her face with a tissue.

"What are you doing here? How did you get in to the garage?"

"Malcolm gave me the remote."

Her brow furrowed. "What?"

"Let's go inside, and I'll explain everything." He followed her into the huge kitchen and took in the marble countertops and the ornate chandeliers hanging above the center island, which could easily accommodate twenty people around it. He'd have bet she and Phillips could've walked around this house for days and not run into each other. Suddenly, he felt like that kid again, the one from the working-class family who didn't know which fork to use.

The dog jumped up and nudged Jack's hand with his head.

"This is Beau." Her voice was wooden.

Jack crouched down and ruffled the fur on the dog's head. Beau's tail thumped wildly.

"Nice to meet you, Beau." He looked up at her. "Malcolm came to see me last week. Told me that someone was after him. If anything happened to him, I was to come see you."

"I can't believe he's d-dead." She stumbled on the word.

"Taylor." Jack took a breath. "It wasn't an accident." There was no easy way to say it, so he just said it. "He was murdered."

She shook her head. "No-no. What are you talking about? He died of an allergic reaction. He's allergic to shellfish. The medical examiner ruled it an accidental death."

Jack persisted. "He warned me that something was going to happen to him."

"I don't understand. Why would he come to you? You hardly know him."

"He said I was the only one he trusted. He's seen me around the Hill, knows my reputation." Jack hesitated before asking, "And I assume he knows our history, that I'd want to help?"

At this she glared at him. "Yeah, well, he should have gone to someone else." She dabbed her eyes with the tissue clutched in her hand. "I still can't believe it."

"Did he say anything out of the ordinary before he left?"

She shook her head. "No. But…" She stood up, pacing. "Well, he *was* preoccupied, distracted. I just figured he was stressed from work. The trip was a last-minute thing, just to blow off some steam. I don't dive. It's something he does alone."

Jack sighed. "He told me he would be killed, that I had to get you. You're in danger. We have to leave tonight."

"Are you crazy? I'm not going anywhere with you. I have to plan his funeral."

He tried a different approach. "Let's just back up a minute. What do you know about this vaccine bill?"

She shrugged. "Malcolm was for it. It was going to help a lot of families that couldn't afford the vaccine. RSV is horrible and the vaccine is costly."

"So then, why did he change his mind?"

She frowned. "What do you mean?"

"He voted no."

"That doesn't make any—"

She was interrupted by the buzz of the intercom.

"Are you expecting someone?" He didn't like this. It was nine o'clock. He walked over to the window. Even with the outside lights on, the thick hedge of boxwood in front of the driveway made it impossible to see anything.

"See what they want, but don't buzz them in."

She gave him a skeptical look, then pressed the button on the speaker on the wall. "Yes?"

"Mrs. Phillips?" a gravelly voice asked.

"May I help you?"

"Sorry to disturb you, ma'am. We're from the Capitol Police. We need to speak with you."

She hit the buzzer. "Come in."

"Why did you do that? How do you know they're legit?"

"It's the *police*. They must have news. What's wrong with you?"

A few minutes later, the flash of headlights shone through the curtains briefly and a car door slammed.

Jack followed her into the hallway, and as she opened the door, he stood behind it, unseen. From Jack's vantage point, he could only hear what was going on.

"May I see some ID, please?" Taylor asked. "What are you doing?" she asked, her tone rising.

Jack heard the storm door being rattled; then Taylor slammed the front door shut and engaged the deadbolt.

The sound of broken glass made them both jump, and Jack grabbed her hand and pulled her out of the hallway.

Her eyes were wide as she said, "When I asked for ID, he tried to open the door."

Jack flew into action. "We have to leave. Now. Get in my car—it's in the garage." He pulled out his gun just in case there were any surprises waiting for them in the garage.

"I have to get my stuff."

He could hear something ramming against the door. They'd be in the house any second.

"No time. Let's go."

"But—"

"Taylor, please!"

The dog whined.

He started the car, not turning on the headlights. "I don't know how we're going to get past them."

She pressed her index finger onto the fingerprint reader pad on the alarm panel, grabbed a key ring from the hook on the wall, then got in the passenger seat. He watched in shock as the ground in front of the car opened into a black void that ultimately revealed a downward ramp.

"What the—"

"It's an underground tunnel. Installed by the previous owners."

This was something new. He pressed on the gas and slid the car into the dark opening. It led them about a mile from the house, still her property apparently, until they came to what looked like a solid concrete wall that was stained red from years of ground water rusting the concrete's re-bar.

"Now what?"

She took the key ring, which had a small LED flashlight attached, and illuminated the wall until she found the oval embossed star on the face of the concrete. Holding the proximity sensor on the key chain against the star, the muted sound of mechanical movement commenced. The wall slowly opened as if it were a garage door.

Jack drove through and cast a sidelong view at Taylor. "Seriously? Was the previous owner regularly hunted by assassins or something?"

"She was a former head of state. It's one of the things that drew Malcolm to the house. He thought it was cool. Like the bat cave or something." She bit her lip. "I always thought it was ridiculous. Never thought *I'd* need to use it."

Jack was relieved to see that theirs was the only car on the road and that they'd make a clean getaway.

"Who do you think was at the door?" she asked.

"I can only assume they're connected to whomever killed Malcolm."

"So it's really true? He was murdered?"

"Looks that way. I know it's crazy, but right now we just need to put some distance between us and them—whoever they are. Let's get out of the state, and we'll stop somewhere for the night. I'll show you everything when we get there."

She ran a hand through her hair and looked at him.

"This is surreal. I can not believe I'm actually in a car with *you* running off into the night." Then her hand flew to her mouth.

"Oh no."

"What?"

"My progesterone shots."

"Your what?"

"Jack. I'm pregnant—with a high-risk pregnancy. I need to take these shots for two more weeks. Without them, I could lose the baby. I have to refill my prescription. We have to go back."

Jack shook his head. "We can't. It's too dangerous."

Pregnant! Phillips had left that little tidbit out. Jack rubbed his temples and gave her what he hoped was a reassuring smile.

"Don't worry. I'll figure something out."

CHAPTER FOUR

The limousine came to a stop, and as Damon Crosse waited for his driver to get out and open his door, he admired the elaborate stone building he had commissioned. Towering iron gates, which surrounded the perimeter of the property, served as a deterrent to the curious; guards stationed in towers, and twenty-four-hour video surveillance ensured that he was informed of all goings-on at all times. He divided his time between this facility, and the one much more secluded and secret, where the important work was being done. But, today was the start of the new fellowship program and he was curious to get a look at the newest recruits. Before getting out of the car, he removed a long white hair from his pant leg. He would have to speak to his housekeeper about brushing Peritas more often. He normally kept the dog with him, but today his schedule was too packed to give him the attention he deserved.

The latest group had arrived last night, right on schedule. Walking the long hallway to the west elevator, he entered and pushed the button, tapping his foot on the descent to the basement level. He emerged and walked down the cold, bare corridor. Entering the room adjoining the barracks, he observed the new group through the two-way mirror. They sat on their bunks, awaiting further instruction. Their excited chatter and delight with the novelty of their circumstances would soon be replaced by an apprehensive awe due to the formidable surroundings. Every group reacted the same way. A knock at the door made him turn.

"You may enter," he said.

"Sir, is there anything else you desire?"

"Everything is as it should be?"

"Yes, sir. The dossiers are on your desk. Everything so far is unremarkable."

"That is all then."

His estate manager cleared his throat.

"What is it, Jonas?"

"He's waiting in your office, sir."

"Very well."

Damon watched as the heavy door closed. He observed them for half an hour. Deciding he had let the visitor wait long enough, he rose and returned to the main level, and to his study.

He stopped before opening the door, pulled out his cell phone, and watched the man on the screen. Dwarfed by the enormous wing chair he sat in, the visitor waited. Despite the chill in the air, perspiration had discolored his thin white shirt, and beads of sweat glistened on his brow. He muttered, "We'll find her sir. Not to worry. Not to worry." His head bobbed as he repeated the mantra to himself over and over.

Damon frowned, put the phone in his pocket, and opened the door.

"So good of you to come." Damon's smooth, deep voice resonated in the room. "I trust you have good news for me?" He seated himself behind the large mahogany desk and looked at the visitor with pursed lips.

The man swallowed. "She got away, sir."

"How?" Damon pressed in a soft voice.

"She must have had someone helping her. Her car was still in the garage." The man hesitated. "We never saw another car. I don't know how she got away. It's like she disappeared into thin air."

Damon said nothing.

The man in the chair flinched, and hurried on. "We'll find out who it is. We will. We've got a lot of men on it, it won't be long. I'm sure, sir—we'll fix it. Stupid, stupid, I know but—"

"Enough," he said. His left hand moved to a small box that sat on the corner of the desk, and with deliberate calm, he pressed the red button. He looked up and studied the visitor for a full minute before he spoke again. "You have failed."

As Damon stood, he nodded toward the back of the room and the three men who had entered silently surrounded the visitor. They didn't need to use any force to subdue him. Everyone in Damon's employ understood the consequence of failure.

He pressed his intercom. "Jonas."

The door opened. "Yes, sir?"

"Send a team to the Phillips house. Have them retrieve the video footage. I want to know who's with his wife, and I want to know yesterday."

"Of course, sir."

CHAPTER FIVE

One hundred and fifty miles later, Jack pulled over at a run-down motel and got them a room. The rumpled man behind the desk looked annoyed at having to tear himself away from his porn magazine to wait on them. In response to his request for a credit card, Jack slapped two hundred-dollar bills on the counter. They disappeared into the man's pocket and a room key appeared in their place. No one else was around, so it was easy to sneak Beau into the room.

The stink of stale cigarettes wafted over Jack when he opened the door. He flipped a switch, and a dingy bulb in a cracked lamp illuminated the room. He threw his bag on one of the two orange Naugahyde chairs next to the small, round wooden table.

Taylor looked around the room, her eyes resting a moment on the double bed, then back at Jack.

"One bed. You should have gotten two rooms."

He shook his head. "Don't worry. I'll take one of the chairs."

She pulled the comforter off the bed, folded it, and placed it on the floor. Jack didn't even want to think what kinds of stains would show up on it under a black light. Sitting on the bed, she called Beau over and patted the mattress until he jumped up next to her.

Jack handed Taylor a protein bar, but she shook her head.

"You have to eat. Think of the baby."

She took the bar, opened it, pulled off a small piece and put it in her mouth. "I don't even have any clothes with me," Taylor said, as she watched Jack put his duffel bag on the table.

"We'll have to pick some things up tomorrow." Rifling through the bag, he brought out a pair of faded blue sweatpants and a Boston University sweatshirt. "In the meantime…," he held his breath as he handed them to her, watching her expression carefully.

Her mouth dropped open. "I can't believe you still have these." She held the shirt at arm's length, looking it over, then shook her head. "You kept them all these years?"

He shrugged. "Couldn't force myself to get rid of them."

She got a faraway look for a minute, pressed her lips together, stood up and walked into the bathroom without another word.

He turned on the TV and flipped channels until he found CNN.

She returned, having changed, and sat down at the table. "Tell me again about what Malcolm said when he came to your apartment."

"He wasn't making much sense, was clearly agitated. He mentioned someone named Jeremy that we need to find, said now that he'd voted against the bill, they would kill him. He also said Brody Hamilton was in on it. He gave me an envelope for you. Then he left."

"Let me see it."

Jack went to his briefcase, pulled out the letter and gave it to her, then sat back down.

She read it, then handed it back to Jack. "Go ahead. You can read it."

My dear Taylor,

Let me begin by how saying I am sorry and how painful it is to know that nothing I can do will fix the mess I've made. No matter how it started, in the end, I did love you. If you believe nothing else, believe that. You will find things out—things that will make you hate me. I need you to understand that what we've gone through in the last two years to create this life you carry, it changed me. Brought us closer and gave me a glimpse into real love—something I'd never known before you. It was your love and the love I already feel for our child that gave me the strength to stand up to them. To finally do the right thing.

There's so much more at stake than meets the eye. For reasons too complicated to explain in this letter, I have changed my vote. Look into the rider. It opens the door for untold evil. And look into Brody Hamilton's record. Once my vote is cast, they will know that I have deserted, and they will kill me. I can't tell you how it will happen, or when but you must know that regardless of what it looks like, when you hear of my death, be certain it was not of my own doing. They are excellent at making things appear as they want. After all, they made up my entire background.

You must find a man named Jeremy. He is the key to everything. He has been in hiding for the past year and has, over that time, built up a network of allies and advocates. I've enlisted the aid of Jack, he has skills you are not aware of, and I believe together you can accomplish what neither of you could do alone.

Trust no one. Not the press, not the enforcement agencies. They are everywhere. Disappear. Go deep. I have already arranged your first stop. Jack knows where to go. Once you arrive, you will find instructions for your next stop. Don't waste time. It is imperative that you get to Jeremy as soon as you can.

I don't deserve your forgiveness but I pray that one day you will find it in your heart to grant it.

All my Love,
Malcolm

When Jack had finished, he looked at her. "Wow."

"Yeah, I don't even know where to start. What does he mean, 'they made up my entire background'?" she asked.

"I don't know. But he told me that he was owned. Hamilton too."

Taylor looked shocked. "No. That's impossible. You must be wrong."

"Look Taylor, I know this is hard to take in, but you need to think. Who else could be involved? He already mentioned Hamilton. What about other politicians in D.C.?"

Jack could see the wheels turning in her mind. Grabbing the cheap, plastic motel pen from the table, she rooted in her bag and brought out a small pad of paper.

"Number one: The rider. Two, Brody Hamilton, and three, Jeremy. Where is this cabin he mentioned?"

"The New Hampshire woods. It belongs to a friend of mine."

19

She looked confused. "Why would he know anything about your friends, and why would he be keeping tabs on you?"

"I don't know."

"How can this be? How did he get through the background checks?"

"That's what I'm trying to tell you. Whoever he works for is powerful enough to build him a bulletproof identity."

The voice on the television got their attention.

"US Senator Malcolm Phillips was found dead in his room while vacationing in Truk Lagoon, a small island in Micronesia, yesterday afternoon. The senator apparently died of anaphylactic shock from a seafood allergy. In a bizarre twist, his wife, Taylor Parks Phillips, is missing. Funeral services are on hold until Mrs. Phillips is located."

Jack changed the channel again. Fox News was discussing the implications of Phillips's death.

"On a more personal note Bill, what do you make of the wife's disappearance? Seems a little strange, don't you think?" A picture of Taylor flashed across the screen.

The news anchor's eyes widened and he turned to his co-anchor.

"It seems there is a new development in the disappearance of Taylor Phillips. She may have been abducted. Take a look at this. A man was captured on video by the security camera."

The footage showed Jack holding a gun as Taylor was rushed into the front seat of his car.

Jack cursed and turned the television off. "How did they get that?"

"We've got cameras everywhere."

"Everyone will be looking for us. We've got to get moving, and we've got to dump my car."

"What about my shots? We need to go back."

She didn't get it. "We can't go back. I'll figure something out. Trust me."

As soon as the words left his lips, he regretted them. Her expression said it all—trust was the last thing she would bestow on

past him, grabbed Beau's leash and opened the door. "I won't be long."

Jack followed immediately behind her. He didn't care if she got annoyed.

They returned to the room without incident. Jack was mentally assessing what he needed to accomplish before they hit the road again. He pulled out his laptop, wanting to see how many outlets had picked up his story. He typed *Manchester v Omega* into Google and his name. This was interesting. Not many papers had run the story. He typed in *Teenage Wasted* to see if others had covered the ruling on the show. The page was full of links—mostly to YouTube. He scrolled down, clicked the first link, and was taken to a video.

It had an adult content warning and he clicked it and waited. Jack watched in horror as a young man demonstrated the most efficient way to set up an autoerotic asphyxiation room. He gave a tour of his room, a list of supplies, suggestions on where to hide them, where to set them up, and promises of a live demonstration to come.

"What are you watching?"

He paused it.

"I did a story on *Manchester v Omega Entertainment*. You know the case I mean? The class action suit about the kids' reality show that went to the Supreme Court."

"Of course. It's been all over the news. Disgusting. I can't believe Omega won."

"Take a look at this. There are hundreds of them."

He hit play again, and they continued watching the video until it ended with the noose around the boy's neck and him winking. Then the screen went black.

Taylor shook her head. "Unbelievable. I wish Omega had lost."

He arched an eyebrow. "A surprising stance coming from a journalist."

She looked at him. "It's not so black and white, Jack. There was an analogous case out of California a few years back, *Brown v EMA*. The state banned certain violent video games from being sold, and the gaming company fought back claiming protection under free speech. The gaming company won, but only because there wasn't enough proof that the games incited violence." She raised her eyebrows and gave Jack a long look. "I think we can safely say that's not the case with this show."

"Listen, Taylor. It wasn't an easy call. On a personal level, I would like nothing more than to shut that show down. I've talked to those parents; they're heartbroken. But I gotta say, it worries me when we start fooling around with constitutional liberties. This case was a slippery slope, dangerously close to censorship. But on an emotional level, I agree with you."

Jack thought about the woman from his last interview. He'd seen a lot of grief, but the abject agony in her eyes haunted him. What could he say to this woman who had saved her daughter from the grips of death years earlier only to have her succumb to it in a misguided attempt to get high? Her words echoed in his mind.

"She spent years working with therapists. She was throwing up every day to look like those airbrushed models on the magazines. Finally gotten the bulimia under control. Was happy. And then…gone. Copying those foolish kids. Gone in seconds."

How do you comfort someone like that? Did he want Omega to pay? Absolutely—but not if it meant screwing with the First Amendment.

"I read your articles." She pursed her lips. "Your follow-up did a good job giving the parents a voice. It's just that Omega's behavior gives all us journalists a bad name."

"Agreed." He stood. "I'm going to run out and get some provisions before we hit the road later. Why don't you start digging and see what you can find out about the bill and the rider? I'll be back as soon as I can."

"Hold on. You can fill my prescription for progesterone." She took the wallet from her purse and began looking through it. "Oh, no."

"What is it?"

"I must have left it in my other bag. Jack, I need it. After everything I've been through, I'm not about to take any chances with this pregnancy. Get me a name of a pharmacy and I'll call my doctor and have a new prescription called in."

"We can't do that, Taylor. It would lead them right to us." Jack was quiet for a moment as he thought. "I have an idea." He didn't know why he didn't think of it before.

"What?"

"My sister's a nurse. I'll see if she can get it."

"Where does she live?"

"Boston. We're headed there anyway."

Relief filled her face. "That would be great. Here, let me write down the dosage."

"You actually remember it?"

"Yeah, I could probably run my own fertility clinic at this point. Get fifty milligrams in oil. Enough for two weeks. Syringes too."

"I'll be back as soon as I can. Lock the door behind me and don't go anywhere."

CHAPTER SEVEN

Crosby Wheeler, CEO of Omega Entertainment looked at the men gathered around the table. He was in a good mood, pleased by his recent win in court. It was unfortunate that the parents of the kids who had died had gotten together so quickly and organized the class action suit. It was ridiculous to pin the blame on his show. That was the problem with society these days—no one wanted to take responsibility for their own actions. Instead of trying to make him take *Teenage Wasted* off the air, they should have been more involved with their kids, known what they were doing, maybe look in a closet or check their cell phone texts. His job wasn't to parent America's children. His job was to entertain.

He had jumped on the streaming bandwagon early. Omega had started small but was now the uncontested leader, made popular by his original programming. He made shows that no one else dared make. He was criticized widely by some, adored by others.

He'd never had any doubt that they would prevail, but it had been an inconvenience having to put a hold on the show until it became official. Luckily, the forced hiatus had only increased interest in it, and he was certain that the losses incurred over the past several months would be made up in no time. He looked at his executive producer.

"Ratings are continuing to climb?"

The man nodded. "Yes, I just got the latest figures."

"Any fallout?" he asked.

"Parents are outraged. They can't accept that they've lost. The other networks are using it to their advantage, hosting parent interviews. We've lost a handful of sponsors."

His new executive in charge of advertising, Adrian Winters, cleared his throat and spoke. "But we've got a long line of others waiting to take their place. I've replaced them at double the price."

Crosby looked at him with interest. He took a sip from his bottle of mineral water. "Do tell."

Winters picked up a mint from the crystal bowl in front of him and unwrapped it. "The media frenzy has caused the ratings to skyrocket. Internet channels are jamming from the traffic. It's an advertiser's dream." He popped the mint in his mouth.

Crosby spoke. "Good work. Email me the list and the new production schedule." He addressed his producer again.

"The kids on the show okay?"

"Mostly. They were pretty upset, but the counselors talked them down, gave out some anti-anxiety meds. They've been compensated."

Crosby nodded. "Good. They need to understand that they are not responsible for the deaths of those kids who imitated them. Make sure their contracts are all up-to-date. We don't need any more lawsuits." He stood and left without another word.

Back in his office, he reviewed the newest script. It was going to make the other episodes look tame.

He opened his email and input the addresses of his top ten YouTubers. He wrote a short note, letting them know what he had planned for the next show and telling them to be ready to imitate it on camera, then post their videos after the show aired.

CHAPTER EIGHT

Taylor had been reading the bill for over an hour, and her eyes were starting to blur. It must be the pregnancy. She moved over to the bed, stretched out, and patted the space next her. Beau jumped up and nestled against her legs. His warm body was comforting, and she stroked his head.

"You're wondering what in the world we're doing here, aren't you, baby?" She sighed.

The enticement of sleep became stronger, but she had to think. *Oh, Malcolm, what did you do?* How could it be that she would never again hear his soothing voice or feel his strong arms around her? That he wouldn't be there with her to raise the child they'd worked so hard to conceive? He'd been her best friend these past few years, the one she'd confided everything in. She still had a hard time believing that his whole identity had been faked. Hot tears wet her cheeks, and she hugged Beau closer to her. The familiar ache returned. Being with Jack after all this time brought it back: the heartache, the betrayal. She needed to clear her head.

"Come on, boy. Let's take a walk." She got up and attached his leash, grabbed her purse, and left the room. Her father would be beside himself with worry after the news report. She had to let him know she was okay. She pulled out her phone and dialed the number to his cell phone.

He answered on the first ring.

"Taylor?" The deep voice of Warwick Parks came over the line.

"Dad?" Her voice broke with emotion.

"Taylor! Thank God. I've been out of my mind. Where are you?"

"Oh, Dad. I don't know where to begin. Jack showed up at my house last night. He said Malcolm told him to come and get me, to keep me safe. It's all so mixed up; I don't know what to believe."

"Listen to me, Taylor. I don't know what in the world he's thinking—whisking you off like that, but the police think he kidnapped you. He's in a lot of trouble."

"He didn't kidnap me. Some men came to the house, and we had to leave. Malcolm went to see him. I can't explain it all now. I just wanted you to know I'm okay. We're trying to figure it out." She heard a long sigh.

"Taylor, you need to come home. You haven't seen Jack in years. You have a funeral to plan. Everyone's looking for you. You can't just run off...I don't trust Jack."

"Dad. Stop. You have to trust *me*. I have to see where this leads. Jack is not going to hurt me." What did she expect? The bad blood between her father and Jack to just disappear?

"Tell me where you are."

"At a motel somewhere. I don't know exactly."

"Where are you going?"

"We're following clues Malcolm left in a letter to me, trying to find someone named Jeremy."

"Are you crazy? This makes no sense. Come home!"

She had to hang up. "I love you. I don't know when I can call again, but I will as soon as I can. Try not to worry." She pressed End.

Beau sensed her mood and jumped, putting a paw on each shoulder, and gave her face three quick licks. Laughing, she rubbed his head.

"No matter what happens, I've always got you to cheer me up." She took a seat on the bench by the motel's front office and lifted her face to the sun. Beau curled up on the ground and rested his head on her foot.

The first time she had seen Beau, he had been a mess. Abandoned on the side of the road, his coat mangy, and with sores all over his legs, it was impossible to see what a beautiful dog he was. Taylor had loved him from the instant his soulful eyes locked upon hers. After a visit to the vet, he began to look better. But Malcolm had been less than thrilled. She recalled their conversation.

"How do you know where he came from? He could be rabid for all we know."

Taylor had been floored. "The vet's checked him out, and he's fine," she'd said fiercely. "All he needs is a little TLC. Please, Malcolm. He needs me." Her voice broke. "And I need him."

He'd softened. "All right, but, at the first sign of any aggression, that dog goes."

She had cupped Beau's head in her hands and lowered her face to his.

"No one will ever hurt you again. I promise," she'd whispered and kissed him on the nose.

Beau had turned out to be a loving, gentle, and loyal companion. It was his calm and nurturing presence that had gotten her through all her days of disappointment and devastation month after month, year after year, when it looked as though she would never achieve her dream of becoming a mother. Despite his teddy-bear nature, he had also turned out to be a fierce guard dog and was particularly protective of Taylor. She had discovered this one day when the cable repairman had shown up at her door. Before she could let him in, Beau had gotten between her and the door, a deep growl rising from his throat. She had tried to calm him, but he'd been immovable. He began to bark ferociously, and, no matter how hard she tried, she couldn't pull him away from the door. Finally, she had to call through the intercom and ask the man to come back later. When she'd phoned her cable company to reschedule, she had been shocked to discover that the man they were to send wasn't due to arrive for another two hours. She had wondered then, who had raised Beau the first few years of his life, and after that she'd never doubted his instincts again.

CHAPTER NINE

The Institute, 1975
May

I look straight ahead as the sedan climbs the long hill, and the stone building comes into sight. It is immense and imposing and makes me think of knights and maidens from a long time ago. A chill runs through me, and I have the urge to scream: *Go back! Let me out!* Get a grip, I think. My overactive imagination is at it again. I was chosen out of thousands for this elite, post-graduate fellowship program in medical research. We will be here for three months during which we will be closed off from the outside world. This is necessary, we are told, to help us to focus on the reason for being here—to get into the top 20% of the program and prove we are worthy of the one-year fellowship, all tuition paid. There is no time for distractions from family, friends, or lovers. I said my good-byes to my parents and my dear sister with the assurance that the months would fly, and before we knew it, we'd be celebrating my elevation into the full-year program. Because, of course, I intend to win. It's my only chance to work under Dr. Strombill, the bioethicist I've admired for years. Now that I am actually going to meet him, to have the opportunity to impress him, I am feeling awestruck and giddy, and I'm never awestruck and giddy.

The car comes to a stop, and the driver walks around and opens my door. I smile at him, and he looks right through me.

"Please proceed to the front steps."

I grab my backpack, throw it over one shoulder, and walk the cobblestone path to the immense structure. I wait for the others to fall in line, and while I do, I study the ornate carving on the door. I've never seen anything like it before; it's a crest and a dragon-like creature. The beast is otherworldly and grotesque but beautiful at the same time. I am oddly drawn to it and reach out to trace the lines of its head when a voice behind me makes me snatch my hand back.

"Put your belongings on the ground next to you. You will have no need of them."

There is an instant outcry of protest, and I clutch my purse to my side as my heart pounds in indignation. But then, the door opens and when I look inside, my indignation turns to awe.

CHAPTER TEN

Jack rushed down the aisle at Walgreens, throwing hair dye, scissors, make-up, and some local maps into his basket. He jiggled his keys while the line moved at a snail's pace. Why were there never enough cashiers? Biting his lip, he tried to stay cool as the elderly woman in front of him fumbled with a stack of coupons. At last, she was done. As she moved away, her foot caught on the rug, and she went tumbling. Jack lunged forward and caught her before she hit the ground.

"Oh my goodness. I don't know what happened."

The contents of her purse went flying. He collected them and handed her purse back. "Are you okay?"

"Thank you, dear. I *am* a little unsteady."

"Let me help you to your car." The blood pounded in his ears, but he maintained an air of calm. The poor woman looked like she was in pain. He was worried that she might not be well enough to drive. It took them ten minutes to walk to her car.

"Do you want me to call someone for you? Are you going to be okay driving?"

"I'm fine, dear. Have a sore hip, that's all. Doctors keep trying to convince me to have it replaced, but I'm no fan of the knife."

"Are you sure?"

She nodded. "Thanks. I'll be okay. You're a kind young man," she said as she smiled at him. Before taking a seat behind the wheel, she leaned in and opened the center console. "I want you to have this." It was a Saint Christopher medal on a chain.

He shook his head. "Thank you, but I couldn't possibly take it."

She pressed it into his hand. "I won't take no for an answer. There aren't too many like you, would stop and help an old lady. Please, he'll look after you." She put a hand on his and held his gaze. "Saint Christopher is on your side."

He doubted that, but he closed his hand around it anyway. Seeing the earnest look on her face, he said, "I *could* use a little help." He gave her an impulsive hug and waited for her to drive away before running back to the store. The line was five-people deep again. He picked up his basket from the counter, and got back in line. No good deed goes unpunished, he thought.

When he was finally done, he threw his purchases on the passenger seat, put the medal in his jacket pocket, and pulled out his cell phone. Finding the contact, he pushed Send.

"Hello?"

"It's Jack. I need you to leave Kyle's truck unlocked with the keys in it. I have to borrow it for a while."

"When?"

"Tomorrow night. I'll text you when I'm close. Also, can you get your hands on some progesterone oil?"

"What?"

"It's a long story. I need fifty milligrams of oil, enough for a couple of weeks. And needles too."

"Is there something you want to tell me? Are you having some gender confusion?" She laughed.

"Very funny. It's for a friend. Don't ask."

"I'll see what I can do. And Jack?"

"Yeah?"

"Be careful."

"Love ya, Sis." He hung up and drove back to the motel. As he got out of the car, he looked toward their room and cursed. Their door was open. Jack broke into a run towards the room.

CHAPTER ELEVEN

US Senator Brody Hamilton watched from the bed as Rita Avery rose and hurried to the bathroom and the steaming shower. He admired the view as she walked away, the perfectly rounded buttocks with the creamy skin, unblemished except for the tiny scorpion tattoo on her left cheek. He knew she was eager to wash away his touch. He found it amusing—the lengths to which she was willing to sink to achieve her goals. He grudgingly admired her tenacity and determination to become the most admired and sought-after lobbyist in the business. Hamilton knew all about her shabby beginnings, her mother's insistence that she attend an upscale school, blind to the fact that their trailer park existence made it impossible for Rita to fit in. Yes, he knew all that and more, but not from Rita—Brody never let anyone get close to him without having them thoroughly investigated. No one would have ever suspected she had grown up in poverty. She carried her Birkin bags like badges of honor—a different one for each season. Brody chuckled.

She came out of the bathroom in a beige Chanel suit, ready for their meeting, her Christian Louboutin alligator pumps clicking on the marble floor.

"Thanks for the tumble, darlin." He liked rubbing it in her face. Hamilton snorted and his naked belly shook with his laughter.

She smiled tightly.

"I'll go on ahead and meet you at the Blue Duck. Everyone will be there soon."

He swung his legs over to the side of the bed where they barely reached the carpeted floor. Grabbing his robe, he put it on and stood. He was all business now.

"Go down the back stairs and out the side entrance."

She nodded and left.

* * *

Hamilton was the last to arrive. Two other men on Rita's team were seated at the table with her.

Rita pulled out a folder from her brown crocodile briefcase and laid it on the table.

"I want to talk about ingredient labeling. The health nuts are pumping out more propaganda about the vaccines. People are asking for ingredient lists. We want to make the lists unavailable."

Hamilton raised his eyebrows. "Do you now? And why, pray tell, should I support a bill that would do that?"

"It should be proprietary. Keep other companies from copying our formulas."

"Don't people have a right to know what they're putting in their bodies?" Hamilton asked. He didn't give a whit about the people's rights, only that the public believed he did.

Rita smiled. "Well, of course we'd label the main ingredients, especially those that are a potential allergen, like eggs. What we don't want to have to specify are the metals included."

Hamilton took a sip of his Johnny Walker Blue, licked his lips, and then took another long swallow. "Metals?"

"Aluminum, formaldehyde, mercury, silicon, polysorbate-80—they've been in there forever without hurting anyone, but people may opt-out if they see all the ingredients."

"Can't blame them," Hamilton said. Let her work for it.

One of the men jumped in. "Look, these are preservatives and bonding agents that are necessary to make the vaccines shelf stable. Sometimes there is a small downside to accomplishing a greater good. We don't want children not to receive lifesaving vaccines

"No. I was walking Beau, and he just pulled up and grabbed me."

"I don't understand how they knew where we were."

Her hand flew to her mouth. "I think I know."

"What?"

"I used my cell phone to call my father."

He felt the blood rush to his face. "Oh, Taylor, I told you not to call anyone."

"I had to let him know I was okay. Besides, we were using your computer; it didn't occur to me that these people were that sophisticated."

He took a deep breath. "I installed a VPN, a virtual private network. No one can track it. I didn't know what we'd be dealing with so I took precautions. You need to take the SIM card out of your phone and give it to me."

"Seriously?"

"Oh right." He grinned. "I supposed you haven't become any more tech savvy?"

"Ha-ha."

He pulled off at the next exit, and removed the card from her phone, and threw it away while she used the bathroom. The last light was fading from the sky as they got back on the road.

"Just who are we up against?" Taylor asked, frustration in her voice.

"Were you able to find out anything more about the bill?" Jack asked.

"It looks pretty innocuous. It was just about adding RSV to the list of illnesses receiving federal assistance for vaccines—a good thing."

"Tell me more about RSV."

"Well, it's a respiratory illness that preemies are especially vulnerable to. I have a friend who had twins and one of hers wound up in the hospital for a month. The treatment is expensive, and the preventive vaccine costs hundreds of dollars even after insurance."

"So why wasn't the vaccine a part of the inclusions in the first place?" Jack asked.

She shrugged. "It's not that common. It's only indicated for a certain subset of children. But for a child in that subset and whose family can't afford to go to the doctor, it can be fatal. Malcolm was sponsoring the bill. I don't understand why he killed it."

Jack wondered the same thing. Obviously, there was more to it. "We need to read the whole bill—see if there's anything else. How many children get RSV every year?"

"I'll check. Let's hope the laptop didn't get damaged when you threw it on the ground," Taylor said. She unclipped her seat belt and reached back to get it.

Jack got a whiff of her hair as she moved past him. Lavender. He heard the twang of the Mac turning on. "Seems to be working." Her fingers tapped the keys." Well, someone's certainly pissed."

"What are you talking about?"

"I Googled RSV, and the entire page is populated with article after article from today. From every news outlet."

"Strange, considering the bill hasn't even been in the news," Jack said.

"There's a segment on *Newsline* tonight too, about a family who lost two of their three triplets. From what I can tell, it looks like the whole Knight news outlet is covering it: in print, Internet and television."

Jack was stumped. This wasn't the type of do-gooder bill the power players cared about. Catherine Knight was the reigning media queen. Her holding company owned television stations all over the world, over thirty magazines, twenty-five major newspapers, myriad radio stations, and the second largest social media platform. Why would she expend resources to make a bunch of noise about something that affected such a small portion of the population? It's not like most people wouldn't already be in favor of increasing funding to make vaccines affordable to children. Someone was trying to stir up a public outcry. But why? And against whom?

"We need to read every line of that bill."

"I'll try and get through the rest of it when we reach Boston. It's over four hundred pages with the rider," Taylor replied.

She stared out the window into the darkness and they drove in silence for a long while. Finally, she spoke. "I never really knew him at all, did I?"

Jack shifted in his seat. What could he say?

"He was fighting his own demons, Taylor. His heart was in the right place at the end."

"I think I knew deep down that he was holding back, that things weren't as they should be, but it was all so intangible. We were both so busy those first few years. Between my hours at the network and the traveling I had to do when working a new story, we hardly saw each other. And then when I couldn't get pregnant he was so wonderful, supportive. It was like we were finally in a real partnership. I don't know what's real anymore."

"I'm sorry, Taylor. That had to be tough."

"That's the funny thing. All—and I mean all—of the women I met in the infertility support groups complained about how insensitive their husbands were, how they couldn't relate to how devastating infertility is. Some of their marriages fell apart over it. But it brought us closer together. He was suffering just as much as I was, and he never said the wrong thing. I wouldn't have gotten through it without him."

Jack didn't feel like hearing what a saint Phillips had been. He drummed his hands on the wheel. "Try and get some sleep. You've been through a lot."

"There's no way I can sleep with all this going round and round in my head."

"Just lean back and close your eyes anyway."

She was out within five minutes. Every turn of their conversation had been rife with minefields. He didn't want to discuss her marriage or her pregnancy. She was supposed to have married him. That had been the plan. She would finish her last year of college, and they would be married the following fall. He'd gotten an apartment in New York and a job with the Associated Press. Taylor used to come down on Friday afternoons, and they'd spend the weekends together exploring the city. They were going to live the life they'd always dreamed of—two journalists in the most important city in the world, the future at their fingertips.

He had never seen Dakota coming. A flash of red hair that framed a face defined by angles and contours, her blue eyes flashed with an intensity he'd found irresistible. He might never have met her if not for his sister. She had talked him into accompanying her to the art exhibit—not his usual Tuesday night diversion. Once they arrived, Jack went straight to the bar, grumbled that there was no beer, and grabbed a plastic cup of wine. Nails with chipped red polish reached out and took the cup from him.

"You don't want that rot. Come with me."

Surprised and delighted by her boldness, he went along. She grasped his hand in hers and led him to the back of the gallery where a small kitchen hid. Picking up two crystal wineglasses, she held a bottle of pinot noir in her other hand and showed it to Jack.

"Much better, no?" She smiled.

"It's lost on me." He grinned. "I'm happy with a cold beer."

She stared at him and bit down on her plump bottom lip, her white teeth showcased by the soft pink hue. He found himself wondering how her lips would feel on his.

"Time to change that. You have no idea what you're missing." Moving towards him, she lifted the glass to his lips.

He took a sip then shook his head.

"Sorry. Still rather have a beer."

The full lips puckered in a pretty pout. "You're a terrible boor." A smile lit up her face, and she put a hand on his shoulder. "No matter. I've decided I like you, and I'm going to keep you."

Jack frowned. "Keep me?"

"Oh don't worry, silly. I mean I want to be your friend. I'll keep you as a friend. Come on, let's see if any of my paintings have sold."

"You're…?"

"Yes, I'm Dakota Drake." She took a bow. "Welcome to my world."

"Stop. Stop. Jack! Beau needs to go out," Taylor shouted.

Jack glanced at her, startled. "Sorry. I'll pull over."

He steered the car to the shoulder and put it in park, then turned on the interior light.

"You stay here. I'll take him. Where's his leash?"

Jack held the leash while Beau sniffed in the dark for a place to relieve himself.

When he had finished, he loped up to Jack and licked his hand. Jack envied the dog his uncomplicated existence. He shook his head and wondered how he had managed to screw up his life so badly.

CHAPTER FOURTEEN

Evelyn was about to leave Damon's office when his phone buzzed again and he put a finger up to stop her. He grabbed it from the desk and swiped. The color drained from his face as he listened to the man on the other end. "You lost her?" he demanded.

"Logan must have had some training," he told Damon. "They got away."

He ended the call and looked at Evelyn, the fury building in his chest. "You know her. What will she do next? Will she call again?"

She shook her head. "I don't know. Maybe he won't let her." She began to say something else, then seemed to think better of it and waited for him to speak again.

If Jeremy had indeed told Malcolm the truth about the bill, and he had passed that on to Taylor and Jack, they would follow the story to its conclusion. They were news hounds after all. He needed to find them before they got to Jeremy. He didn't share this with Evelyn. He leveled his gaze at her. "Figure something out. Use your talents. Find a way to make her call."

CHAPTER FIFTEEN

The Institute, 1975
May

The entrance foyer is enormous, and there are racks lined up on the marble floor, each tagged with a sign bearing a name. Clothes hang there—*uniforms* is perhaps a better word. Shiny black jumpsuits with a red scorpion embroidered on the lapel. I take one from the rack and hold it up in front of me. It appears to be a perfect fit. There are slippers too, and scrubs, cotton shirts, blankets and pillows on a shelf below. I notice a Dopp kit and pick it up. Inside are toiletries— toothbrush, mouthwash, shampoo, and soap. I look around at the others. Everyone has the exact provisions. They have thought of everything.

Our driver clears his throat, and we all turn to look at him.

"You may follow me. Pull your cart behind you. We're going to your quarters."

His face is as expressionless as it was when he first picked us up, and I wonder at his lack of affect. I have an urge to reach out and poke him, try and provoke a reaction. But of course, I don't. I make my face a mask and follow along with everyone as if this is the most natural thing in the world. We are led to an elevator and go down in groups. No one speaks while we wait our turn. I have to pee, but am embarrassed to ask. He comes for us, and we descend six floors, and when the elevator opens, we are faced by a steel door. A woman stands next to it, in a black jumpsuit, and smiles.

"Good evening, students. Welcome." She is pretty, not much older than me, and her eyes are kind.

I feel myself relax and gratitude rushes through me at her warmth.

She opens the door, and we push through with our new belongings.

There are beds lined up on each side of the room, army-barracks style, and others have already staked their claims and are sorting their things.

She turns to me and puts a hand on my arm.

"Maya, you're over here." She leads me to a bed at the end of one of the rows.

I am surprised that she knows my name.

"I'm Evelyn. I'll be your coordinator for this session. Anything that you need, any problems you have, you can come to me."

"Thank you," I manage, my voice cracking. I look around. "Are we *all* staying in here?"

"Part of being here is learning how to think differently. Does it matter when you treat a patient, if the person is male or female? Does your examination differ?"

I shake my head.

"Of course not," she says. "You would find it absurd if a male patient refused to let you examine him because you are a woman." Her hand sweeps across the room. "It is no different here. This is where you all sleep, no matter your sex." Then she laughs. "Trust me, at the end of the day, the only thing that will be on your mind is sleep."

She leaves me then, and I watch her walk over to someone else. I think about what she said and I guess it makes some sense.

* * *

Today is the first day of classes. We are awakened early, though I don't know the exact time, as I no longer have my watch. We all wear our black jumpsuits and slippers. There are about thirty of us, and I dress silently, averting my eyes to avoid looking at the other half-naked bodies in the room and hoping they are doing the same. Despite my conversation with Evelyn, I am still unnerved to be quartered with the men and didn't sleep well last night. I whisper to Amelia, the woman assigned to the cot next to me. "Don't you think they should separate the men from the women?"

She doesn't turn to look at me, but casts a glance in my direction out of the corner of her eye and answers, her words barely audible, "Shh. They'll hear you."

I bite back my retort, disappointed to realize that she's a rule follower, and that I won't be finding any companionship in her. We were told during initiation to keep to ourselves and focus on one thing only—being chosen as one of the final twenty. The competition is going to be fiercer than anything we'd experienced at medical school. Our ability to display a singular focus and to shut out everything around us is one of the things we will be judged on. I can see that Amelia is as serious as I am about being one of the twenty admitted to phase two. Okay then, we won't be friends.

The bell rings, and we walk single file behind our training coordinator to begin a day filled with lectures. I am excited, wondering when I will get to meet him. We are taken in groups of five to the elevator and up six floors.

We are ushered into a classroom. It is nothing special, could be any classroom in any high school. There is a large screen at the front. A man walks in the room, and I bite my cheek to refrain from gasping. It is him—Dr. Strombill. He is shorter than I expected, almost diminutive, and I wonder if this can be the man who has written with such passion and brilliance. He stands in front of us, silent, assessing, and seems to examine each of us before he finally opens his mouth to speak. When he does, all my doubts dissolve, and his passion is so palpable I almost believe I can reach out and touch it.

"Welcome. The fact that you are here is evidence of your

extraordinary talent and dedication. But more will be required. Innovation. Three-dimensional thinking. You must be able to see into the future and stride into the unknown. You have spent years being indoctrinated into the established way of viewing medicine. But we are to revolutionize the face of medicine, to see the big picture and make the difficult decisions that will advance medicine and treatment far above where we are today." His Austrian accent is slight, melodic.

He walks from the front of the room without another word and turns off the lights. The screen comes alive, and we are looking at an older man lying in a hospital bed. I watch as the man on the screen gasps and wheezes in a vain attempt to get air into his lungs. His sallow skin is stretched tautly over his skeletal face, and his pained grimace reveals brown teeth. He croaks out a hoarse request.

"Nurse." It comes out as a whisper.

His bony fingers press repeatedly on the call button as a look of distress fills his face. When there is no response, he sags backward, and his head hits the pillow in despondent resignation. The nurse finally appears, then frowns when she sees that the sheets are wet. She sighs.

"Let's get you cleaned up, Mr. Smith. Lemme get some help in here."

Two medical aides appear with another bed, and together they move the frail body into it. The man she called Mr. Smith grimaces in agony as they jostle him, and he cries out.

"Leave me in peace! Why can't someone make the pain stop?" His anguished cries are punctuated with bouts of coughing and gasping.

The screen goes black, and light floods the room.

"What you have just seen can be prevented." Dr. Strombill leans forward and peers over the dais at the students in the front row.

His voice rises. "You must be the voice of that poor man. It is up to you to make sure that a human being does not endure that kind of suffering. It is your moral imperative, your sacred duty as doctors, as purveyors of mercy, to spare your patients from this degree of pain and indignity."

He scans the faces and looks pleased. "Who of us wants to spend our last days on earth filled with pain, fighting in vain for every breath? No. It is indecent. We cannot allow people to linger indefinitely until their disease-ridden bodies finally give up and free them from their torment and anguish."

A timid hand waves.

"Yes, you." He points at Amelia.

"What is the alternative? If we don't give any treatment, the patient will still suffer from the effects of the disease."

He looks at her, and a frown pulls at his mouth. "I assume you have heard of euthanasia?"

A look of shock appears on her face. "Are you suggesting that we actually kill people? Put them down like dogs?"

"And are *you* suggesting that a dog has more right to compassion than a human being? What is the profit in prolonging the life of someone who will be left with nothing but pain and indignity?"

I hold my breath, waiting for her response. Can't she see she's making him angry?

Her cheeks are flushed. "But it's illegal."

He walks toward her. "It is *now*. But that is changing and we must lead the charge."

"But sometimes a terminal patient *does* recover. How are we to know which are hopeless cases and which are not?" She looks around the room, waiting, I think, for someone to come to her defense. No one does.

Dr. Strombill's cheeks grow blood red, and a vein throbs in his forehead. He points a shaking finger at her.

"That is what is wrong with this country. Over-indulged children who grow up to be spoiled adults. The world does not have at its disposal the resources to squander on lost causes. Have you considered the financial and emotional toll on the family? Do you have any idea how difficult it is to watch someone you love wither before your eyes until they are nothing but an empty shell?" Spittle flies from the corners of his mouth, and his eyes are slits.

Every eye in the room is on her. With tears streaming down her face, she stumbles to her feet and runs to the door, leaving her notebook on the desk.

Dr. Strombill turns to the class. "She won't be needing this anymore." He knocks the book to the floor. "I trust no one else has any questions?"

CHAPTER SIXTEEN

They arrived at their destination.

"Where are we?" Taylor asked.

"Outside my sister's house. Come on. Time to ditch the Mustang."

They quickly moved everything from the car to a truck; then Jack told Taylor to get behind the wheel of the truck.

"Follow me."

She drove behind him until they reached the Charles River, where they pulled into a secluded clearing set back from the road, and she put the truck in park and got out.

"What are you doing?" she cried at the sight of him positioning his beloved Mustang on the precipice of the hill, aimed at the river below.

"Got to get rid of it or they'll know where we are. Can't very well leave it at my sister's and implicate her."

"Oh, Jack! You love this car. You've spent hours and hours working on it and now you've got to get rid of it because of me."

"It's not your fault."

"If Malcolm hadn't involved you in this, we wouldn't be here right now."

"Don't blame yourself," was all he said. He couldn't bring himself to admit what he really knew: she would never have married Phillips if Jack hadn't been such a fool.

She turned around and placed a hand on the roof the car.

"I still remember when you brought it home. Your father had a fit, said it was a death trap." She laughed. "By the time you were finished with it, he loved it almost as much as you did."

He swallowed the lump in his throat. His best memories with his father were because of this car; working on it was the only time he had connected with him. A heart attack had taken his father right after his fiftieth birthday.

Taylor looked at Jack. "Do you really have to get rid of it? Can't we hide it somewhere?"

He shook his head. "No, it has to be this way." He stood straighter. "It's just a car. Step back."

Taylor took a last look, squeezed his hand, and stood back.

He leaned down and pushed. The car ran slowly down the hill until it reached the water. Jack held his breath as it began to sink, and when it was no longer visible he opened his mouth and exhaled. *Time to keep moving.*

An hour later, he pulled into a rest stop. Jack's sister had come through with the progesterone oil, and now, he followed Taylor into the cramped bathroom, arousing looks of curiosity and a few disapproving glares, so that he could give her the shot. The thick viscous liquid necessitated a large-gauge needle, and Jack cringed looking at the size of it.

"I'm used to it, Jack. It's no big deal."

She winced as the needle went in, and he slowly plunged the oil into the area right above her buttock. She rubbed the spot, then gamely smiled and thanked him for helping her.

They grabbed some drinks and snacks and got back on the road.

She was snoring, and he chuckled to himself. She would die of embarrassment if she knew. His attraction to her was still strong, and he felt like a heel, but he had enjoyed the glimpse of her slim hips when he gave her the shot. Being with her again made him wonder, for the thousandth time how, he had ever walked away from her. He had sacrificed her happiness as well as his own, and he hadn't even had the guts to tell her himself. It still shocked him to remember how selfish he had been.

After the art show, he had gone home and berated himself for flirting with Dakota. What was wrong with him? He was in love with Taylor—she'd been the only one for him from the time he was old enough to think about girls that way. Their relationship was story book—girl next door, high school sweethearts. So when there was a buzz on his intercom at 3:00 a.m., he should've known better than to answer it. Half-asleep, he pushed the button, and her throaty voice floated into his room.

"Hey, Jack. Whatcha doing?"

"Sleeping," he'd mumbled.

A laugh came over the speaker. "The night is young. Buzz me up, I have champagne."

Against his better judgment, he had. He'd intended to tell her that he was involved already, then send her on her way.

She'd walked in his apartment, gone straight to the kitchen, opened the cabinet, and gotten two glasses, all like she'd lived there forever. She poured them each some champagne, leaning against his counter, her full lips shiny with gloss, just begging to be kissed.

He took the glass from her and threw it back in one gulp.

"Listen, Dakota. I like you, but I'm—"

She moved toward him and put a finger on his lips. "Shh." He caught a whiff of her perfume, something spicy, musky.

And then they were kissing, and he was lifting her shirt off. The whole thing felt like a dream, and he half expected to wake up in the morning alone. When the bright light of day shone through the curtains, he'd realized with a sinking feeling that he'd screwed up. Seeing the long, red hair fanned out on the pillow next to him—the pillow where Taylor's head should have been resting, made him sick with guilt. He'd never been with anyone but Taylor before that night. Dakota had rolled over and looked at him, the expression in her eyes taking his breath away. There was something in those eyes that said, *I know you—you belong with me,* and he was torn in two, paralyzed by confusion. She closed the space between them, folding her body into his, and he felt himself respond. Like a drug, he had wanted more, needed more, and there was no turning back.

After that, he and Dakota became inseparable. Her loft was a block from his apartment. They spent all their free time together. He was bewitched. She was fascinated by everything Jack had to say, loved to read his articles, would look at him like he was the only person in the world.

After a month, he still hadn't told Taylor. He didn't know how. For the first time in his life, he lied to her. Told her he would be away on assignment. He knew he had to break the news, but how?

He had planned on going up to Boston on Friday and telling her in person. Dakota was cooking dinner when he mentioned it.

"I need to tell Taylor about us."

She'd turned from the counter and sat down across from him, taking his hand in hers.

"Of course. Do you want me to go out for a while so you can talk in private?"

He rubbed her hand. "No, I have to do it face to face. I owe her that."

A frown marred her face, and her lips turned up in a tight smile. She withdrew her hand and stood, turning her back to him. "Oh. When are you planning on going?"

Jack came up behind her and wrapped his arms around her waist. "Don't be mad. We have a long history together. I can't just call her up and tell her I've fallen in love with someone else."

She turned around and pressed against him, cupping his face in her hands. "I know. But I can't stand the thought of losing you."

"You're not going to lose me. Not ever."

"Of course, you have to go. I was just having a moment." Her tone became light. "I would expect nothing less from you, my knight in shining armor."

He smiled, relieved, and she reached out and grabbed his hand.

"Dinner won't be ready for another half an hour. I know what I want for an appetizer."

They fell on the sofa together, limbs tangled, lips locked and he could think of nothing else but the way she made him feel.

When they got the phone call on Thursday inviting them to a last-minute anniversary celebration in Las Vegas for her Aunt Sybil and Uncle Marcel that weekend, he'd modified his plans and made arrangements to go up to Boston the following weekend instead.

They arrived in Vegas late Friday night and Jack wasted no time in teaching Dakota blackjack. The party for her family wasn't until Saturday, so they had the first night to themselves. As the chips accumulated and the liquor flowed, a pervasive euphoria filled Jack. He looked at Dakota and felt his heart swell.

Marcel walked over, clapped Jack on the shoulder, and gave him a broad smile.

"How're you kids doing?" He glanced at the pile of chips in front of Jack. "Looks like you're in the winner's circle. We're turning in for the night. See you tomorrow."

"Good night, Marcel."

Dakota got off her stool and, swaying, put an arm on Jack to steady herself. "Hey, handsome. Ready to call it a night?"

They walked arm in arm from the casino to the elevator.

She started to laugh.

"What's so funny?"

She pointed to the sign by the elevator.

"The chapel of love. I was picturing us standing in front of an Elvis look-alike getting married." She doubled over, laughing.

Jack chuckled and they both began to sing: "Going to the chapel and I'm going to get married. Going to the chapel and I'm gonna get maaaaried…"

The both stopped and looked at each other.

"Would it be too crazy?" he asked.

Dakota bit her lip. "Nothing seems less crazy."

He couldn't think of anything he wanted more. The truth was she owned him already.

"Let's do it," he said.

The rest was a blur. Say this. Sign here. Kiss the bride. And then it was done. They were married. They left the chapel and walked into the cool evening air. Suddenly he was sober. What in God's name had he done?

CHAPTER SEVENTEEN

The Institute, 1975
June

Amelia is gone and despite her giving me the cold shoulder, I feel bad for her. To get thrown out on day one is humiliating. I can't imagine having to go back to my parents and tell them that the two thousand dollars they spent on the program had been flushed down the toilet. On the other hand, one down, eighty-nine to go. She should have kept quiet, kept her doubts to herself. It's not as though the idea of euthanasia doesn't give me pause. Even though I hate to see anyone suffer, I *am* concerned about a course of treatment that requires a doctor to determine when a life should end. But I was smart enough to keep it to myself. How *are* we to decide when enough is enough? Now I'm not suggesting that we not play God because I'm not convinced that there *is* a God in whose hands to leave such decisions. As a woman of science, I have left behind my childhood fancies about God and angels and saints. I leave that magical thinking to my mother. So, while I have no religious ground to base my objection on, I do believe in the sanctity of life. The question is, what constitutes life? A pain-filled existence with no chance of recovery? I think what Dr. Strombill is trying to teach us is that we have to keep an open mind if we are to learn anything; otherwise, what is the point of being here?

It's been a month now, and no one else has been dismissed. I see my own exhaustion mirrored in the eyes of others. We are pushed beyond our limits, but not one of us complains. No one wants to look weak. Each month, we are grouped in thirds, rotating at the end of the month so that we have the chance to work with everyone. We are given a survey at the end of each day on which we write two names—the person we feel has worked the hardest that day, and you can't name yourself—and the person who we believe cut a corner, or didn't push him or herself hard enough. The voting is supposed to be confidential, and when we finish our time here, the votes will be tallied and will factor into who makes it to the next stage. Alliances have already formed. I have identified five people similar to me, and we have figured out a way to work the system. Brian came up with a code. When we sit together for dinner in the evening, he tells a story from medical school. When he picks up his napkin and wipes his mouth, we tune in to the next sentence. The first letter of each word spells the name of the person we are to write down as the lazy worker. Then, whomever he gives a cookie to, is the one who we write down as working the hardest. Every other day, no one gets a cookie, and we vote on our own for the best worker, just so no one becomes suspicious.

It is the sixth and final lecture of the day. I am in the front row, where I sit every day, waiting for him to take notice of me. I *must* be chosen for phase two. The desire to beat them all out consumes me.

Today he leans on the desk and tosses a ball back and forth between his hands as he speaks.

"What if I were to tell you that we are making strides in gene therapy? That we are working to isolate the genes that cause diseases and replace then with healthy genes?"

There is a murmur of approval throughout the classroom. I lean forward in my seat, my body quivering with excitement. This is exactly the type of research I'm dying to be part of.

He looks up at the ceiling as he talks and spreads his fingers wide as he gesticulates. "Imagine. One day a world with no disease, no suffering." His face darkens. "But there are those who warn of abuses, of playing God. Why should we not play God? If we can improve on his flawed design, should we not?"

I raise my hand. He nods in my direction.

"They are afraid." My voice falters, and I clear my throat, trying again. "Of progress, there will always be those who stand in the way of progress."

He smiles. "Yes, Maya! And do we let these naysayers, these cowards, stop our progress?" He answers his own question. "Of course not. But how? How do we stop them?" He walks toward me, puts a hand on my shoulder.

"Maya?"

"We become more than scientists. We become persuaders, convince others who can help us—lobbyists, politicians. Find those who hope to gain from our research and use it to our advantage."

He claps his hands together and laughs. "Very good, Maya. You are learning fast."

His comment garners looks of jealousy in my direction. I smile at him, unfazed by the reaction of my classmates, concerned only with Dr. Strombill's opinion.

CHAPTER EIGHTEEN

Jack disengaged the GPS in the Nissan, then glanced at her. "Keep an eye out while I do one more thing." He got out of the truck and opened the hood. After a few minutes, he returned, holding a small chip.

"What's that?"

"A device placed on all cars made after 2000. It's an internal GPS, so that the car can be located. The government's been installing them on cars ever since 9/11. Of course, the dealers have turned it to their advantage. They sell it as a way to find your car if it's stolen. What they don't tell you is that it's automatically on every car anyway."

Taylor studied Jack. "And you know this how?"

He shrugged. "If I told you, I'd have to—"

"Not funny," she interrupted.

"A few years back, I took a break from life and did a piece on the cartel kidnappings in Colombia. I got a job as a bodyguard, made some connections with the other bodyguards there. One was ex-military intelligence. Let's just say I learned a lot."

She was looking at him like he'd lost his mind.

"You took a break from life by going to Colombia and protecting people from drug lords? Don't you need training for something like that? Why would they hire a journalist?"

"Aw shucks. Thanks for the vote of confidence." He gave her a wry smile.

"You know what I mean."

He didn't want to get into all of it with her. "I do have a black belt, and I took one of those civilian training courses."

"You mean like Blackwater?"

"Something like that. I needed to do something different for a while." He didn't tell her that it was what saved his sanity, that if he hadn't been able to get out of the country, away from everything and everyone he knew, he probably wouldn't have made it.

Her eyes widened. "Was this after…" She couldn't bring herself to say it.

He looked away and started the car. "Let's hit it."

After an uncomfortable silence, Taylor finally spoke. "How long till we get to the cabin?"

"Maybe three hours."

She ran a hand through her hair. "I hope there's running water. I'm in desperate need of a shower."

Jack nodded. "It'll have everything we need."

"Jack, listen. I really need to get word to my dad that we're okay."

"They'll be an untraceable phone waiting there for us."

"Good."

"But, Taylor, I'm not so sure anything you say to him will make him feel okay about your being with me."

She raised her eyebrows. "I'll make it clear that's it temporary. He knows I would never be *with* you again." Her tone was sharp, and she turned in her seat towards the window, as if she couldn't get far enough away from him, and Jack knew that that message was meant for him as well.

CHAPTER NINETEEN

The Institute, 1975
July

I am approached by one of the instructors and shown to a private room. I blush with pleasure at being singled out. My unwavering attention is paying off.

My belongings are already there, and I am told to sit and wait. A few hours later, I am escorted out of the building and to a waiting limousine.

"Where are we going?" I ask the driver.

"To another building on campus."

I lean back and look out the window, intrigued. We drive for over thirty minutes, each mile seeming to take us deeper and deeper into uncivilized terrain, trees and branches obscuring the view of everything but the road in front of us. At last, we stop, and I gasp as I open the door and step outside. I am standing in front of a castle. A real castle! I crane my neck to look at the top where I count at least eleven turrets. It is something out of a fairy tale, and I hug my arms around myself, too enchanted to speak at first. Finally, I manage.

"What is this place?" I ask. The neo-Gothic architecture looks familiar to me. I've seen it somewhere, in a picture or postcard.

"It is a replica of Hohenzollern Castle," he replies.

"The German castle, right?"

He nods with a bored expression, as if we're discussing the weather. "Of course, on a much smaller scale."

I wonder again what I'm doing here and what in the world this has to do with my research fellowship.

"Follow me," he says, and I walk behind him up a steep hill that leads to a tremendous iron door, feeling as though I've time traveled and am about to encounter knights in all their splendor waiting on the other side.

When we enter the cavernous hallway, there are indeed suits of armor, but they are empty, their owners departed long ago. My heart is pounding as I try to take it all in, when I am whisked down the hall by a woman. She leads me into a room that has a doctor's examining table in the center and a counter littered with medical supplies. I am directed to sit on a table, which is covered with a paper sheet.

"What's going on? Where am I?"

She hands me a robe. "Congratulations. You've graduated to the next phase."

I look at her, dubious, wondering if I'm dreaming this. "I still have two months to finish my fellowship. This doesn't make sense."

She ignores my objections. "Everyone has to undergo a physical before moving on to phase two," she states.

I take a deep breath. This feels wrong, but I'm afraid to jeopardize my chances.

"What do you want me to do?"

I sit on the examining table, covered only by the paper gown I was instructed to put on. She sits in the corner, reading a magazine. I have kept silent but can no longer contain my curiosity and clear my throat in an effort to gain her attention. She ignores me.

"Excuse me."

"Yes?" she says, not bothering to look up.

"Can you tell me why I need to be seen by a doctor?"

"It's just a standard physical."

I look up at the ceiling and try to distract myself while I wait. *What is taking so long?* My face grows warm as impatience gets the better of me. I am about to jump down from the table and put my clothes back on when the door opens. I smile at the man in the white coat, hoping to connect with him.

He doesn't smile back but simply moves his hand in a shuffling manner to indicate I should lie back. He holds a syringe in the other hand.

"What are you doing?"

"Relax. It's something to calm you."

I inch away from him. "Stay away from me."

The woman is by my side in an instant. She takes my hand in hers. "It's okay, Maya." Her voice is sugar. "Look at me."

The distraction is enough. I feel the sting of the needle, and the next thing I know I am lying down with a pillow under my hips.

She is sitting in a chair in the corner of the room again.

I rub my eyes. "What happened?"

She pushes a button on the counter.

The doctor returns.

"What did you do?" I manage to croak out.

He looks at the woman.

"Make sure she doesn't move. He will be in to talk to her later."

I try to sit up but before I can, a strong arm comes down on my arms and holds me still.

"You heard what the doctor said. Do I need to strap you down or are you going to be a good girl and stay still?" There is no compassion in her eyes.

I drop my head back onto the table. What have I gotten myself into? All of a sudden my ears are wet, and I realize I am crying. I make no move to wipe away the tears. I won't give her the satisfaction. I lie still, staring straight ahead and make my mind blank.

CHAPTER TWENTY

Senator Hamilton played solitaire on his phone while he waited for the tedious proceedings to finish. Knowing the outcome tended to make a bill vote boring. Three more and he could get out of here and enjoy the steak he had been thinking about all morning. He licked his lips. The clerk continued with the roll call vote.

"How do you vote Mr. Marin?"

"Aye."

"Mr. Marin, aye."

"Mr. Plomkin?"

"Aye."

"Mr. Plomkin, aye."

Hamilton didn't look up from his phone.

"Ms. Linway?"

Finally, last one.

"No."

Hamilton's head snapped up. He must have heard wrong. He turned around to look at her, but she wouldn't meet his eyes. The bill was dead.

He strode from the room and rushed to his office. Within minutes, four Congress members arrived.

Hamilton picked up the phone.

"Hold my calls."

Wheezing from the exertion, he took a long sip of water and wiped the perspiration from his forehead with his handkerchief. He looked at the man sitting across for him.

"Would you mind telling me what just happened? We engineered this to be a close vote. How did we lose Kansas?"

The only woman in the room cleared her throat. All eyes turned to her.

"She's pregnant."

"So?" Hamilton's eyes narrowed.

"I think it colored her perception. She just got the news yesterday."

Hamilton glared at her. "Senator Marcus, when did you find this out?"

She gulped, her face red. "This morning."

His voice rose. "Why didn't you tell me? I would have found someone else for the swing vote."

"She's my friend, and she asked me to keep it quiet. Besides, she promised it wouldn't change her vote."

Hamilton wanted to strangle her. "And you believed her?"

A congressman on his left interrupted. "It's a minor setback. There is more than one way to achieve our goals. Remember how long it took to make screening mandatory? The rest of the bills have passed quickly and mostly unnoticed. The bio-ethicists have done their jobs well. Everyone wants healthy children. We'll make some minor modifications to mollify our constituents and get them on our side."

Hamilton exhaled and leaned back. Maybe he was right. On its surface, the bill was a win-win. It covered a wide spectrum of birth defects and chronic illnesses that were detectable in the first trimester of pregnancy. Any of the conditions included would qualify as a pre-existing condition that would be excluded from coverage, thereby, in practical terms, mandating the termination of the pregnancy. Since pre-screening had become mandatory, these birth defects had been reduced by 40 percent. They had garnered widespread support from special interest groups whose mission it was to optimize health care. It was the fervent belief of those supporting the bill that this was the path to eliminating diseases and freeing up resources to work on curing other diseases that were not yet preventable. They were on the forefront of a better, more perfect world. Hamilton didn't care a whit about any of that. His name was on the bill, and he'd be damned if some uterus with legs was going to be his undoing.

He pulled out his phone, clicked the Twitter app and typed:

Thanks to all who supported #healthy #children #bill. Unfortunately, no win this time. #HCB

CHAPTER TWENTY-ONE

The Institute, 1975
July

When he walks into the room, I feel a momentary flicker of hope. Surely someone this beautiful is no one to be feared. His face is almost perfect, marred only by a small, round scar on one cheek. Otherwise, it is a face to rival any movie star's—chiseled cheekbones; straight Roman nose; full lips. My gaze moves to his eyes and then my hope crashes.

I have never before seen what I see in those eyes. They are predatory and penetrating. Something intangible terrifies me when I look into them. There is a heaviness in the air, an invisible darkness that threatens to invade me, and I want to cover my eyes like a child and pretend I am invisible. He looks at me as if we know each other.

I take a deep breath, affect a bravado I don't feel, and swing my legs off the bed, ready to stand.

"Don't get up. You need your rest." His voice is deep, pleasant.

"Who are you?"

His lips curl in a smile. "All in good time, my dear." His tone is mocking.

I take a deep breath and stare at him. I am afraid to speak.

He pulls a chair next to my bed and sits. "You are a brilliant young woman. It's why I chose you."

"What have you done? Why am I here?"

He arches one eyebrow. "You have been chosen to bear my child."

His child? My stomach tightens, and I feel sick. I glare at him. "Did you rape me?"

A look of repulsion transforms his face, and the corners of his mouth point to the floor.

"Please, Maya. I am not an animal. Think. There are other ways to impregnate someone. Rape you? What a nauseating thought."

"Why? Why would you hope to impregnate me?"

"We do not hope. We plan. I have your entire medical history; you have been monitored for the past month. I'm fairly certain that you are pregnant."

I jump off the bed and began to pace. "Why in God's name?" I scream. I don't understand. Why would he need to do such a thing? With his looks, I am sure there was no shortage of willing women.

"God has nothing to do with it. You need know nothing but this for now. You have been chosen from thousands. You should be pleased. You have not only made it to the top of the class, you have made it to the top of the world."

"I don't understand. I came here to learn. You can't do this! Who are you?"

"Damon Crosse. I am the one in charge here. You were selected from a great many to come here—but not for the medical internship." He stands and walks to the corner of the room, picks up a folder, and opens it. After reading something inside, he closes it and returns to the chair.

"It was very close. I almost chose someone else. But your pedigree was better."

What is he talking about? "Pedigree? I'm not a dog."

He smiles again. "No, Maya, you are more like a brood mare."

"Go to hell, you bastard." Spittle flies from my mouth.

He looks at me with no change in expression.

"I'm getting out of here. I'm going home. This is insane!" I rant.

He withdraws from the room without another word, and then the men arrive. They push me down on the bed and strap me into a white vest.

"You're making this harder than it has to be," one whispers in my ear.

I scream until my throat is raw. I can no longer move my arms, and the more I struggle, the tighter everything becomes. I don't know when I finally fall into an exhausted sleep. When I awake, he is there again. Watching. Calm. Cold.

"The sooner you learn to accept things, the better."

"I'll never accept being held prisoner. Why have you done this?" I croak, my voice barely audible.

"In good time. In good time you will know the part you will play, but not quite yet."

"I need to move. Take these off."

He frowns. "You must learn the proper way to address me. You may request but never demand." He stands up and hovers over me. "Do you understand?"

My stomach tightens. I nod my head.

He sits back down. "Good."

"Would you please take this vest off me?"

"Not yet. When I believe you can be trusted, then I will have it removed. In the meantime, we shall continue our chat."

I lie there while he sits, seemingly bored, and indifferent to me. I fear I shall never see my family or anyone else again.

CHAPTER TWENTY-TWO

The country road was full of bumps and potholes. Taylor winced as she was bounced again, and her head bumped against the headliner.

"Sorry 'bout that. Almost there."

"Hope I don't give birth early," she joked.

He gave her a worried look. "That's not possible, is it?"

She shook her head. "No. It's too early. I was just kidding. It's hard not to be preoccupied with the pregnancy." She didn't know why she felt that she needed to explain but she did. "I've had some miscarriages, and I'm considered high risk. That's why I need the progesterone shots for the first eight weeks—it helps decrease the chance of it happening again. This is not the best time for me to be stressed out."

His hands tightened on the wheel. "I wish Malcolm had told me."

"Yeah well, I don't understand what was going on in his mind. Truthfully, if those guys with guns hadn't shown up, I'm not sure I would have believed any of it was real. I just want to find Jeremy, whoever he is, and get some answers."

The scenery began to change as the road narrowed, and civilization faded away. Everything was a green blur. Never had she been in the middle of so many Evergreens. As they crested the top of the hill, she saw what looked like a brown rectangle nestled in the patchwork of forest. As they got closer, a small A-frame log cabin appeared. The enormous trees dwarfed the dwelling, and Taylor shivered, thinking of old horror movies involving isolated houses.

Jack pulled into the gravel drive.

They walked up to the door, and Jack took the key from his pocket and opened it.

Beau began running around the house in frantic loops. After about ten rounds, he bounded up to Taylor and prodded her to pet him.

"Poor guy, stuck in the car all that time. Maybe we can walk him a little later?" she said.

Jack looked at his watch. "Let's get settled first."

He seemed familiar with the place, as he walked over to a lamp with a base made of miniature canoes and turned it on. The amber glow made the room cozy and inviting, and she went over to a plush brown sofa and ran a hand over the velvety fabric. Large windows with sheer, white curtains on two walls looked out at the barricade of trees, and she suddenly felt safe and cocooned.

"Why don't you take a shower and change, and I'll fix us something to eat?" Jack said.

"We don't have any food."

He opened the refrigerator, which was filled to overflowing with a huge variety of meats, fruits, and vegetables.

Taylor's stomach growled in anticipation. "Where did that come from?"

"Let's just say I have resourceful friends."

"Good to know."

"How about an omelet?"

"Sounds perfect."

Taylor freshened up and then sat down at a wooden table by one of the windows. She took a bite from the still-steaming omelet. "Delicious! What kind of cheese is this?"

"Goat. I also chopped some dates in."

She raised her eyebrows. "Impressive. Last time you made me something to eat it was a lumpy peanut butter and jelly sandwich."

"I seem to remember your liking those sandwiches." He laughed. "Remember in fourth grade, you would trade me your turkey and cheese for my PB&J?"

She had forgotten that. "They were good. My mother's never tasted the same. The bread was wrong, and so was the peanut butter. You always had Wonder Bread and Jif." She used to feel so bad that Jack's mom didn't get up with him before school and make him breakfast or pack him a lunch. He had been taking care of himself for as long as she could remember. He became such a regular fixture at their dinner table that, after a while, her mother automatically set a place setting for him.

"I'm happy to make you one any time you want."

His tone was flirtatious, and she bit back a light-hearted response and finished eating. That was a lifetime ago, and they had both changed.

She brought his laptop to the table and opened it. She had gotten through the rest of the bill last night and was now looking at the rider. Now this was interesting. "Jack, I think I found something."

He walked behind her and looked at the screen where she was pointing.

"Look at this. It's talking about a TB vaccine. Doesn't one exist already?"

He shrugged. "I've never heard of one. Don't know."

"Well, this rider claims that one is in testing now and that once it gets FDA approval, it can be mandated in case of a national health emergency."

"Mandated for kids?" Jack asked.

She shook her head. "No, no. And this has nothing to do with the main bill. This would make all health care workers have to get the vaccine if there was a breakout, and the language around what a breakout is goes on for pages."

"So what? Don't they already have to do that with flu shots?"

Taylor thought a minute. That was true, but something was niggling at her. "Yeah, but I think that's more a hospital requirement. This would make it federal law. Right now, states mandate those decisions." She kept reading. "Here. If the incident rate rises above .05 *everyone* would be required to get the vaccine."

"Define incident rate."

"The number of cases per one hundred thousand. The incident rate is now .03"

"I guess that's a significant increase, not sure if it's enough to justify forcing the vaccine on the entire population," he said.

She swiveled around to face him. "Jack. Why would Congress pass a law about a vaccine that doesn't even exist yet?"

"Good question. I wonder which drug company is developing it."

She turned back around and started typing again.

"Hmm."

"What?" Jack asked.

"There *is* already a TB vaccine. BCG. Says here it's been around since the 1920's but is not highly effective. Hold on." She typed in "more effective TB vaccine."

"So there's the Tuberculosis Vaccine Initiative, a non-profit working together to find a better vaccine."

"Interesting. I'm assuming they partner with drug companies. Can I take a look?"

She slid the computer over to him.

He clicked on through the website. "Yeah, they do. So, we need to find out who's working with them on this new TB vaccine. They receive funding from grants and donations and industry. We have to figure out a way to get a hold of their annual report."

Taylor got up and took their dishes to the sink to wash them. "So in the meantime, what are we doing here?"

Jack walked over to the fireplace. He pushed aside the mesh curtain and reached inside. Taylor watched as he dislodged a brick and pulled out an envelope. He dusted off his sleeve and walked over to her.

"Our next set of clues." He held the envelope up.

"If I didn't just see it, I wouldn't believe it." She shook her head.

Jack ripped the envelope open and took out a map and a note. He scanned the note then waited for Taylor to come over.

"Does this mean anything to you?" He handed it to her.

She read it aloud. "Go to the library in Claremont, New Hampshire. Taylor, find your favorite book. The one that has always spoken to you of resilience and fortitude. There, you will find the address. The number can be calculated by multiplying the number of letters in her maiden name times 6 and adding 7. The town bears the same name as the town where her true love returns. The street name will be in the book." She smiled. "He's talking about *Gone with the Wind*."

Jack chuckled. "Don't tell me—your favorite part is 'I don't know nothin 'bout birthin' babies'."

Taylor smacked him on the head with the letter. "Very funny. He meant the scene where Scarlett swears she'll never be hungry again." For a moment, she forgot about Malcolm's deception and remembered only the intimacies they had shared. She felt a wistful longing for him.

"I'd have pegged you more like Prissy," Jack said.

She laughed and was surprised to find that the familiar mischievous look in his eyes lightened her heart. For a split second, it was like old times, before any of the complications, when they were just two best friends looking for their next adventure.

She pursed her lips. "And you bring to mind the dashing Charles Hamilton." That would fix him.

Jack fell back against the cushion and clutched his heart. "Ah, Scarlett, you have cut me to the quick."

She became serious. "So, we need to go to Claremont and find the book to get the actual address for Jeremy's place. We can figure out the number: her maiden name is O'Hara, five letters times six equals thirty plus seven means the street number is thirty-seven."

Jack nodded. "So, the town. He said where her true love returned. Where did Ashley go?"

Taylor shook her head. "Her *true* love. Ashley was only who she thought she loved. She didn't realize until too late that she really loved Rhett and that's when he left to go back to Charleston." She was annoyed that she had to explain it. Everyone knew Scarlett never really loved Ashley. Even Malcolm got that. She realized Jack was talking.

"What?" she said a little too snappishly.

"There's a Charlestown on the map, that must be what he meant. It's not far from here." He circled the two cities. "We're a little more than an hour away. Now all we need is the street name."

"We need the book. Let's hope no one's checked it out," she said. "I'll be right back. Need to use the bathroom."

She closed the bathroom door and took a deep breath. She had actually been flirting with him. What was wrong with her? They weren't away on vacation. She was angry at herself for letting her guard down so easily. *Remember what he did. He is not the Jack you used to love.* She pulled down her jeans and sat down on the toilet seat. It took a few seconds for her to register what she was seeing. Blood.

No. Not again.

She grabbed the counter to steady herself.

"Jack," she yelled.

He came immediately.

"I think I'm losing the baby."

CHAPTER TWENTY-THREE

Crosby glanced down at the alert on his phone and saw the tweet from Hamilton. He pressed the intercom for his secretary. "Get me Winters."

She buzzed back and let him know he was holding.

Crosby picked up the phone again. "We need to change the lineup on *Behind Closed Doors* Friday night. Slot in the episode of the family with the disabled kids." He clicked off.

Crosby Wheeler took a sip of his water and waited for the video to load.

* * *

Red letters slowly appeared on his computer monitor until the title of the show filled the screen—*Radical Reality: Regrets, Recriminations, and Reflections.*

The camera zooms in on a stark-white kitchen with bare counters. A harried-looking woman stares at the camera, runs a hand through disheveled hair, and begins to speak in the voice of one battle weary and defeated.

"It's Friday morning, but it could be any morning. One day dissolves into the next, the same as the one before, our one and only goal to make it through until we have the blessed reprieve of sleep. I'm Monica. Welcome to my personal hell."

The camera follows her into the living room, where two children, somewhere between eight and nine, sit, strapped into their individual wheelchairs, heads tilted, eyes unseeing, drool running from their mouths.

Monica ignores her daughters and sits down on the worn-out sofa, sinks back and closes her eyes. The sound of her footsteps has elicited a moan from one of the children. Monica opens her eyes and points to the girl nearest to her.

"Meet Cindy."

Cindy knocks her head back against the chair and moans again.

Monica rises and walks over to the child, pushes the hair from her forehead, and whispers, "It's all right. I'm here. Everything is okay. Shh."

A shrill yell interrupts her ministrations.

"That's Cindy's twin sister, Lydia. She doesn't like it when I talk to Cindy."

Lydia continues to scream.

Monica raises her voice in the direction of Lydia. "You have to wait your turn."

Finally, she gets up and goes to her other daughter, cupping Lydia's cheek with her hand, and Lydia lifts a hand and clumsily swats her mother's away. "Nah nah nah," she continues in a keening wail. Monica speaks reassuringly to her until she at last quiets down.

"How about listening to a nice television show while I get breakfast?" Monica forces a cheerful tone, then changes the channel to a cartoon. Looking at the camera, she whispers, "Follow me into the kitchen, and we can continue our conversation."

She begins to cut up fruits and vegetables for a smoothie she will make for her girls, explaining they have a hard time chewing. She sits at the table again, puts her head in her hands, and heaves a heavy sigh. "People tell me all the time that I'm a hero." She shakes her head. "I'm no hero. I had no idea of the kind of life I would have to lead to care for two seriously disabled children."

The woman holding the camera is an attractive woman in her fifties with warm, compassionate eyes. She reaches out to cover Monica's hand with her own. "Monica, I know this is terribly difficult for you. We so appreciate your giving us a glimpse into your life." She pauses and then continues. "Can you please share your story with our viewers?"

Monica wipes a tear from the corner of her eye.

"When the girls were in utero, everything looked fine. Their development was on track, and the ultrasounds showed two normal babies. Most people who meet them think that they were born prematurely, but that's not the case. It wasn't until they were born that it was discovered that they both suffer from a rare genetic anomaly. If the genetic testing had been done in utero, it would have been discovered before they were born and all this could have been avoided."

The interviewer looks shocked by the statement. "Are you saying that you wish they had never been born?"

Monica returns her stare without flinching. "I am saying that I wish they didn't have to have a life of suffering. They can't see. They will never walk or speak or have any semblance of a life. I don't know what they are thinking or feeling. All they do is sit in those chairs all day and scream and moan. Do you have any idea what it's like to change the diaper of a nine-year-old? To have to treat the diaper rash and painful sores that come from sitting in a wet diaper?"

"I am so sorry. Of course, I have no right to judge. Please go on."

Monica stands up and begins to pace. "What is going to happen to them when their father and I are gone? Who will take care of them then? All our money is tied up in caring for them now. We've spent a fortune making this house wheelchair accessible, so that we can take them out occasionally. And when we do...the stares...you wouldn't believe how cruel people can be."

The reporter shakes her head. "That's why it's so important for your story to be told so people can understand what it's like. We are so grateful to our sponsors for their support."

* * *

Crosby shut the laptop. The show was perfect. He just needed to check one more thing.

He buzzed his secretary again and told her to get the executive producer.

"Louis, how are you handling the legalities surrounding the mother on RRR show?" he asked once he had him on the phone.

"We have a disclaimer in the rolling credits stating that she is the stepmother. We were very careful with the dialogue, so that she never makes a claim that she was pregnant or is their birth mother."

"You've taken measures to ensure she won't abandon them in the middle of the season?"

"Yes, sir. Her contract is solid. She'd have to pay back all the money. But if for any reason she breaks it and leaves, we can use that to our advantage, show how this has devastated their marriage. By the time we reveal the entire story—that the mother died in childbirth and Monica is a latecomer to their care—it won't matter. Everyone will be invested in the story by then."

"Good." Crosby hung up.

He rose and, grabbing his cashmere blazer from the credenza, slipped it on as he walked out the door. "Call my driver and tell him I'm ready," he told his secretary without breaking stride, and inserted the key into his private elevator.

"Yes, sir. Before you go…"

He turned. "Yes?"

She tilted her head. "Would you like me to have dinner sent over for you and Mrs. Wheeler tonight?"

"No, Millicent. I'll cook it myself this evening."

He didn't miss the look of sympathy on her face. She said nothing—she knew what a private man he was. After ten years, they both knew no more about each other than they did on day one. She had never asked him what was wrong with his wife, knew only what he had told her—that she was confined to a wheelchair and under the daily care of nurses. She had tried to probe once, but he had cut her off. He wasn't blind to her attraction to him. Nor did he miss the looks that told him she'd be more than happy to fulfill any duties his wife was unable to. He made it very clear that a personal relationship was off-limits and that he was prepared to fire her if she didn't take the hint. She accepted her role and things remained professional between them.

"Good night," he said briskly and entered the elevator.

CHAPTER TWENTY-FOUR

The Institute, 1975

August

I am being held prisoner in a beautiful room high in the castle, like a princess in a fairy tale, alone and forgotten. Maroon velvet drapes with thick, gold sashes adorn the windows that reach to the floor. Murals of kings and their ladies watch me from the walls. My bed looks as though it was hand carved. The beauty in its detail would bring me joy if I were here under different circumstances.

He has left me alone for three weeks. The only contact I have is the cursory greeting from those who bring me my meals and take me to the gym for my exercise, and from the doctor, whom I assume will be following my pregnancy. I am a caged animal. He does allow me to keep a journal, and before I go to sleep at night, I pour my frustration out on to the page. I have no illusion of privacy, but do it nonetheless. I have missed a period. Still no scientific proof that I am pregnant, but I know that I am with child. My body feels different.

He comes into my room, and the very air changes. I can barely breathe. He gives me one of his cold smiles and sits in one of the velvet-cushioned chairs next to the ornate, wooden table.

"You seem calmer, Maya. Are you beginning to settle in?"

"What choice do I have?"

"What indeed? To set your expectations, I will tell you what lies ahead. You will stay here during the entirety of your pregnancy. If you do as you are told, you will earn some freedoms. For one, I will continue to provide you with paper and pen. Two, you will receive a menu and may choose your meals. Three, you may use my library—when escorted of course. When you have delivered my child, you will be set free."

"And if I don't cooperate?"

He frowns. "If you don't cooperate, you will find yourself very uncomfortable indeed. Needless to say, you will enjoy none of the aforementioned privileges, and you will be moved to a padded room where you will be restrained in order to keep the child safe."

"I'll cooperate," I lie.

"Wise choice, Maya. I will return tomorrow. I think you will be most interested to learn what awaits the child."

He leaves.

"Help me, God," I find myself saying aloud even though I have long ago given up any belief in a supreme being. I wish I still retained a kernel of that faith. But then, I reason, what good would faith do me now, and why, if there was a God, would he allow me to be imprisoned here? No. The only one I can count on is myself.

CHAPTER TWENTY-FIVE

The Institute, 1975
September

Another two weeks have passed. Every day, I tense in anxious anticipation when my door is opened, then fall back in blessed relief when it is not him. I was taken to see the doctor five days ago. This time I didn't bother to engage him. He drew my blood and gave me a pelvic exam.

I hear his footsteps, and I steel myself. The door opens, and he enters. His emerald eyes find mine, and I am unable to look away. His gaze holds mine hostage—I am immobilized. It sears me, that look, and I want to scream, to tell him to let go, but no words come. I muster all my strength and squeeze my eyes shut, hoping with everything that I have that I will open them to find it's all been a bad dream.

His laughter causes my eyes to fly open.

"Maya, Maya. A bit childish don't you think?"

He smiles that perfect smile, and I marvel again at the beauty of his features. How can someone so beautiful be so ugly?

"Please let me go. You don't need to do this."

He shakes his head. "I can't let you go. The rabbit died."

So, it's been confirmed, then.

I shiver and shake my head. I don't want his child inside of me. The violation is overwhelming, and I break out into a cold sweat. "There must have been any number of women who would have been willing to give you a child. Why me?"

He sits down on the leather chair across from where I sit.

"I chose you for a specific reason. Your family has something I want."

"What do you know of my family?" My heart skips a beat.

"Much."

His smug manner infuriates me. I want to reach out and scratch his face until it bleeds. I must know. Has he been following me? My parents and my sister? Are they safe?

"My family has nothing to do with this. What is your interest in them?" I demand.

A frown mars his face, and his voice is stern. "I am the one who will ask the questions. Have your parents ever mentioned any valuable treasures or relics they brought with them from Greece?"

My mind races. "I don't know what you're talking about."

He leans back and pours himself a glass of water from the crystal decanter seated on the tray on the table. Taking a long sip, he stares at me the entire time, then puts the glass down. I have to tear my gaze away from his again.

"Your parents grew up on the island of Patmos, and they left right after World War II."

How does he know this?

He continues. "Patmos is the island where Saint John lived for many years."

"So?" I say in a voice more rebellious than I feel.

"There were a great many religious relics hidden there. The Germans found most of them, except for…" He stands and turns his back to me, weighing, I think, whether or not to continue.

"That is all I will say for now," he finally says. "Think, Maya. Think about your family stories. What has been handed down. Try to remember so that I don't have to pay a visit to your parents and ask them." He lets the words sink in, then adds, "That would be an unfortunate turn of events for them."

I have no idea what he's getting at, but he has to leave my parents out of it. I try to get more information from him.

"Then tell me, if you are to be the father of my child. You know about my family. What about yours? Where is your family? Your parents?"

He seems to consider my question, looking off into the distance. He turns and takes a seat again.

"Do you want to know about my family? Do you suppose I have a loving family like you? What do you know about need? About cruelty? My father lived to be cruel. Should I tell you one of my childhood memories?"

He doesn't wait for my answer.

"I bet you had a birthday party every year, yes?"

I nod.

"Of course you did. Well, I never did. Except when I turned eight. He brought home a dog. A beautiful, fluffy white dog. I was too young to know it was a trick. I took care of that dog—fed it, walked it, cleaned up after it, made sure it was no trouble at all because I knew what he did to anything that caused him trouble. I came home late that day, ready to take him out. My teacher had wanted to see me after class. My father was waiting for me. Had the dog on the leash and was sneering at me and I knew it meant big trouble.

"'You're late boy,' he said. 'The dog wet in the house.'"

"I knew he was lying."

"'You know what that means dontcha?'"

"I ran for the leash, tried to wrest it from his hands, and he laughed." 'You scrawny punk. You think you can take this from me?' "He kicked me hard. Then he started kicking the dog."

"My screams filled the air, and the more I screamed, the more he laughed. I covered my ears to drown out the sound of my dog's cries. After an eternity, all was quiet again. I didn't want to look. But he made me."

"'Clean up this mess boy. Next time make sure you're on time. Poor dog would still be alive if you hadn't been late.'"

My blood runs cold as my imagination paints the horrific picture. I want to say something, but no words will come.

He arches an eyebrow, leans back in his chair, picks a non-existent piece of lint from his black turtleneck, and looks at me. "No words of wisdom for me?"

I feel sorry for him despite myself. I look at him, searching for any trace of that eight-year-old-boy. Sitting in front of me is a man who appears to be devoid of any vulnerability.

"That's so terrible. I'm —"

"Don't waste your pity on me, I have no need or desire of it. I tell you this so that you may understand my strength, what I have been through to become who I am today. My father paid for his abuse. After my worthless mother died choking on her own vomit, it was just him and me. But I was bigger by then. He couldn't hit me anymore. I towered over him. He could still make my life miserable, but not for long. Everything changed when I went to work for the only man in town worth his salt. He taught me everything that I needed to know, took me in like I was his son."

"Who?" I ask.

"You will meet him soon enough. He's the one who started it all. Would you like to see some of the work that's being done here? Work you would have been a part of if you didn't have a greater purpose?"

I can't tell if he's mocking me or not. Anything is better than sitting in this room with nothing to do but think.

"Yes."

"Come, then." He stands and beckons for me to follow. Before he opens the door, he stops and turns around.

"Don't think of trying anything stupid. Talk to no one. Just follow me."

I nod.

No one is in the hallway, and I follow him down the empty corridor until we reach a small elevator. He inserts a key, and the door opens. He waits for me to enter and then joins me in the small space, his breath so close that I want to hold mine to avoid breathing any air he has exhaled. Then I remember he has already contaminated me, and my stomach turns.

The elevator doors open, and I follow him again, this time to a room with a large window into a classroom with a two-way mirror from which we can watch those in the other room undetected. He sits down without a word, and I take the empty chair next to him.

The children are sitting in rows, both feet on the floor, hands folded, and eyes on the teacher at the front of the room. They are elementary-aged, maybe third or fourth grade. Their teacher is scowling at a student standing in front of her and holds the bunched-up fabric of his shirt in her hand. I want to go through the glass and pull him away from her. He looks terrified, and his small hands are bunched into fists.

"Can anyone tell me what Matthew has done wrong?" the teacher asks.

No one raises a hand.

She lets go of his shirt, then pushes him, and he falls to the floor. "He gave his answers to someone. That's what. Why is that wrong?"

A little girl holds up her hand. "Because it's cheating?" It comes out as a squeak.

The teacher walks over and puts her face inches from the child's. She mimics her. "Because it's cheating?" She yanks hard on the girl's pigtail. She straightens, then raises her voice. "No! Not because it's cheating. Anyone else?"

A few hands shoot up.

She points. "Malcolm, how about you?"

"Because he got caught?"

"Exactly. Good job." She hands Malcolm a candy bar.

"Only stupid, careless children get caught. Sometimes in life, cheating is necessary. But if you're going to break the rules, you make sure to cover your tracks." She walks back over to Matthew. "Get up. Go back to your seat and don't ever let me catch you again." She turns to the class. "What is the cardinal rule?"

"Don't get caught," they answer in unison.

"Very good. Now it's time for musical chairs. No lunch for the loser."

"What is this? Why is she so horrible to the children?" Outrage has turned my voice shrill, and my face is hot.

He sneers at me. "What you see as horrible, I see as necessary. These children don't need coddling. They are going to be extraordinary leaders one day. They need to learn life's lessons early."

"What lessons? That adults have the right to abuse children? That lying and cheating is good? I would have never agreed to be a part of any of this."

He shakes his head. "This wasn't part of your training. I show you this to give you a complete picture of the empire my child will one day inherit. These children are lucky. Where else would a group of orphans have the opportunity to be educated by the brilliant minds here at the Institute? And what other orphans are being molded into adults who will have impeccable pedigrees and be groomed for positions of untold wealth and power? But first they need discipline and direction."

"Where did they come from?"

He laughs. "They are brought to me. They are throwaways, disposed of by irresponsible garbage not fit to be called parents. Without us, they would be nothing. One day, these children will be judges, politicians, business magnates."

I see where he is going with this. "And you will pull their puppet strings."

"The others coming through here, others like you, we recruit from the top universities. They are all vetted and solidly indoctrinated before they reach this advanced phase of the program. But there is something to be said for getting them while they're young."

He stands. "Just think how much more my own flesh and blood will be capable of."

I cannot speak. Images flood my mind of my child being raised in this hellhole, and I gasp for breath and double over. The prospect is unbearable. I must find a way to escape. Surely even death is preferable to the fate that awaits my child.

CHAPTER TWENTY-SIX

Jack saw Taylor to the bedroom and got her settled under the covers.

"Has it stopped?"

"I think so."

"Good. Lie on your left side. Hopefully you're only spotting. We're going to have to lay low for a few days. You should stay off your feet."

She stared at him. "Since when did you go to medical school?"

He looked at the floor. "Dakota started spotting in her third month, but it passed." He cleared his throat. "I'll let you get some rest. I'll be in the next room. Yell if you need anything."

She closed her eyes. Hearing Dakota's name, it all came rushing back. She recalled the day she found out that Jack had betrayed her. Evelyn had been waiting for her when she got home that day for school break. She'd given Taylor a long hug.

"How was the traffic?"

"Easy drive. No problem. Dad home?"

"Not yet. Let's go into the kitchen. I'll make some tea."

She patted Taylor on the shoulder when they got to the kitchen. "Taylor, sit down. I have something to tell you."

"What's wrong? Is my father okay?"

"Yes, it's something else. Sit." She took a deep breath.

Taylor pulled out the chair and sat down—and waited.

"It's about Jack," Evelyn finally said.

"What about him?" Taylor asked in a shaking voice.

"There's no easy way to say it. He got married."

Taylor shot up from her seat. "What? What are you talking about? What do you mean he got married?" She could barely speak. "We're supposed to get together this weekend."

Evelyn answered with exaggerated calmness. "I know it's a terrible shock. His mother is very upset as well. She got the call last night. He met her last month apparently. They ran off to Las Vegas and eloped. I'm so sorry, Taylor."

Taylor ran into the bathroom and slammed the door shut. Sinking to her knees, she vomited in the toilet. Sweat broke out on her face, and falling back against the wall, she hugged herself, and wailed. How could this have happened? *Jack, oh Jack, how could you do this?* She stayed that way for a long time.

Eventually, she found the strength to stand up, and when she did, she ran from the house and got into her car, with no idea of where she was going; she needed to move. In a haze, she drove down Connecticut Avenue, her thoughts racing as she tried to make sense of it. This wasn't just some random boyfriend—this was Jack. He knew everything about her and loved her anyway—or so she had thought. They had nursed each other through all of life's bumps, knew all the family skeletons, commiserated over every challenge, every rejection, every hardship. How could he do this to her? And who was the woman? His wife! It was impossible. She would go to New York and confront him. He owed her an explanation at least.

She didn't know how fast she was going, but before she knew it, she was in front of his apartment building. His Mustang was there. She ran up the three flights and pounded on the door, her face hot, her heart hammering. The door opened and a creature with flame-red hair and icy-blue eyes stood there, coolly appraising her.

"Can I help you?" Her voice was husky.

"Where's Jack?"

She arched a perfectly shaped brow. "And who are you?"

Taylor pushed her way into the apartment. "I'm his girlfriend. Jack!" she yelled.

The woman's manner was infuriatingly calm. "He can't hear you, Taylor." She drew her name out, mocking her. "My *husband* is in the shower."

Taylor spun around and glared at her. Suddenly, she couldn't breathe, and the room began to spin. She put a hand on the wall to steady herself while the woman continued to stare at her.

"I think you'd better leave."

Taylor ran past her without another word, got in her car, and gunned it. She cried the whole way back to BU.

The rest of the semester was torture. Visions of Jack with Dakota taunted her every waking hour. She imagined them in bed. Her hands everywhere Taylor's should be. His lips on her mouth; their bodies intertwined. It was unbearable. The worst betrayal of all was that he hadn't even told her himself, just discarded her like a broken toy, unwanted and forgotten. It was beyond her comprehension. She tried to throw herself into her studies, but concentration eluded her, and she failed all her courses. When she returned home for summer break her father was furious. The confrontation took her by surprise. She had never seen him so angry.

He stood in the marble foyer, waiting for her to come inside. In his hands was a letter.

"What were you thinking? Did you even attend one class? Do you realize you've put your entire future in jeopardy?"

She couldn't take her eyes off the vein throbbing in his forehead. Mumbling a quiet, "I'm sorry," she tried to walk past him.

He stepped in front of her, blocking her. "Not so fast, young lady. I'm not finished. Come in to my study. We are going to talk about this."

She walked behind him, with her head down, and slunk into the chair across from his desk.

"Taylor, look at me."

She lifted her head.

"One more semester! One more and you let yourself go from dean's list to this." His voice rose with each word. He threw the paper on the desk.

"I tried, Dad. I did the best I could. All I did was study."

"Thirty thousand dollars! I may as well have thrown it in the trash."

Taylor's eyes filled, and she turned her head.

His tone softened. "Taylor, listen to me. I'm sorry you're hurt, and I wish I could make it all better." His brows knit together in a scowl and he stood up. "Frankly, I'd like to kill him!" He slammed a fist onto the desk, and Taylor jumped. He walked over to her and put a hand on her shoulder, lifting her chin with his other hand so she would meet his eyes. His finger traced the hollow of her cheek.

"You've lost so much weight. My dear, you have to move on. Jack has his own life and you need to make yours too. I've spoken to the dean and he's willing to let you come back next semester."

"I don't—"

"Stop. You will go back and by the fall you'll be ready."

"What if I can't do it?" She felt like she'd never be herself again.

He pursed his lips. "You will." He looked up at a noise at the door, and Evelyn came in holding a brochure.

"Here." She pushed it into Taylor's hand. "Your father and I were thinking that a nice trip to Europe would do you a world of good. You can go to Italy, Spain, and then spend a month in Greece, on your mother's island. Ikaria? Isn't that it?"

At the mention of her mother, a fresh wave of grief enveloped her.

She handed the brochure back to Evelyn. "Thanks, but I don't think a trip to Europe is what I need."

The next day she paid a visit to her old parish priest. She hadn't seen him since her mother's funeral, but he greeted her warmly, as if no time had passed.

"So wonderful to see you, Theophaneli." She hadn't been called that since her mother died.

She swallowed the lump in her throat as they hugged. He motioned for her to sit on the love-seat in his office, and he took a seat facing her.

"I guess you're wondering why I'm here after all this time."

Suddenly, she felt awkward and second-guessed her decision to come.

He raised his eyebrows and stroked his beard. "Why *are* you here?"

"Because everything's a mess, and I don't know what to do." She began to cry.

"It's okay, *pethi mou*, let it out," he said, handing her a box of tissues.

"It's the only place I could think to come." Her lip trembled. "I miss her so much, Father."

"She would be happy that you came here. She would tell you to turn to God."

She felt the bite of anger rising in her. "Where was God when she was being raped and murdered?"

"Theophaneli, these are questions we wrestle with on this side of heaven. I don't know why she had to suffer that way, but God did not abandon her. He was with her. We aren't puppets. He gave us free will and that is a double-edged sword that the human race has been contending with since the fall of Adam and Eve."

She was only half listening. She had heard it all before. Man's fall. God's grace. Good and evil co-existing in this hell we call earth. She didn't like who she became when she contemplated such things, hated the cynicism that wound its way up from her core until she was thinking and saying things that sounded like someone else. She preferred to keep a lid on those feelings. So, what *was* she doing here? She sighed. She was trying to get close to her mother the only way she knew how. Her mother had loved this church, spent countless Sundays worshipping, and nights and weekends on committees to raise money for the various charities the church supported.

"Father, I was wondering if the foundation my mother started to support SOS Children's Village has already taken its annual trip to Greece."

Taylor had gone there with her mother when she was ten. She still recalled her excited chatter on the plane. Her mother had warned her that this was not their usual vacation to Greece, had tried to prepare her for what they were in store for. She had been shocked to learn that there were so many children with no parents or family to look out for them. That was the summer she grew up and was awakened to the world outside their privileged enclave in Chevy Chase. She had wanted to bring all her new friends home with her, share her things with them. She and her mother had spent eight weeks there. From that point forward, Taylor had earmarked half of her allowance to send to the children without families in Greece.

Father Ted shook his head. "Not yet. As a matter of fact, there's a meeting Tuesday night to finalize the group. Why do you ask?"

She knew what she had to do. "Because I want to go too. Is there room?"

He smiled.

"Of course, *pethi mou*. We would love to have you."

Taylor opened her eyes and took long, deep breaths. She would not lose this baby. No matter what Malcolm had done or what was waiting for them when they found Jeremy, she would protect this child.

Beau approached the bed whining softly, and rested his head on Taylor's stomach. She stroked his silky head. He looked up at her adoringly, his luminous, brown eyes on her. He was her golden child, and she loved him without reservation. If only he were enough. Beau stretched out on the hardwood floor next to the bed to take up his watch over her and her unborn child. She closed her eyes and waited for the blessed escape of sleep.

* * *

Evening had fallen and Taylor dozed on. Jack's nerves were frayed— he had to do something. There was no way he would be responsible for another baby dying. He had to get her checked out before they hit the road again. *Think, think.* He flipped open the burner cell and punched in the eleven numbers. It was answered on the first ring.

"Hit it."

"It's Logan. Thanks for the set up."

"What's up?"

"I need a doc—obstetrician. Can you send someone ASAP?"

There was a brief silence. "Soonest will be tomorrow. I'll see who I can find in the area."

"Thanks." Jack hung up and went in to the bedroom to check on Taylor.

Her eyes fluttered open at the sound of his footsteps. "What am I going to do?"

"We're going to get you looked at to make sure everything is okay. I've called a buddy about getting a doctor here. He'll be here tomorrow. In the meantime, you need to stay off your feet."

"Can you feed Beau and take him out?"

"Of course." He squatted to the dog's level. "Come here buddy." Beau was so reluctant to leave Taylor's side, she had to coax him to go with Jack.

"It's okay. Go ahead," she said.

The golden retriever ambled over to Jack and looked back at Taylor.

Jack smiled. "Good boy. Let's let your mom get some rest, and you and I will take care of business."

After Beau finished, Jack grabbed a Coors from the refrigerator and sat down. If it weren't for the fact that they were on the run, this could be a nice little slice of domesticity. How great it would be if they were here on a little get-away, if he hadn't screwed everything up.

He downed a couple more beers while sitting and remembering, and finally, when his thoughts started turning maudlin, he switched off the lamp and got up.

"Let's go check on her," he said to Beau and tiptoed into the bedroom. The light from the hallway was bright enough for him to see that she looked like she was sleeping. He was about to turn and go to his room when she spoke.

"What time is it?"

"Almost ten. Sorry if I woke you."

"You didn't. I've been lying here for a while, just worrying."

He didn't know what to say and finally came up with, "You should probably try to rest."

She flicked on the lamp on the nightstand and sat up, propping a pillow behind her. "Can you sit with me for a little?"

He sat down in the chair by the bed before she could change her mind.

"I've been thinking about this baby, wondering how I'm going to keep it safe. I always thought that was a simple thing, you know, that the hard part was getting here, after all the treatments and disappointments, that once I was pregnant, the hardest part was done."

"It's going to be okay. The baby's going to be fine." A meaningless platitude. He didn't have anything else to offer.

She shook her head. "I'm not even talking about this." She gestured around the room. "I mean, just, in general. I was so busy trying to get pregnant, I never thought about the fact that this little life would be looking to me for all the answers. Poor thing."

"Poor nothing. That baby couldn't have a better mother. I've never known anyone as fiercely loyal to those she loves as you."

She shrugged. "Will it be enough? Will *I* be enough?"

He wanted to tell her that she didn't have to be, that he'd be with her to help her if she let him. Instead, he said simply, "You will be plenty."

She closed her eyes and yawned.

"I'll let you get some sleep," he whispered.

Without opening her eyes, she said, "Would you mind staying until I do?"

He'd do her one better. He'd sit in that chair all night and make sure nothing came near her or her baby.

CHAPTER TWENTY-SEVEN

The Institute, 1975
September

I have learned more about his upbringing, of the mother who did nothing to protect him from a father who delighted in tormenting and abusing him. Things changed when he turned fourteen.

He sits expressionless and tells his story. "My father couldn't keep a steady job. He worked odd jobs for the other families until they fired him for showing up drunk and belligerent. So he found a job for me, told me it was time I pulled my own weight. There was a man everyone knew only as 'the cripple in the big house'. He had plenty of live-in help, but he was looking for a companion, someone young to play chess with, to entertain him. The rest of the boys in the town were cretins, too busy drinking beer and driving around in their ridiculous jacked-up pickup trucks. Even though I was worthless in my father's eyes, he couldn't deny my intelligence. It was his one source of pride. He offered me up to the man as a sacrificial lamb. It was a Saturday.

"'Come here boy. I done got you some work.'"

"'Where?'"

"'Workin for the cripple up on the hill.'"

"'I hear he's a pervert.'"

"My father lifted his shirt and scratched his skinny belly.

"*'So what if he is? What's he gonna do, chase you? He's in a chair for crying out loud. So, if wants to cop a little feel, let him. What's the difference? You sure as hell ain't getting any action from the girls, ugly as you are.'*"

"*'I won't do it.'*"

"He took a long pull from his cigarette. The next thing I knew; the hot end was on my cheek. I jumped and put my hand up to my stinging flesh. That's when I made up my mind. I would figure out a way to get rid of him forever."

So, that's where he got the small scar. His hand goes to his cheek and he unconsciously rubs it. He is on his feet and has a faraway look in his eyes I haven't seen before.

"That is all for today."

"Wait," I whisper.

He looks at me, and the faraway look fades. In its place is hatred, the fierceness of which terrifies me.

I force myself to speak despite the pounding of my heart warning me of my folly. "Your father used his power to control you, and you hated him for it. Don't you see that you're doing the same thing to me?"

He stares at me and says nothing for a full minute. Finally, he speaks. "I am disappointed in you. Did you think such a transparent attempt at pop psychology would work? I won't even dignify that with a response." He shakes his head.

"I'm just saying—"

He puts a hand up to silence me. "You're trying to analyze me. It won't work. I have a purpose, and it won't be thwarted. A shame, really, that your education had to be cut short. You could have been a part of the work here, but at least your contribution will live on. Come, I'll let you have a look at how the training progresses."

We sit in another of his screening rooms. There are ten beds in a row, all with white sheets and wool blankets. Next to each is an IV stand with a liquid-filled bag. My stomach tightens as my imagination goes wild imagining what is in those bags. Dr. Strombill walks in, followed by a number of students from my fellowship group, as well as some students I've never seen before. They stand around the perimeter of the room and listen to him as he begins. He holds a stopwatch.

"Are they a new group?" I ask.

"They are recent law graduates, here for a special training program."

I am about to ask him more when Dr. Strombill speaks.

"It is all well and good to watch films and have discussions on the merits of euthanasia." He stops for emphasis. "But it is quite a different thing to experience the agony of disease as well as to make the difficult decision to end a life."

My leg twitches, as if it knows before I do, that something terrible is about to happen. He begins to speak again. "In a few moments we will begin the experience. Medical students, please take a paper from the bowl on the left."

I see Brian dip his hand in and pull out a small piece of paper. I wonder what it says. Dr. Strombill moves to the middle of the room and addresses them.

"Find the person who goes with the name on your paper. That will be your patient. Lead him or her to a bed and have them lie down."

He waits until they have all taken their places.

"You can now insert the IVs into your patients."

Brian raises a tentative hand. "May I ask what is in them?"

Dr. Strombill's bushy eyebrows shoot up. "You may indeed. It is diazepam. It will counter the effects of the strychnine, so that we won't lose our patients. It will not eliminate the pain or convulsions, but it will keep them alive."

I gasp. In Brian's eyes, I see the horror I'm feeling mirrored. It is very likely that they *will* lose some of the patients. I know what the law students do not—strychnine attacks the nervous system, and most people die of asphyxiation, but only after all their muscles spasm and contract into tight balls. The pain will be horrific. I begin to hate Dr. Strombill now, this man whom I have idolized. I turn to Damon.

"How can you allow this? It's inhumane."

"Ah, Maya, you are upset." His voice is soothing, and he puts a hand on my arm. "My dear, sometimes drastic measures are required to pave the way for the greater good. The patients here are the future lawmakers, judges, and politicians. They must experience the agony and pain we subject people to when we refuse to allow a way out of their suffering."

I shake my head and pull my arm from him.

"You're crazy. You don't have to inflict pain on someone for them to have empathy. Not everyone is a cold, non-feeling monster like you."

"Quiet. You're missing it." He points toward the window.

Dr. Strombill resumes his instructions. "Doctors, you will administer the drug on my cue." He holds up a small cup containing the powder to be swallowed. "The onset of pain will be sudden and will continue for the next thirty-six hours, when you will be carefully monitored. There will be no relief for you unless you ask for euthanasia, in which case, you will be given morphine for the pain until the poison is out of your system. If you do not opt for euthanasia, you will be given no pain killer."

One of the law students raises his hand.

"I don't mean to be impertinent, but why would anyone not ask for euthanasia if it's just an experiment and would end the pain sooner?" His Southern accent is strong. He smirks and looks around at his fellow students as if he's just solved the riddle of the enigma.

Dr. Strombill purses his full lips. "Because, Mr. Hamilton, five percent of the dosage pumps will give you enough morphine to stop your heart entirely."

They all stare at him.

Dr. Strombill sighs. "In other words, you might actually be euthanized. We will see who can live with the pain and who can not. It is time."

Brian hands his patient the cup. The woman's face is ashen, and she has wrapped her arms tightly around herself. Brian looks down at the floor, avoiding meeting her eyes, but I can see the terror in them.

He tears open the alcohol patch and rubs it on her arm. He finds a vein and inserts the catheter.

Dr. Strombill clicks the stop watch. The room is silent, and the air is thick with anticipation. The red hand on the stopwatch dances in circles, ticking off the minutes. A cry stabs through the silence. A second scream, then a third, and soon there is nothing but the agonizing sound of human misery. Then the twitching begins. Arms and legs jerk into the air in a grotesque ballet. I want to shut my eyes and cover my ears to drown it out. I sit helpless, watching as the poison progresses, and I cannot tear my eyes away as the men and women in the beds jackknife into contorted poses of agony.

My face is wet with tears. There is no decency in Damon—his father has killed it. What might he have been in different circumstances? If, instead of abusing and torturing the little boy he once was, someone had loved and nurtured him? I think of the baby growing inside me and am filled with an intense agony I have never experienced before. What lies in store for him or her? Will my child become as consumed with evil as Damon? I cannot contemplate the possibility that my child will grow up to be like its father. *Dear God, help me. Help my child*, I pray silently. *Don't abandon us to this insanity.* Does God hear me? Or am I praying into a void?

Chapter Twenty-Eight

The Institute, 1975
September

"Take me back to my room. I can't watch anymore." Bile rises in my throat, and I put my hand up to my mouth reflexively.

He gives me a look of pure disgust. "I'm disappointed in you, Maya. You're not the scientist I thought."

"That's not science," I say.

I shudder to imagine what other experiments are being conducted here. What astounds me is the fact that no one in the room raised an objection. Not one person refused to participate in that horror show he calls science. Surely I would have been different, would have walked away. Wouldn't I?

He is silent as we walk down the hallway to the elevator. I feel as though I've aged years in an hour. My heart is heavy, and I find it difficult to take a breath. When we reach my room, he doesn't follow me in, and I'm relieved to hear the click of the door behind me. I fall onto my bed and close my eyes, but the images haunt me. I can't erase the picture of those men and women in agony. I clutch a pillow to my chest and let go, crying until I have no tears left, my body wracked with sobs.

Hours later, I refuse the tray of dinner brought to me—the nausea returns when I take one whiff of the beef stew. I think of our conversation about my parents, and I wonder again at what Damon meant when he asked if I knew of any treasure from Greece. I try to remember anything, the stories my mother told of those days on the island, but there is nothing about a treasure. Maybe it's all a misunderstanding. I cannot bear to think of him going near my mama and papa.

I hear footsteps and brace myself. The door opens and he walks in, carrying my tray.

"You have to eat, Maya. The baby needs the nutrition."

"How do you expect me to eat when everything you do and say makes me sick?"

A flash of anger crosses his face. "This is not open for debate."

I get up from the bed and face him.

"I don't like red meat. I've told you that before. You can force me to stay here, but you cannot force me to eat."

He arches one eyebrow. "The iron is necessary for you and the baby. Maybe I can't force you to eat. But I *can* have you restrained to a bed and hook you up to an IV."

I see red. Before I can stop myself, I rush toward him and rake his face with my nails. I feel something wet and am gratified to see it is his blood. His hand goes to his cheek and he looks at his fingers as he pulls it away again. He grabs both of my wrists and holds them tight while I struggle to free myself. I want to hurt him more.

He speaks, and the calmness of his voice chills me. "It's good to see you have a strong will. I made the right genetic choice for my child."

He still holds my wrists, and they begin to ache. I take a deep breath, trying to calm myself, as reason returns. "Please let go."

He studies me for a moment. "If you ever strike me again, I will have your hands amputated."

It is then that I vomit all over him.

CHAPTER TWENTY-NINE

Jack was jittery. He hadn't slept well, had worried through the night that Taylor might take a turn for the worse. Every time he started to doze off in the chair, he'd hear a sound escape her, and he'd startle awake, afraid she was losing the baby. She was awake now, and had agreed with Jack that she should stay off her feet until the doctor examined her. He glanced at his watch. A little after noon. *When was he going to arrive?* He decided he may as well do something productive while he was waiting, so he took a seat at the kitchen table and studied the map Phillips had left for them. A knock at the door made him jump. He was pretty sure it was the doc, but just in case, he grabbed his SIG and held it behind his back when he went to the door.

"Who's there?"

"The doctor you ordered."

Jack relaxed, tucked the gun behind the small of his back, between his jeans and shirt, and opened the door. The man had to lower his head to get through the doorway.

Jack gave him a quick once over. His blood ran cold when he realized the man didn't carry a doctor's bag.

"Who are you?" Jack asked. The man lunged toward him. Jack realized he'd made a mistake, and went for the gun but the man was quicker. He pulled Jack to him, wrapped his arm around Jack and pressed a knife against his neck.

"Where is he hiding?" he asked.

"Who?" Jack asked, playing dumb.

The man tightened his grip. "Don't play games with me Logan. You know damn well who. Where is Jeremy?"

Jack could barely speak with the vise-like arm compressing his throat. He had to think. If he gave him nothing, he and Taylor would both be dead. *Think. Who was this and who did he work for?* Had Craig double-crossed him? No way. Jack held his hand out in surrender, and the man let go.

Jack coughed and tried to regain his voice.

"Have an idea. Don't know exactly," he croaked out.

"Tell me what you know," he demanded.

Jack coughed again, stalling. Then he saw Beau peeking out from the bedroom from the corner of his eye.

"Give me a second. I'll get you what I have." Jack quickly assessed his surroundings, ready to grab the fork from the table when he heard a deep growl. Beau flew from the next room toward the man's neck in a single lunge. The intruder toppled over immediately, and the knife fell from his hands to the floor. Jack didn't hesitate. He grabbed the gun from under his shirt, and fired. He needed only one shot.

"Good boy!" He hugged the dog with relief.

Taylor rushed in. "What's going on?"

Jack looked from Taylor back to the dead man, splayed on his back just feet away.

"That's not the doctor, is it?" she whispered.

"No. Unfortunately no doctor's coming. Somebody double-crossed my friend. We've got to get out of here."

"What are we going to do with him?" If she was shocked by the sight of a dead man lying there, she didn't show it.

"Leave him. You're in no shape to lift him, and I can't do it alone." Jack had a feeling that his friend Craig would never be coming to the cabin again. He felt sick, knowing that by reaching out to him, he was responsible for his friend's death. But there was no time to think about it now.

"Throw your stuff into a bag and let's go."

Fifteen minutes later, they were in the truck driving down the dirt road away from the cabin. Taylor turned around just in time to see the lights go back on.

CHAPTER THIRTY

The Institute, 1975
October

I have just finished my breakfast—bacon, eggs, and toast. I force myself to eat despite the fact that I feel like my appetite will never return. I am tired all the time, and my breasts are sore.

The door opens, and he comes in.

"It's a beautiful day outside. Why don't we take a walk?"

I jump at the chance to leave these four walls, even if it's with him.

He picks up one of the sweaters that he's provided. "Better bring this along. I don't want you catching a chill."

I bristle at his solicitous comments and the charade of civility he affects. I grab the sweater without a thank you and follow him out the door and down the hallway. I can see from the windows that the sun is shining and for a moment my heart lifts. I've missed being outside, seeing the sky and the feeling of infiniteness surrounding me, instead of the confinement of my room. We go down in the elevator and emerge on the ground floor. People are coming and going, but no one pays attention to me, and everyone looks away from him deferentially. He opens the iron door, and I walk outside and feel the cool breeze kiss my face. I want to run and never stop. The leaves are beginning to turn, and I pick a fallen maple leaf from the grass. It is bright orange, and it makes me want to cry. Everything around me is a symphony of color, and the beauty overwhelms me. My isolation has made me forget what a beautiful world it is.

We walk down a cleared path that leads to a large pond at least two miles in diameter. A paved walking trail encircles it, and I wonder if it's used by the students in phase two. This morning we are the only ones walking.

He begins to speak, and I brace myself for another tale from his childhood.

"The best thing that ever happened to me was meeting Friedrich. He was a genius. He taught me how to play chess, what books to read, how to understand what was important and what was not."

I say nothing and file the information away, categorizing it, analyzing it, in case it can be useful to me later.

"When I was fifteen, we made the plan. It was time for me to go and live with him. Late one night, after my father had finished his bottle of bourbon, I lit the match that would burn that ramshackle hovel to the ground. I barricaded his bedroom door shut. I superglued the windows so he couldn't push them open and let the smoke out. Thanks to his paranoia, he'd had bars put on them years before, so there was no way he could climb out. Then, I stayed outside and listened for his screams. What music they were to my ears. I knocked on the window. He turned and looked at me, wide-eyed and crazed. 'Help me, you worthless punk,' he said, and I raised my middle finger, smiled and watched as the flames licked at his filthy pajamas. He cursed me as the fire engulfed him. Once I knew he was beyond saving, I left. They never connected me to it. The house had burned to nothing, and they assumed it was an accidental fire."

"Wasn't there an investigation? Didn't they look for you?"

He sneers. "We were trash. Dirt poor, lowest on the rung in a Podunk town with crooked cops and small-minded people."

"Didn't anyone see you living in the house on the hill?"

He waves his hand dismissively. "Are you being deliberately

obtuse? The point of the story has nothing to do with how I escaped. But I'll satisfy your curiosity. We moved."

I shiver in spite of myself and avert my eyes. I can't deny that I am glad he escaped from his father, but it shocks me that I'm not more horrified that he did this. He has drawn me into his past, and I feel myself rooting for his escape, angry at this abusive monster that has so warped him. But even as the thought crosses my mind, it occurs to me that he will never escape his father. And then I shudder when I consider the fact that he was able to stand, watching and unmoved to mercy knowing his father was inside burning. What hope do I dare have if he was capable of such an act when he was still a child? His father has turned him into a sadistic murderer. Could he have been saved if Friedrich had been different?

We walk in silence for the rest of the time, and I am surprised by how tired I am. When we return to my room, I thank him, but only because I hope that we will do this again.

He turns to leave when I ask, "Why was Friedrich in a wheelchair?"

He turns back and answers. "He was diagnosed with Parkinson's disease after the war, when he was in his sixties. Only a few years before I met him, but by then it had progressed aggressively."

"Did they try Levodopa?"

"Yes, of course. It worked for a while, then stopped. They classified him as a non-responder."

"Is he still alive?"

His lips part in a smile. "Why don't you see for yourself?" He looks above my head, to somewhere on the wall, and nods. I follow his line of sight and squint. It is then that I see it—a small hole. My face is hot, and I glare at him.

"You've been spying on me all this time?" The fact that someone has been watching while I take my clothes off, sleep, talk to myself—it's unthinkable. "Have you enjoyed seeing me naked, you pervert?"

He laughs again. "I'm no pervert, Maya. No one cares about seeing your body, especially as it grows fat. We're just making sure you don't try and hurt yourself or the baby."

The blood rushes to my head, and I turn away from him and walk to the window so he can't see the tears running down my face.

Ten minutes later, the door opens, and I turn around. Steel-blue eyes lock with mine. The white hair is receding and reveals a still-smooth forehead for a man who looks like someone's grandfather. His features are unremarkable; in fact, he is rather benign looking. His thin lips are a straight line, and he looks at me as if he knows me. When he crosses the threshold, I see he holds a cane in his left hand. It is a struggle for him to walk.

Damon runs to him, placing a hand on his back and helping him to a chair.

"Father, can I get you some water?"

He waves him off, impatient with the fussing, and lands with a thud in the chair.

"Hello, Maya. It is a pleasure to finally make your acquaintance."

The German accent is thick. "You're Friedrich?" I ask.

A look of disdain appears, and he looks up at Damon, shaking his head.

"The youth today—no respect." His eyes settle on me. "You must call me Dr. Dunst."

He spits the words at me, and I recoil. I see it now—the same predatory look that Damon has. They may not be related by blood, but they are the same. He looks at me, expectantly, and I say nothing, watching the fury build in his eyes.

He leans back in the chair, pulls a silver case from his suit pocket, and extracts a cigarette. His hand shakes as he fumbles trying to ignite his lighter. After several failed attempts, it spits out a flame. Dunst takes a long pull and blows smoke rings. I cannot stop looking at his mouth making the small *o's*. He holds the cigarette in the air, and my eyes are drawn to a purplish discoloration on his skin. Damon sets an ashtray on the table next to him.

"I have met your parents."

My heart skips a beat. "When?"

He arches a white eyebrow. "Before you were born. It's been almost thirty years. Back when I was stationed on their island."

"During World War II?" I ask.

"When else?"

It dawns on me with sickening certainty that this man before me must be a Nazi. Can this very ordinary, frail, old man be one of the legion of fiends responsible for the anguish and slaughter of millions?

"You are a Nazi?" I whisper.

He looks at me as if I were a cockroach under his foot. "I am an American citizen, a respected scientist. Your country says so." He laughs.

"But you were part of the Nazi regime that occupied my parents' island?" I know it is true, but I need to hear it from his lips.

He shrugs. "I was not there on holiday." He pulls a bottle of eye drops from his pocket, leans his head back, and squirts two drops into each eye. A thought occurs to me, and I continue to watch him.

Damon moves a chair next to his and sits.

"Did your mother talk about bringing something of value with her to America? Of hiding a treasure?" Dunst asks.

Again, I search my mind for any memory, but I still remember nothing. I shake my head.

"She never talked about some coins, silver pieces?" he persists.

They are both staring at me with an intensity that makes my skin crawl.

"My mother doesn't like to talk about those days. The occupation was hard on them. The Germans"—I give Dunst a pointed look—"were cruel. They took whatever they wanted with no regard to anyone or their feelings. Everyone was starving while they ate like pigs and—"

"Quiet." Damon's command slices through the air, and I feel the anger emanating from him. Dunst seems unaffected by my outburst. I suppose he is used to the hatred of others.

Dunst sneers at Damon. "Don't waste your energy. Her opinion matters not." Then he leans forward and enunciates very slowly. "Think hard, Maya. Try to remember where your mother might have put them."

"Why are these coins so important? What are they?"

Neither of them answers.

"How do you expect me to tell you anything if I don't know what they are?" This provokes a reaction. I am lying, though. I have no knowledge of anything at all related to treasures or silver from Greece. But I want to know what they are so desperate to find.

They exchange another look, and Dunst nods his head so slightly I wouldn't have seen it if hadn't been looking.

Damon turns to me and says, "The thirty silver pieces Judas received for betraying Jesus."

CHAPTER THIRTY-ONE

Taylor grabbed Jack's arm. "Someone's back at the cabin!"

Jack swore. He had to gather his thoughts. So, the man hadn't come alone. If Jack hadn't realized right away that he wasn't legit, the man likely would have continued with the charade until he found the map and instructions. Then he would have killed them both.

"He must have had a partner. They're going to make it look like I'm a killer."

She gasped. "What?"

Jack looked at her.

"My fingerprints are all over that cabin and so are yours. I think I was set up." He hit his hand hard on the steering wheel. "I don't understand how they found us. It's my friend Craig's cabin, and he's the only person I talked to. He's the one I told you about, the ex-military guy I worked with in Colombia."

"If Malcolm knew about the cabin, maybe whoever's after us did too."

Jack bit his lip. "Maybe. But the guy said he was the doctor. So somehow he knew about the conversation I had with Craig."

"Could Craig's phone have been tapped?"

"Doubtful. It's a burner. And no one could have traced the call—we didn't talk long enough."

He had a sinking feeling he knew what had happened. "I think they were there when I called Craig. Whoever we're up against must have one massive intelligence network. If they've investigated my

117

background, they'd know Craig and I worked together in Colombia. They must have gotten to him, made him pretend to agree to send someone, and then killed him once we hung up."

"How are we going to fight against someone so ruthless? Who are these people?"

"I wish I knew. Damn it! Craig didn't deserve this. We can't reach out to anyone, Taylor. Not your Dad. None of my friends. I can't be responsible for putting anyone else in harm's way."

They had even less time now. By tomorrow morning Jack's face would be all over every news station, every paper, every media outlet. He might even make the FBI top ten. If they arrested him, Taylor would be on her own—an easy target. His thoughts turned back to Taylor.

"How are you feeling? Any more spotting?" he asked, worry suddenly flooding him.

She shook her head. "No, not since yesterday morning. I'm hoping it was a fluke."

"I wish I could take you to the doctor, but I really don't think we can take a chance right now."

He felt so impotent. He'd promised Malcolm he would keep her safe. How was he supposed to do that when he couldn't even make sure she received proper medical care?

"Jack?"

"Yeah?"

She cleared her throat. "What happened with the baby?"

He felt the color rise to his cheeks, and he tightened his grip on the wheel.

She pressed on. "I read about it and followed the trial. Did you have any idea she was capable of something like that?"

He sighed. "Things were bad for a long time. I tried to help her, but she didn't want any help. All she wanted was an audience for her suffering. I was ready to leave her when she told me she was pregnant. I couldn't bear the thought of putting a child through what she was putting me through. She was five months along when she told me. She was so thin; I couldn't even tell."

"Did you tell her how you felt?"

"She didn't care how anyone else felt. I don't think she even wanted kids. It was just another way for her to manipulate me."

"What do you mean?"

He didn't want to rehash it all, but she was looking at him with that expression, the one that said *you can tell me anything.* "She refused to take her pre-natal vitamins. She drank wine and let me know that the baby's well-being was at her whim."

"That's horrible. I can't imagine. Couldn't you talk some sense into her?"

"I tried. It backfired. She held that baby hostage, and I had no choice but to go along."

"Tell me the rest," Taylor whispered.

Jack shook his head. "I can't talk about it, Taylor. Please." Jack was sorry for what he'd put Taylor through, but it was a long time ago. She had no right to go dredging up memories that he wanted to keep buried.

Chapter Thirty-Two

The Institute, 1975
October

My mouth drops open.

"You're serious?"

"This is a waste of time. The girl knows nothing." Dunst leans on his cane and struggles to a standing position. As he stands, his eyes roll back in his head, and he faints. Damon catches him just before he hits the floor.

"How long has that been happening?"

Damon lays him on my bed and pushes the button next to it to call for help.

He narrows his eyes at me. "Why do you care?"

"I think he's been misdiagnosed."

"What are you talking about?" He whips around and looks at me.

Before I can answer, the door opens and a large man pushes a wheelchair in. Dunst has started to rouse and is mumbling. Damon helps him to a sitting position, where he falls back one more time until, finally, he begins to stabilize. They settle him into the chair and wheel him out. He looks straight ahead, completely ignoring my presence, embarrassed, I assume, by his show of weakness.

Damon escorts him to the hallway and I hear the murmur of conversation. A few minutes later he returns.

"What do you mean you think he was misdiagnosed?"

I see hope in his eyes, an expectation perhaps of good news. What I have to tell him is not good though—not for him or Dunst, but I feel no sympathy for either.

"The dry eyes, the skin discoloration, the fainting upon sitting up or standing—they are symptomatic of something more. I believe he has multi-system atrophy. It mimics Parkinson's but is much more aggressive and debilitating."

He rushes toward me, his hands poised to strike me, and I shrink back.

"You're wrong." He pulls back suddenly and appraises me as if seeing me for the first time. His voice is calmer now. "Why didn't his neurologist figure it out?"

"When was he diagnosed?"

"1957."

"It wasn't fully understood until 1969. And it looks the same as Parkinson's in the beginning. The fact that he stopped responding to Levodopa is a red flag. Did he continue to see his neurologist?"

Damon shakes his head, looking at the floor.

"When the medicine stopped working, he went a few more times, but there was nothing else they could do. He said it was a waste of time."

"One thing I don't understand is how is it that he's walking? If he's had the disease for almost twenty years, he should be completely bedridden by now."

"It's has to do with the coins," he says.

"What?"

"During the war, Friedrich was part of a unit that specialized in religious relics. He was Himmler's second-in-command and was responsible for finding artifacts and relics for the cause. The silver coins have special powers."

He walks over to the table and pours a glass of water for himself. "When Satan entered Judas, his touch was conveyed to the coins that were held in Judas's hands. Friedrich has been trying to find them for over thirty years. In the hands of someone who knows how to use them, they are powerful indeed. Friedrich dispatched a team to search for them after the war. He found ten, and that was enough to heal him. For a while."

The manner in which he conveys this information is shockingly banal, as if the story is commonplace. The fact that Dunst worked directly for Himmler chills me to the bone. "He wants the coins to heal himself again?"

"He needs to be healthy to continue his great work."

"How could you give your allegiance to a Nazi?" In truth, I am not surprised that a man who would do what he has done to me would align himself with such evil. But I ask him anyway.

He sits down, crosses his legs, leans back into the leather chair and clasps his hands together.

"He is a brilliant scientist, a visionary." He shrugs. "The Nazi party was lucky to have him. Their cause was misguided. He served his country but never believed in the Nazi cause per se. But he was passionate about the work of the Ahnenerbe."

"The Ahnenerbe?"

"The Ancestral Heritage Research and Teaching Society. The group Himmler started. Friedrich led the charge in searching for relics in Rumania and Greece. Before that, he had worked in their top-secret section, the Institute for Scientific Research for Military Purposes, doing scientific experimentation. But he found the occult more compelling. When he learned about the coins, he knew he had to have them. They have a rich history. They were handed down from Abraham all the way to Peter. They were even given as a gift to Jesus himself, by a king whose son Jesus healed. But Jesus knew the destiny of the coins, and he refused them, and they went instead into the treasury. Do you know what happened next?" he asks.

I remember my Bible history. "Of course. Judas went to the chief priests and agreed to betray Jesus, and they agreed on a price. He was paid the thirty silver pieces in exchange for his betrayal. Judas led them to Jesus when there was no crowd around and kissed him."

"Not quite right, Maya. He tried to kiss him, but Jesus stopped him and asked: 'Are you betraying the Son of Man with a kiss?'"

Is he quoting Scripture? I narrow my eyes. "*You* read the Bible?"

"Sunday school every week until I was twelve. My good Christian parents might have beat me at home, but they looked after my soul. But go on, Maya. What happens next?"

"Why ask me? You seem to have all the answers."

"Okay, I'll tell you. Poor Judas, he ended up regretting his actions. When he saw they were going to put Jesus to death, he went back to the chief priests and returned the thirty silver pieces, and confessed his sins, but it was too late. So he hanged himself." He shrugs. "The chief priests decided they couldn't keep the money in the treasury, as it was blood money. Instead, they bought the Potter's Field—a burial place for strangers—called the Field of Blood to this day."

"What happened to the coins after that?"

"According to legend, the owner of the field threw them into a fountain in Solomon's temple. They were taken from there and paid to the guards stationed at Jesus's tomb. When Mary Magdalene came to the tomb to tend to Jesus's body, they were in such shock that he was gone, they gave the coins to her. Mary handed them over to Peter. Peter kept ten, gave ten to Matthew and ten to John."

"The same Saint John who wrote the Gospel?"

He nods. "Yes. But then that John gave them to John of Patmos, the author of Revelation. The monastery on the island is named after him. During the war, when Friedrich was stationed on Patmos, he searched the cave where Saint John had lived, and ordered an archeological dig of the area near the cave, but they couldn't find the coins. He found the ten that Peter hid while he was on Ephesus, but nothing on Patmos. Their healing power got him out of his wheelchair, but it doesn't last forever. He suspected that someone on the island was hiding them. He went from house to house with the soldiers, but his search was interrupted by the end of the war."

"Where are the other ten?" I ask. "The ones Peter gave to Matthew." It feels surreal to be sitting here talking about the saints from the Bible as though they are people I know.

His face clouds over. "They are supposed to be in Jerusalem. We are still searching and we *will* find them. But he needs more time. We know your parents have ten. That will be enough to help him for now."

"How can you know that my parents have them?" This seems utterly preposterous to me.

"I went back on Friedrich's behalf, when I was eighteen. Took a tour of the monastery, visited the site where Friedrich believed one of the islanders may have buried them after the war was over. It was obvious that it had been disturbed, that someone took them. I talked to the islanders, got a list of all the families who had left. I've spent the past ten years interviewing them. I found out something very interesting at the last stop."

He doesn't wait for me to say anything.

"I found out that your mother was the sister of one of the monks at Saint John's monastery. Your uncle had been entrusted with guarding the coins. I am told he gave them to her to bring to America."

It can't be true, I think. *My parents are just normal, boring people.*

"I have been watching them, watching you. I was delighted when you decided to pursue the fellowship we offered you."

"You lured me here because of this connection?" I sputter. "I know nothing of these coins. They have nothing to do with me."

"On the contrary, Maya. You have history in your blood. You are related to one of the monks in service of Saint John. My child will have even more power when he comes of age and holds those silver pieces. He will rule the new order."

"I hope you never get your hands on any of them. And just so you know, Friedrich's decline will be swift and brutal. He won't have the ability to rule anything, not even his own body."

He lunges toward me, his hand coming so fast, that I feel the slap before I see it. The sting is so sharp; I feel my cheek vibrating. But, I don't regret speaking up. The look of anguish my words have caused him was worth it.

He is on his feet within seconds, striding to the door. "What a pity for the world that your keen diagnostic talents will die along with you," he throws over his shoulder as he leaves.

Chapter Thirty-Three

Brody Hamilton held a chair for Rita Avery. Even though Rita knew him well, and there was no need for beating around the bush, he wanted to have a little fun. He smiled at her.

"Well, my dear. What have you got for me today? What new deceit awaits the good people of this country?"

"Now, Senator, that's not fair. I'm just trying to make sure my clients stay solvent so that we can continue to enjoy the fruits of their labor." She paused and pulled a plastic container from her purse, took out a pill, and swallowed it. "Case in point—without these antibiotics, I'd be home in bed right now."

He raised an eyebrow.

She continued. "We would like to remove the contraindications handed out with the medicine. It's a huge waste of money—no one reads them anyway. Not to mention that it's ecologically irresponsible. Instead we want to put a web address on the bottle's label where customers can look them up."

It started as a chuckle, but within seconds, he was doubled over laughing. "Ecologically irresponsible? Oh, my dear. You have hit a new low."

She waited for him to finish.

"Ah." He sighed. "I needed that laugh." He became serious again as he spoke. "Well, I'm just a small-town country boy, but I have to wonder, what about folks who don't have a computer. You know, the majority of your market, those over seventy-five?"

Her shiny, glossed lips parted in a fawning smile. "There will also be the option to request the literature from the pharmacist."

Sipping his Johnny Walker Blue, he rubbed his chin with his free hand. "Just a suggestion, but maybe you ought to lead with that. Tone down the altruism. Aint' nobody gonna believe the drug pushers give a whit about the planet. That dog won't hunt. Make it about efficiency. Cost savings passed down to the customers. Have it to me by the end of the week."

She nodded in agreement. "Thank you, Senator."

He fidgeted with his fountain pen after she left. It would be easy to get this one through. She was right: no one did read the inserts. This bill was only the beginning. The framing for what was to come later. One step at a time as his grandma used to say. Everything that happens starts one step at a time.

CHAPTER THIRTY-FOUR

As they drove in the darkness, more memories rushed back to Taylor, memories she hadn't let herself think about in ages. Jack was inextricably entwined with her past. She could barely think back to any event without seeing his face. Some of her most cherished memories of childhood included him. Of course, it wasn't all good. There were the times Jack had come running to her house, the pain fresh in his eyes, after a shouting match with his father when he'd forgotten a chore, or hadn't completed it to his dad's standards. She'd wanted to make it all better for him, make him feel loved. When they were still little, she'd grab his hand and pull him outside; then they'd jump on their bikes, pedaling as fast as they could, to see who was the quickest. That always got his mind off things. When they were finished, her mother would make them chocolate milkshakes, and they'd talk and giggle, as if nothing were wrong.

As he got older, the stakes increased. No matter what he did, it was never enough for his father. Jack had to go out for the varsity football team, make the honor roll, and hustle to get more lawns mowed or driveways shoveled than anyone. But the thing that had infuriated Jack the most, was his father's insistence on Jack being an altar boy and pushing him toward the priesthood. As the only son of a large Catholic family, they pinned all their hopes on Jack becoming a man of the cloth. What they didn't realize was that'd he given up on the church long before he'd graduated high school. He confessed to Taylor that he'd lost faith in a religion that spat out rules with no regard to how they affected its members. He'd watched his mother battle depression his entire life, and refuse to get any help. Her friends told her to pray more, to give it to God. It wasn't until years later, that Taylor realized it was postpartum depression made worse by her almost constant state of pregnancy. Jack's bitterness with the church had always been a source of tension between him and his parents.

When he'd gotten the letter from Columbia University, Taylor and her family had been the only ones cheering for him. If it hadn't been for the football scholarship, she doubted he would have been able to go, even though his father's tire store had grown to include chains in ten states, and they could easily have afforded it.

She remembered that his father had made a spur-of-the-moment trip to Jack's apartment in New York the weekend before he died. But they hadn't talked about it at the funeral—she knew Jack better than to press him. She'd meant to draw it out gradually, over the months following, but never got the chance. He'd met Dakota soon after.

"Jack?"

"Hmm?"

"That weekend, the one before your father died. I've always wondered, did you resolve things with him?"

He gave her a quick glance, then his eyes went back to the road. "It's strange. But I think maybe he knew, somehow, that he was on borrowed time. You know, he never once came to see me at school, except for graduation of course. Then out of the blue he calls and says he wants to come see where I live."

Taylor waited for him to go on.

He sighed. "I asked if he wanted to see the sights. As close as we lived to New York, he'd never been. But no, he said, he just wanted to spend some time with me. We went to McSorley's and threw back some of their ale. He told me he was proud of me." He cleared his throat. "That's the first time I ever heard him say that."

"That must have made you happy."

Jack shook his head. "It pissed me off. Why did he have to wait twenty-four years to tell me? All my life, I was never good enough, and then suddenly he's proud of me? We spent the rest of the night talking sports."

She was sorry to hear it, but she supposed it was unrealistic to expect one weekend to undo years of strife. "He loved you, Jack. In his own way. He did the best he could."

"Sure." He paused. "There *was* something else."

"What?"

"He told me that I'd made the right choice with you. That you were the real deal and to never let you go."

She felt like all the air had been sucked out of her lungs. "He—"

Jack tapped the steering wheel. "Guess it's a good thing he didn't live long enough to see that I'd disappointed him once again."

CHAPTER THIRTY-FIVE

The Institute, 1975
October

"Any message you'd like me to take to your parents?"

I feel my blood turn to ice. "No," is all I can manage. He can't go near them. Please let him only be taunting me.

"Since you don't have any useful information, I have no choice but to go to the source."

I scramble to come up with a solution.

"Let me talk to them. They'll tell me. I can find them for you, get the coins for you in exchange for my freedom."

He laughs at me. "You have no bargaining chips. Once they know I have you here, they'll hand the coins over, I'm quite sure."

My parents were expecting me home a month ago. I wonder if they believe the lies they have been told by Damon's people. That I failed out of the fellowship and took off to parts unknown. They may believe that I was ashamed enough not to return to them. It's a feasible cover story, considering how I've always defined myself by my accomplishments. They must be so hurt. But my sister will know better. She knows I would never do that to her. I know with certainty that she is searching for me. Oh, how I miss her.

I think back to the last Sunday we were all together. Mama always made a big dinner, and I went when I could. As soon as she and Papa would return from church, my mother would cook—homemade meals full of calories and love. Over dinner she would tell me about the priest's sermon. She was always trying to talk me into going to church with them, but I refused. How many times did my mother look at me, tilt her head, and cluck her tongue? *Maya, my girl, God loves you. Don't you know he loves you?* After dinner, we'd linger, sipping our coffee, and sampling the assortment of pastries sitting in the middle of the table on a large platter. I close my eyes, and will myself there, to that table I took for granted, where my papa's smiles warmed me, and my mama's hand fed me. What I would give for one more dinner.

"I suppose you think your parents are wonderful, don't you?" His voice brings me crashing back to the present.

I don't know whether he expects an answer or not.

"Well, Maya? Are they? Are they wonderful?"

"They're good parents," I stammer. "We never wanted for anything. They did their best to provide good futures for us." I become emboldened. "They sacrificed to pay for medical school for me and my sister." I sit up straighter. "Yes, they're great parents."

He laughs. A soft, mirthless laugh. "You are a fool if you believe that. Sacrificed? Nonsense. You fed their ego, fulfilled *their* purpose in your life. Two doctors in the family. How admirable. What good parents. They didn't do it out of love for you. No, they did it purely for bragging rights."

I shake my head, lift my hands and cover my ears. He's wrong. My parents love me with all their hearts, and I love them. But, I'll never get to tell them that again. I don't want to hear any more of his vile perspective on human nature. I will not allow him to steal my past. To pervert my memories.

He stands up. "Cover your ears all you like. The fact remains: no one loves anyone but themselves. The sooner you accept that fact; the sooner you'll learn not to be taken advantage of."

"Not taken advantage of?" I explode. "I'm a prisoner. I've lost everything. My freedom—even the right to my own body. You dare to lecture me on how to live? What choices are left to me now?"

He advances until he is towering over me. I recoil and slide back.

"Why are you complaining? You always wanted to be the best. You've beat out everyone for the privilege of bearing my heir. You should pat yourself on the back that you were picked. You are elite. But remember, pride goes before destruction and a haughty spirit before a fall." He laughs again. "Imagine that, *me*, quoting from the Bible."

I won't accept responsibility for his insanity. Yes, I was proud, but I don't deserve this. I can't bear the thought of him getting near my parents. If he's going to tell them he's holding me prisoner, that must mean he intends to kill them.

"Please don't hurt them," I beg him.

"I don't make promises I don't intend to keep."

CHAPTER THIRTY-SIX

They had been driving for a few hours. Taylor looked at Jack's hand shifting gears and remembered his touch. He had strong hands. They were nice hands, she thought, not too big but still masculine. They were hands you could depend on. Or they were once. *Forget about his hands.* What was wrong with her? She sighed.

"Let's look for a place to stop for the night," Jack said.

Half an hour later, they pulled into the parking lot of a small highway motel. Jack pulled his baseball cap down as far as he could and went to the front office. Minutes later he returned with a room key.

At least this room had two double beds. She was exhausted and climbed into one immediately. Beau hopped up and nestled by her side. Her mind was racing. A part of her wanted to call out to Jack, to feel his arms around her and relax in his comforting embrace. It would be so nice to just pretend everything was good between them. She shifted again, restless. *Stop thinking ridiculous thoughts.* She felt disloyal to Malcolm, then a quick surge of anger when she remembered she didn't owe him her loyalty any longer. She didn't even know who he really was. She had married him thinking he was a straight arrow, someone who would never betray her. She still didn't understand how she could have been so easily deceived.

Watching as Jack bolted the door and pushed a chair against it for good measure, she noticed how the T-shirt he was wearing showed off his muscled back and trim waist. The stirrings of desire fluttered as she remembered the feel of those strong arms. She flipped over to face the wall, her back to him, and pulled the covers up to her chin.

When he got into bed and turned the light off, she closed her eyes, but sleep wouldn't come. She kicked her leg out from under the sheet, trying to find a comfortable position.

"You still awake?" Jack whispered.

"Yeah."

"Did you have any idea about Malcolm? Any suspicions that something was off?"

"Of course not. Some journalist, huh?"

"It's not your fault. People aren't always what they seem, and we want to see the best in those we love."

They had both married frauds, she realized. But surely, there had to have been more to her marriage than Malcolm's deception. She couldn't believe that everything between them had been a lie. No one could be that good an actor. Lying there in the dark, it felt comforting, unburdening, to talk about it.

"I met him the night *Twenty-Four Seven* was running a story that had taken me a year to produce. I was exhausted and exhilarated. It was about Operation Paperclip, a covert program that smuggled Nazi war criminals to the US. I was going to my dad's to watch it, and Malcolm had been invited to dinner."

"He was friends with your father?"

"I guess. I'm not sure how Dad knew him. It was the first time I'd ever seen him. At first, I wasn't interested, thought he was too old and too typical, Washington-power type. Then I found out that he'd lost both his parents when he was a teenager. It made me feel close to him."

"I can see that. What you went through, losing your mom—not many people get what that really does to you."

She thought back to the days following the funeral, after everyone had gone back to normal and expected her to do the same. All except Jack. He'd been by her side, not asking anything of her, instead offering a steady and consistent comfort.

"I'll never forgot how you helped me through it. Looking back, I don't know how you stood it."

"What do you mean?"

"All those nights when I snuck next door to your house and crawled in your room, and you held me while I sobbed. That went on for months. It had to get old."

She heard him shift in his bed. "It never got old. But it broke my heart."

The raw pain of that memory took her by surprise, and she brushed a tear from her cheek. Trying to lighten the mood, she said, "At least you were rescued when they sent me away to boarding school."

A hard edge came into his voice. "I still don't understand how your father could do that."

She didn't blame her dad; it had been Evelyn's idea. "The wrong wife can make you do things you never thought you could." Of course, he knew that better than anyone. All of a sudden, she didn't want to talk anymore. "Good night."

"Taylor...Good night."

Memories bombarded her, playing like a video reel. Images of Jack faded and were replaced by Malcolm. After Jack, it had felt impossible for her to trust again. The hard shell she'd built around her heart had served her well. She had gotten her career on track, she was doing work she loved, and she was happy. When she finally opened her heart again, she'd believed she had found someone who would never hurt her. The bond she and Malcolm had shared over the tragedies they had suffered and then their ardent desire to create their own family had eradicated any remaining reservations she'd had about opening herself up again. Malcolm's betrayal wasn't just hurtful though—it had caused her to lose faith in herself. If the second time she had trusted someone she'd been wrong again, what did that say about her? Now that she knew Malcolm was devoid of the very integrity and honor she'd been so sure he possessed, she wondered how she could have lived with him all those years and never known. Maybe there was some part of her that sought men who were incapable of true intimacy. Masks. Everyone wore one. She was done being a fool. She would take nothing and no one at face value ever again.

CHAPTER THIRTY-SEVEN

Crosby hit the play button on the video streaming on his computer. The latest episode of *Teenage Wasted* was ready to be aired, and he was taking one last look. These were college kids—eighteen and nineteen years old. What they were doing was illegal everywhere in the states—everywhere, that is, except for where it was filmed, in Nevada. If anyone bothered to read the disclaimer, they would see that it was a scripted reality series and mostly fabricated.

Two girls are sitting in a dorm room, talking.

"It's easy, Mindy. And when you graduate, you have no debt."

"I don't know." The other girl looks at her fingernails. "I don't think I could do it."

The first girl stands, brushing her long, blonde hair from her shoulder with a manicured hand. She walks to her dresser, opens it, pulls out a wad of cash and fans it in front of Mindy's face. "Fine. I'm going shopping with my little tip here. You can let that cheapskate of a boyfriend touch you for free. I'm doing exactly what you are, but instead of being paid with dinner or a movie, I'm getting what I deserve, not to mention my tuition paid."

Mindy looks up at her friend. "How did you even find out about it, Lucy?"

Lucy smiles and sits back down. "That's the great thing. It's super easy and organized. It's run by a girl just like us, and she vets all the guys. You can even pick from a picture and get a cute one. They're older, but, you know, handsome. Just rich older guys bored with their wives. It's fun really. They have these on every campus."

Crosby stopped the video. It was just enough to titillate and get people thinking. He had no doubt that men of a certain age and resources would begin Googling to find willing college girls. Cash-strapped girls would do the same. He sent an e-mail to his YouTube contingent, and closed the laptop. After the show aired, there would be a plethora of videos of good-looking young women singing the praises of such a service.

Of course, there wasn't really an escort service on every college campus. Yet.

CHAPTER THIRTY-EIGHT

The Institute, 1975
November

He hasn't come for three days now. I am going crazy with worry, imagining all sort of scenarios with him and my parents. Desperation has driven me to prayer. If there's any chance that someone up there can hear me, I have to try. I hope with all my heart that they give him what he wants and he doesn't hurt them. But I don't believe that's possible. I think of a story my mother used to tell me when I was a little girl. It was about three men in Babylon who refused to worship a gold image made by the king because they would worship only their God. They were thrown into a fiery furnace so hot that it burned the soldiers who threw them in. The next morning, they were all still alive, not a hair on their head singed. The king was astounded, promoted them to better jobs and ordered everyone in the land to worship their God. I remember asking my mother why they didn't just pretend to worship the image, just say something to save themselves. She told me that true faith requires sacrifice, and that to love our lives more than we love God is not serving Him but ourselves. So, I asked if God would always step in and rescue His people like that. She hugged me, put her hand on my face and said that, no, not always in this life, but yes, always in the next.

My door opens, and it's him. I hold my breath, dreading what he has to say. His eyes are stormy, and his face looks tense. He slams the door behind him and stares at me.

I stand and put one hand on the table behind me, steeling myself for whatever he is going to say. He just looks at me, until finally I can't stand it anymore.

"What happened? Did you see my parents? What did you do?"

"Yes, I saw them. You look like your mother."

"Please!" I shout. "Just tell me. Are they alive?"

"They were when I left them."

"What do you mean?"

He sits.

"Patience, Maya. I was waiting for them when they returned from church. They're very polite. When I mentioned I knew you, they let me right in. Gave me coffee and some delicious Greek pastry." He taps his index finger against his chin. "Theeplis, I think they're called?"

I want to scream. I tap my foot and wait for him to get on with it.

"I told them I'd worked with you here. They're quite heartbroken that they haven't heard from you."

"Stop toying with me." I can't stop the tears now.

"Indeed. Well, I got around to the real purpose of my visit. When I asked about the silver pieces, it was obvious by their reactions that they knew exactly what I was talking about."

I hold my breath, waiting for him to continue.

"Your father was the first to figure out that I wasn't just someone who knew you. He demanded that I return you to them. He's a brave man."

"You're loathsome."

His eyes narrow. "Do you want to hear the rest or not?"

"Go on."

"I promised I would let you go if they told me where they hid the coins. Even told them they have a grandchild on the way. That garnered a mixed reaction." He looks at me with a triumphant expression. "You should have believed me when I told you they didn't really love you." He pauses for effect. "They said no."

All the breath whooshes from me.

"They said no?" I whisper.

"Oh they blabbered on, said how much they loved you, but they had a sacred trust in guarding the coins. They couldn't betray it or betray God. The fools."

I sit up straighter. "They are not fools. They knew you wouldn't let me go. You're the fool if you think you can trick them so easily." I want to wound his pride, to say anything to wipe that smirk off his face.

He arches an eyebrow. "It doesn't matter. We'll get it out of them. They could have done it the easy way."

"What are you planning to do?"

He stands. "It's done. Friedrich's men are interrogating them. They're extremely skilled in getting information."

I clutch my chest as a knifelike pain sears me. "You're torturing them?"

He tilts his head. "Well, *I'm* not."

"You monster!" I pick up the crystal decanter from the table and throw it at him, narrowly missing his head. It crashes to the floor.

He shakes his head, steps over the broken pieces, and opens the door.

"I'll send someone in to clean this up." And he leaves.

I walk over to the mess and begin to attend to it myself. Making sure my back is to the camera, I take the largest jagged piece and slide it into my pant's pocket.

CHAPTER THIRTY-NINE

Dakota sat in the common room of Bellevue staring straight ahead, missing nothing. The chaos surrounding her made her want to scream, but she swallowed her rage and remained silent. To her right, a woman carried on an animated conversation with no one, gesticulating, grimacing, and flailing her arms about. Dakota wanted to slap her, tell her to shut up, but she kept her expression neutral. Across the room, a man pinched his own arm every few seconds then yelled "Ow stop!" No one paid any attention.

She had been here a long time—since the day she had plunged the knife deep into her abdomen, determined to rid herself of the leech that was making her fat and tired. She had finally made Jack understand how miserable she was at being forced to accommodate the intruder that was taking over her body. In the beginning, when she still looked pretty and thin, she had liked the attention. Everyone was congratulating her and smiling, making her feel so special. But then things began to change. Her breasts were sore, and her legs turned lumpy with ugly blue veins. She had to pee constantly, and she was always exhausted. She was sick of being told what to do. No drinking, eat right, take your bloody vitamins. And Jack, always looking at her as though she was doing it all wrong, like he didn't trust her with his precious child. She knew what he had planned, could see the disdain in his eyes when he looked at her. He was biding his time until she had the baby and then he would leave her.

Take the wretched thing and start a life without her. Well, she wouldn't let him. The baby was in her body and he would never get his hands on it. She chose the day knowing he would be working late. She intentionally started a fight with him so that when he came home and found her he would blame himself. The last words he said to her—that she made him say to her—would haunt him forever. She recalled the conversation with satisfaction. Her vitamins had been sitting on the table, unopened.

"Haven't you been taking these?"

"They make me sick."

Jack exhaled slowly. "It's important for you and the baby."

She stuck out her tongue. "All you care about is the stupid baby."

Jack gave her a withering look. "Stupid?"

She put her face inches from his and sneered. "Stupid. Just like its father. Stupid, stupid, stupid."

He grabbed her by the shoulders. "What's the matter with you? How can you talk about our child like that?"

"Because, Jack, as you've pointed out, I don't have a maternal bone in my body."

He was speechless.

She goaded him. "Say it."

"Say what?"

"Say you're not cut out to be a mother."

He turned his back on her and walked toward the door. "I'll say no such thing."

She ran up to him and grabbed his arm. "Be honest for once in your pathetic life. Maybe then we can start to change things. Say it!"

He spun around, defeat in his eyes. "You win, Dakota. You're not cut out to be a mother."

"Ha." She was triumphant. "I knew you felt that way. Get out of here."

When he got home that night to find her bathing in her own blood, she was nearly unconscious. She was determined to hang on until he appeared, so that she could whisper the condemning words to him: "I guess I'm not cut out to be a mother."

The lawyers advised her to plead insanity, and the court-appointed shrink had diagnosed her with bipolar disorder. Her attorney argued that the pregnancy hormones had sent her over the edge. She was more than happy to go along with them. She knew how to play the game. So here she was, waiting like a good little girl to see the useless doctor and continue to feed him the lies that would get her released. She had studied hard for her role as the improving patient and had no doubt her brainless doctor would soon let her out.

He opened his office door and called her in.

She bestowed her most enchanting smile on him. It was so easy. It bored her to death. She spoke her well-rehearsed lines, cried when appropriate, made her voice catch in the right places. He was nodding at her now, his facial expression one of earnest empathy.

She was a great actress. Her stint with Jack had been her longest-running role. Oh, the long seasons of depression left her bored, but the one thing that kept her going was her amusement at his clumsy attempts to cheer her up. He was pathetic, and his codependent behavior sickened her. When she was tired of being "depressed", she would miraculously recover and become the Dakota he loved once again. What delight she took in the knowledge that his happiness was short-lived and at the complete whim of her moods. She threw herself into their lovemaking with one goal—to enslave him. She reveled in the sexual power she held over him. She broke him down, built him up, and broke him down again, all the while mocking him in her mind. She was sorry when the role came to an end, having grown fond of the game and crushing his spirit. She got her parting shot in though—cutting the baby out of her stomach had been her idea—her masterpiece. She wanted to destroy him, make sure he would be no good for anyone else. She did so knowing she would have to pay for it but it was worth it. The session was almost over.

She dabbed at her eyes with a balled-up tissue and looked at the therapist. Her lip trembled.

He stood. "Dakota, I'm so pleased with the progress you've made. I do think you're ready to take the next step."

She feigned grateful surprise. "Really, are you sure, Doctor?"

He smiled at her. "Yes, quite sure. You are ready. I'll make my recommendations at your hearing."

Dakota thought he looked pleased with himself. Soon she would be free of this place and back where she belonged. She had played her hand well and was ready, finally, to claim her reward. She couldn't wait to be with him again. The only man she considered her equal and worthy of her devotion. Damon Crosse.

CHAPTER FORTY

The Institute, 1975
December

My baby is growing strong. I am informed at my weekly exams, that all is going perfectly. The heartbeat is strong, and I'm gaining just the right amount of weight. How could I not, with my diet so carefully controlled? I am visibly pregnant now. I've been brought pants that stretch to accommodate my growing belly and loose fitting tops. A drab uniform of solid colors and practicality. Dreams of beautiful maternity clothes, a loving husband, and joyous expectation will all go unfulfilled.

It has been a week since he went to see my parents. I haven't seen him since, have been left on my own to do nothing but worry. Even though I would never let him know, when he first told me that my mother refused to turn over the coins, I *was* wounded. How could she not do anything in her power to save me? All because of a legend about some pieces of metal? Because that's what it must be. Legend. An inanimate object has no power—at least that's what I thought at first. But now, I wonder. Dunst is a renowned scientist. That's what got him his entry in this country. And he believes in the power of the coins. And what about the claim that they healed him? I wish I could do some research, find out more about them and their history. But all

I have to go on is what they tell me. And if my mother and father, whom I know with certainty *do* love me, wouldn't give them up, then maybe, just maybe, they do contain the power he claims. What I said about them knowing he wouldn't release me—I want to believe that. And maybe it's true. But deep inside, I know their faith is stronger than I ever realized. It's hard enough to sacrifice your own life for your faith—but the life of your child? The only way that is possible is to have an unshakable belief that to betray your faith would have monumental repercussions and that the stakes are truly of eternal significance. Now that I am to become a mother, I already feel an overpowering love for my baby. I would lay down my life for this child without a second thought.

So, are my parents fools? Is their faith misplaced? I am beginning to think *I* am the fool. When did I give up on my faith? I search my memory and try to remember what it was that turned me away. Did something happen to shatter my belief? Some terrible trauma that made me realize there was no God? I can think of nothing. The reality is, I just drifted away. There was no defining moment, no betrayal on God's part, no reason other than it was easy to walk away. I gave my allegiance to myself and to science. I didn't think I needed God or anybody else. Is it too late for me to turn back now? I kneel by my bed, the way I did as a little girl, and clasp my hands together.

"Dear God, I don't know if you can hear me, but I hope you can. If there was ever a time I needed to know if you are there, it's now. Please give me a sign, anything, that you exist, that you love me, that I'm not doomed to die in this place with no hope of a life after." I stay that way for a long while, my head bowed, my spirit still. Then I feel my baby move. It is nothing more than a flutter at first, so subtle, I'm not sure if I imagine it or not. But then, another movement—this time stronger—and a kick. I look up and whisper, "Thank you."

Chapter Forty-One

They were back on the road and Jack was worried about Taylor. The strain was taking its toll on her. She had dark circles under her eyes, and she was barely eating. They had fallen back into an easy companionability, and it struck him again how much he had missed her. He was overcome with tenderness for her, and he had to fight a sudden urge to reach over and stroke her cheek. It was becoming harder and harder to be with her and *not* be with her.

He cracked the window and breathed in the cool air. There was a welcome sign ahead. They had made it to Claremont. A few miles later he spotted a motel and parked.

"I'll get us checked in. Keep the doors locked."

He was back quickly, and she looked up as he got back in the car.

"Any problems?"

"Nope. I gave the clerk an extra bill to let us bring Beau."

"Good thinking."

In the room, Taylor threw her bag on the bed and sorted the dishes and food they had picked up for Beau.

"Tomorrow we'll go to the library and find the address. This time tomorrow night we could be talking to Jeremy," Jack said.

Taylor nodded at him absentmindedly while she fed Beau.

"Any luck on tracking down the pharma company involved with the vaccine?" she asked.

"No, but I did some digging on Brody Hamilton and he *has* sponsored a number of bills relating to Alpha Pharmaceuticals,

149

mostly lessening of regulations, like labeling and side effect warnings."

"Could you find a connection between them and the latest bill? Or the vaccine?"

He shook his head and put his palms up. "Nothing."

"Shoot. Let's hope that Jeremy can shed some light on it," she said without much enthusiasm.

"We'll know soon enough."

They were getting closer to unraveling the mystery, and Jack should have been relieved, but he realized that he was reluctant to complete this mission. He didn't want to let her go—let her go *again*, that is. But he was being a selfish jerk. She deserved better than him, and he owed it to her to leave her alone, to find love again with someone who wasn't jaded, hadn't ruined his life and everyone's around him. No. It was good that things were coming to a close. He would deliver Taylor safely to Jeremy, figure out what they needed to do to take down the bad guys, and would go on with his life.

CHAPTER FORTY-TWO

The Institute, 1975
December

I fear my parents are dead, and I dread finding out. I can't bear to think of what has been done to my dear mama and papa.

I pray every day now. Last night, I felt a peace wash over me, covering me like a warm blanket. It was comforting and strangely tangible, emanating from a source outside of myself. My hand goes to my neck, and I grasp the christening cross that I've worn each day of my life since I was thirteen. Until now it had ceased to hold any significance, other than nostalgic. But now, it is my most precious possession, my only real possession, and merely feeling it against my skin fills me with hope. I think of all it symbolizes and make myself meditate on its meaning. I wonder why he has allowed me to keep it, but I don't dare ask for fear he will take it.

With every fiber of my being, I rebel against the lies he tries to instill in me. That I carry within me the continuation of evil. I won't accept it. I hold fiercely to the belief that I am connected and forever bound to the God of the universe. Damon may hold my body captive, but he will never touch my soul. How ironic that I owe my salvation to the man who imprisons me. Would I have turned back to God if I'd been allowed to continue on my chosen path? Medicine

151

was my god. Education was my god. And yes, I even made myself into a god. What a terrible thing pride is. If it were only my life to be lost, I could almost be grateful, for in losing it I have found it. What grieves me with unrelenting desolation is the knowledge that I am leaving my precious child, alone and unprotected, helpless to resist the evil that will encapsulate him. I will pray for this child until my dying breath.

I am talking to my baby, telling him how much I love him—I feel I'm having a boy. I tell him stories of his family. The yia yia and papou who would spoil him, the aunt who would adore him.

I don't know how long he has been standing outside my door, only that he has overheard some of it. He opens the door, stares at me, and then begins to laugh.

"Love! My child will have no need of this emotion full of fallacies. They say God is love. My child will have nothing to do with either. Don't waste your time, Maya. You are merely the vessel. You will have no influence on what my child thinks, feels, or believes. He is going to be powerful. More powerful than you can ever imagine. I would have thought that would have been enough for you. Your ego should love that, no? You, the mother of the most powerful man in the world?"

"You are insane!"

"Insane? Far from it."

"What has happened to my parents?" I demand.

His gives me a contemptuous look, and his lips form a scowl. "No matter what we did, they wouldn't give up the hiding place. They admitted they brought them from Greece, but they refused to say where they are hidden." He shakes his head. "I don't understand it. They were unshakable."

"What did you do to them?" I choke the words out. I don't want to know, but I have to suffer too, must know what they went through.

He makes a dismissive gesture with his hands. "It doesn't matter. They are gone now. Your sister will believe that they had an ordinary automobile accident. Nothing to arouse suspicions. And we will keep watch on her. Surely there will be something in the will or in their papers that she will find and lead us to the coins. We will wait for as long as it takes."

My grief is intermingled with relief. They won't kill my sister. She is useful to them. I can only hope that my parents took the secret of the coins with them to their graves.

He stands and paces. "What would make someone so stubborn? Their faith could not be broken, no matter how hard we tried." He brings a fist down on the table so hard that the glass on it tips over and water runs off.

My parents didn't die in vain. Now I understand the faith my mother told me about—the one that sent those three men into the fire. I sit up straighter and stare into his eyes.

"My child *will* return to God one day."

He looks at me with such murderous rage that I shrink back, afraid he will strike me. He comes close to me, until he is just inches from my face, and I can feel his breath on my cheek.

"My child will never worship your God. He will rule nations, and be responsible for turning others *away* from your God. Know this, Maya: your prayers are impotent. His destiny is sealed."

I bite my lip and take a deep breath. Then a thought occurs to me, and I move my face even closer to his, in our own twisted version of chicken.

"We shall see about that, *Damon*. We both know how the story ends. I assume you have read Revelation, the book written by Saint John on Patmos. The Battle of Armageddon will see your master thrown into the pit forever. Christ will be victorious. The battle is already won."

His eyes narrow to slits, and he flies from the room, and the lock clicks behind him. My heart is still pounding, and I breathe deeply to regain my equilibrium. I begin to wonder if I've gone too far. When dinner time comes, there is nothing but beef stew. He knows I hate beef. By morning, I am ravenous but its red meat again. A bloody steak this time. So, he will have the last word after all.

CHAPTER FORTY-THREE

The cocooned darkness of the limousine enveloped Dakota. She rested her head against the soft leather and closed her eyes, her stomach fluttering in exquisite anticipation of the evening ahead. The iron gates opened, and they drove through and onto the immense property. Thirty minutes later, they were in front of the sprawling castle, and Dakota was escorted up the familiar steps to the hand-carved wooden door that would lead her back into the only domain in which she felt at home.

Damon was waiting for her in his private chambers. They said nothing to each other. She went to him and caressed his face, lingering on the rounded scar on his left cheek. He allowed her this one touch—only one and only her. She reveled in the knowledge that no one else ever had or ever would get this close to him. She knelt before him and bowed her head.

"Master. Thank you for calling me home. I am ready."

He placed a hand on her head. "You have served me well. Rise. There is still much to do."

"It is my greatest honor."

He nodded.

"Your room is ready. They are waiting to examine and prepare you."

He pointed to the door. She knew better than to attempt to use her charms on him. He wanted to be alone and nothing she would say or do would dissuade him. She wanted more, but she would bide her time.

She nodded to him and left, closing the door softly behind her.

* * *

Dakota was still groggy from the anesthesia, and it took her a few minutes to get her bearings. She blinked until her vision cleared. Glancing to her right she saw him sitting there, staring at her.

"How many did they get?"

Damon looked pleased.

"Eight. You're a very fertile young woman." She was thrilled. Her position was now assured.

She laughed. "Good to know. How many are they going to fertilize?"

He looked bemused. "What does it matter to you?"

Not the answer she was looking for. She sat up and smoothed her hair back from her face. She wouldn't allow him to cut her out. "Who is the surrogate?" After her self-inflicted abortion, her uterus was no longer viable.

He rose. "Don't concern yourself with the details. You are being spared the indignity of another pregnancy. That's all you need to know."

"Shouldn't I have some say in who hosts my babies?" She didn't care about the embryos that would turn into babies. She did, however, care very much that she be afforded the respect she deserved in providing them.

He gave her a sardonic look. "I'm well aware of your maternal instincts. These children will be kept far from you."

* * *

Damon Crosse left the room without another word. He went to his library and sat down at his desk. There was a knock on the door.

"Yes?"

Jonas poked his head in. "Dr. Whitmore would like a word with you, sir."

"Send him in."

The doctor came in and stood until Damon invited him to sit. This was a man he had known over thirty years, yet their relationship was still as formal as it had been on the day they'd first met. The doctor looked at the floor, then at his fingernails, and finally at the folder on his lap—anywhere but at Damon.

Damon cleared his throat and the doctor reluctantly met his eyes. "Well?"

He blinked repeatedly, then pushed his wire-rimmed glasses up to the bridge of his nose.

"I'm running out of patience," Damon warned.

"It seems that, ahem, your sperm count is quite low."

Several seconds of silence ensued before Damon spoke. "How low?"

The doctor looked down at his feet. "Nonexistent actually. I'm afraid that even intra-cytoplasmic sperm injection won't work. I see no viable options here."

Damon nodded. He would not react. "That is all."

The doctor rose and hurried out of the room.

How could this be? It had never occurred to him that he had anything to worry about. If the idea of producing a specimen wasn't so disgusting, perhaps he would have made provisions earlier. It had taken him months to provide the sample for Jeremy. He wasn't wired with a single sexual urge. He was horrified at the messiness of it, the loss of control. It was something he would never understand. The irony. How many men had lost kingdoms, untold wealth, all they held dear, because of sex? He was not susceptible to such yearnings and for that he had always been grateful, but now it had the power to be his undoing. Never one to wallow in regrets, he stood and began mentally preparing for his next steps. He was filled with renewed resolve as he pondered his good fortune in concocting a contingency plan so long ago. He went to his bedchamber and packed his suitcase. He rang for Jonas, his thoughts racing while he waited.

"Yes, sir?" Jonas came into the room.

"I'll be gone for a few days. Please see that everything runs smoothly in my absence. What time is the new group scheduled to arrive?"

"Five o'clock, sir."

"I presume everything is prepared?"

Jonas nodded. "Of course, sir."

Damon sank down into the soft cushion of his silk chaise, suddenly tired. He felt all of his seventy years. In the space of an hour, he had gone from a vital thriving man to a withered shell. No. He raised his head. He was Damon Crosse. He was never out of options. He knew where he must now focus his efforts. It would take longer, but in the end, all that mattered was that he had a suitable heir. Perhaps this was better after all.

CHAPTER FORTY-FOUR

The Institute, 1975
December

His revelations leave me breathless and heartsick. Is there no one who can stop him? He interrupts my desperate prayers.

"A futile effort, Maya." He laughs derisively. "Don't count on any help from your God. He has abandoned you just as you will abandon your child." He sneers at me as he lifts his coffee cup to his mouth.

"Shall I continue? Let me see, where did I leave off? Ah, yes, the legal victories. Our plans are to make sure that prostitution will be legalized in more and more states. This has been in motion for some time. The fools believe that legitimizing it will contain disease and eliminate the victimization of women, but things will only get worse. We will be able to entice more women in to prostitution with promises of safety and easy income." He laughs again. "So much easier to continue forcing the downtrodden into the trade because no one bothers investigating suspicious circumstances. You'd be amazed at what poverty can do. Already parents are willing to sell their children for a loaf of bread. Soon, they won't even feel any guilt about it and more will follow. Women will become another commodity in a world for sale. Many more young men will lose their virginity in this manner and look at sex as purely recreational. We will succeed in separating sex and love at last."

I can keep quiet no longer. "Why?" It is the only question worth asking.

"The more we can increase the antipathy between men and women the easier it will be to perpetuate these crimes against women and pervert the men. Men will pull away from God out of shame and women will do it out of a feeling of abandonment."

"It sounds like you are trying to create hell on earth."

He smiles. "Nicely put. Don't you want to know the role your son will play?" He laughs again. "Soon we will reduce the time required for divorce to a matter of days. By the time we're finished, there won't be a shred of moral decency to be found anywhere. But my best is still to come. One day, it will be virtually impossible to give birth to anything but a physically perfect child."

"I don't understand."

"Genetic testing. We will use it on pregnant women, and if the child has a birth defect, we will mandate abortion."

"You're crazy! A law like that will never pass."

"That's what they said about abortion. It will happen, and when it does, it will make the abortion rates skyrocket." He was gleeful.

"What does increasing the abortion rate do for your cause?" I ask.

His eyes look upward. "There's nothing more precious in the eyes of God than new life. Anything I can do to destroy those lives, I'll do."

I am without words. The more I am forced to endure his lectures, the more tainted and soul sick I feel. I say the only thing I can think of to make him angry.

"You won't prevail. No matter how important you think you are, there will always be many more good men and women who will fight you."

"Good men and women? There are no *good* people. They are all self-interested, easily manipulated little pawns. I'll show you."

I shake my head.

"I don't want to see any more of your work."

He grabs my arm. "It's not a request."

Still, I refuse to move. "Why do you care what I think? What difference does it make if you show me these things?"

"You will accompany me to this meeting but you will say nothing. Do you understand? Or should I have your sister brought here?"

"I understand." I stand and follow him from the room. He has taken my parents from me, and I can't let him take her too. Despite all he is capable of, I cling to the hope that he will keep this promise to me. Do I believe she is truly out of danger? As long as she is his only connection to the coins, I think she is. But I can't take any chances.

He opens a door to a boardroom and sits at the head of the table. He points to a chair on his right, and I take a seat. There are three people sitting at the long, chrome table. No one asks who I am; they only glance quickly in my direction.

"Good day, doctors. I trust you have found it easy to work together and come up with a program with which you all agree? Let us hear from the psychiatrist first."

A man who looks to be in his mid-forties, balding, with round-rimmed spectacles answers, "It has been most interesting to hear the opinions of my esteemed colleagues. I now have a better understanding of neuroscience, as well as sexual medicine. We have put together a protocol which we believe will please you." He hands Damon a folder.

Damon opens it and makes a face. He looks disgusted. I get a glimpse of a naked woman being restrained. I can't see the rest of the photo, but my imagination fills in the blanks.

Damon puts the picture back in the folder and throws it down. "How does it work?"

The psychiatrist looks at the woman next to him and then back at Damon. "I will let Dr. Droskin, our neuroscientist, answer that."

Droskin speaks. "We will combine video, magazines, books, and auditory measures to stimulate the subjects and to measure which has the greatest and most immediate effect. Video will leverage the mirror neuron tendencies by zooming in and making the subject feel he is experiencing what is happening on the screen. We will measure response to stimuli and whether we can change the sexual appetite by repeated exposure to negative stimuli if it follows positive stimuli closely enough."

Damon is nodding. He turns his attention to the last man in the room. "Let's hear from our sexual medicine specialist."

"In a nutshell, we show them something that turns them on. Right after, we show one of the scenarios they find abhorrent—rape, torture, bondage. We see if repeated exposure to the negative, closely after erotic stimulation, eventually pairs the two scenarios until the subject is aroused by all the scenarios. It is our theory that sexual predators are made, not born. If we can understand the process behind it, we have great hopes of curing them."

The psychiatrist picks up the thread. "Most of these criminals have been exposed to this behavior from their male caregivers. They have been subjected to torture and abuse themselves, then forced to participate in these crimes until their sexual appetites are perverted. We will attempt to replicate this to see if our theories are indeed correct. We will also inundate them through their auditory channel, with the sounds of women pleading, anguished cries, and so on, until they become desensitized to them. It is a protocol that we've—"

Damon interrupts him. "So you believe you can find the key to how rapists and sadists develop?"

"That is our hypothesis. We can begin tomorrow."

Crosse stands. "I look forward to your updates." He turns to me. "Let's go."

As we walk down the hall I can't help but see how pleased with himself he looks.

"They think they're working on a cure, but you're going to use it to make sexual predators."

He smiles at me. "Ah, Maya. You're catching on."

"If they're looking for a cure, why wouldn't they take existing deviants and try to do the opposite, to make their appetites normal?"

"It's too late by then. Those men are too damaged. We need to reach people earlier. The research wouldn't bear it out, and I couldn't find anyone to agree to experiment on children. This way, if it works, they can reverse the methods to be used on younger subjects that are pulled from such circumstances."

I shake my head. "It's a specious argument. Your scientists are charlatans."

"They are not your traditional doctors. If, at first, they worried about turning normal men into rapists and sadists, their egos allowed them to believe the lie—that they could turn them back. They are lured by the promise of becoming pioneers, of discovering a cure for what is currently incurable. To turn a predatory sexual deviant into a contributing member of society is the head shrinker's holy grail." He arches an eyebrow. "See? Self-interest at work once again."

"And how are you going to implement this into society? Are you going to kidnap young men and brainwash them?"

"Of course not. I will implement another training program at The Institute and rewire the brains of our future leaders. I'll be judicious, but done to the right men, the consequences will be far-reaching. You'd be amazed at what men will do to satisfy their deviant urges. Only a little tweak here and there to a select few—I can't risk turning out an army of sociopaths, after all, I need to keep control."

I hate him with every fiber of my being. I want to crush him. I want to watch him bleed and die. I now understand how someone can murder. I know we are supposed to love our enemies, but this man standing before me is not worthy of love. There isn't a shred of humanity in him. If I didn't know better, I would believe he was the devil incarnate. I can't allow him to raise my child. I must figure out a way to prevent this child from being born alive. I will find a way and hope that God will forgive me.

CHAPTER FORTY-FIVE

"Do you have everything?" Jack and Taylor were ready to go to the library.

"Yeah, I think so."

She was quiet as he drove. "Jack, do you mind stopping? I want to get a ginger ale. My stomach is upset."

"Everything all right?"

"Of course everything is not all right. My husband's dead, our lives are in danger, and I don't even know what we're doing. What if this is just a huge wild-goose chase? And when it's all over, then what? I thought I had a good life with Malcolm. Turns out he was a liar too."

Too? Jack thought. Was that how she saw him? A liar? He pulled up to a 7-Eleven and put the car in park. He turned to face her. "Come on, Taylor. I know you're grieving for Malcolm, but time will heal."

Anger flashed in her eyes. "Is that what you think, Jack? Time will heal? Let me tell you something—it doesn't heal. It only numbs the pain tearing your heart apart until you can't feel anything anymore. It wasn't supposed to be like this." She poked him in the chest. "You and I were supposed to be together. But you ran off and married that psycho!" Taylor threw the door open and ran into the store leaving Jack alone and shaken.

Jack sat shamefaced, Taylor's words still ringing in his ears. He looked at Beau, who had leaned forward and licked his hand. "At least you're not mad at me, huh, fur ball?"

He stroked the soft coat absently and thought maybe it was a good thing that Taylor had gotten angry. It was time they cleared the air. He wanted to explain about Dakota, but how? He barely understood it himself, and he had no excuses or explanations for what he had done. He couldn't blame her for hating him. Despite the roller-coaster existence, it had never occurred to him to leave Dakota in the beginning. No matter how low she sank, how nasty she became, he stood by her and opened his heart again when the loving Dakota returned. He held no grudges, never threw her heartless words back at her. For her part, she seemed to have amnesia regarding her black spells. There were never any apologies, no pleas for forgiveness. She accepted it as her due that he would be there, on the other side of her depression, waiting for her return to him. His friends told him he was crazy, that he should leave. It was out of the question. Was he happy, they wanted to know? Happy? Had he ever been happy? In those rare moments of self-reflection, he would admit that yes, he had been happy—when he had been with Taylor. She'd been the only bright spot in a childhood marred by many seasons of melancholy and moroseness.

How had he failed to see it? He'd replicated his childhood when he'd married Dakota—it was the same wretched, unpredictable, insanity-filled life. Each pregnancy his beautiful Irish Catholic mother—with a poet's soul and a mournful heart—endured had plunged her deeper into depression, her emergence from the depths more arduous with each subsequent baby. Jack was her second. For as far back as he could remember, she had always been pregnant. When he left home at eighteen, he had seven siblings and a mother barely functioning. He'd begged his father to do something. Get her help. Stop knocking her up. They were Catholics, his father reminded him. Birth control was a sin. His father rebuked him for interfering with their "personal business" and insisted there was nothing wrong with his wife that a little time wouldn't cure. Taylor had been his mooring. Her family became his, and he spent his evenings at their dinner table, wishing they were his family instead—until the day when he knew he wanted much more from Taylor than to be a brother. How different both of their lives would have been if he'd kept his word to her. God knows he had paid the price for his mistakes—was still paying it every day. But that did nothing to alleviate Taylor's pain or to absolve him for causing it. Taylor approached the car looking sheepish and got in.

"I'm sorry, Jack. I don't know what got into me."

He shook his head. "Don't apologize. You were right. I should have never married her. To say I'm sorry doesn't even begin to cover it, and I don't know what I could ever say to make up for what I did."

She ran her hands through her hair.

"It's water under the bridge. Long time ago," she said quietly. "The stress of all of this, it's making me a little nuts."

"No, it's not. Taylor, can we please talk about it? I can't stand to have this huge thing between us. I know what I did was unforgivable. I'd like to at least try and explain."

"I don't think I really want to rehash it all. I know things didn't turn out well for you, and I'm sorry." She looked down.

He didn't mince words.

"Are you talking about the baby?"

She looked up. "Yes." She ran her thumb back and forth over her fingernail. "How could she? I'll never understand it." She shook her head.

Clearing his throat several times he finally answered. "She blamed it on me."

"What?"

"She hated being pregnant, gaining weight. She used to berate me daily about what I'd done to her."

Taylor said nothing.

"The day it happened, we'd had a fight. She kept egging me on, trying to get me to say that I thought she'd be a terrible mother. I finally did. I've never seen a look of triumph like the one on her face that day. When I came home, I found her in the tub. Right before she passed out she told me it was all my fault."

Taylor was horrified.

"Jack, don't you see that she'd planned it all along? No woman is going to cut a child out of her stomach just because of a few words. No sane person would do that."

He put his head in his hands. "I know that intellectually. But I still feel responsible. She killed my child just to spite me. That's how much she despised me. How could I fall for a person like that?"

Taylor pursed her lips. "How did you?" It came out as a whisper.

He was anguished. "I wish I knew. It was the worst mistake of my life. Will you ever be able to forgive me?"

She closed her eyes and finally answered, "I don't know if I can."

CHAPTER FORTY-SIX

The Institute, 1975
December

I retrieve the shard of glass from my hiding place and slip it into my pocket. I dare not try anything in my room or my bathroom—I know he has cameras everywhere. But today he is taking me to the screening room. He wants to show me the television programming of the future. I plan to ask to use the bathroom in the middle of it, and then I will do what needs to be done.

"Would you like to see an example of one of these shows?"

Not really, I want to say, but I know he'll show me anyway. I merely nod.

"This first one will be what we'll call a 'true life show.'"

"A what?"

"A show where the characters are real people, not actors. Cameras will follow them, and we'll get a glimpse into their actual lives. What you're about to see is the model for one of these shows."

The room goes dark and the screen lights up. Red letters appear one at a time until the title is displayed: AFFAIRS OF THE STREET. It looks like a normal neighborhood backyard barbecue. There are five couples sitting around a fire pit, drinking alcohol, laughing and talking. One of the women stands up and walks over to a hot tub.

"Anyone want to join me?" She takes off her top and her pants and climbs into the steaming water in nothing but her bra and underwear.

A few more people follow suit until there are just two people left sitting on the patio.

The woman who is left behind goes into the house, and the others are drinking and laughing, seemingly oblivious.

A short while later, the man she was sitting with goes inside.

The camera cuts to the interior of the house, to a bathroom, where the couple is kissing and peeling off each other's clothes.

The woman throws her head back and laughs. "I wondered if you'd follow me in."

He looks at her. "I've been wanting to do this to you all night."

The next scene shows them getting into the hot tub five minutes apart. She sits down next to another man.

"There you are," he says. He looks at one of the women sitting across from him. "Didn't know if she'd get in. She's a little sensitive about that all baby fat she's carrying around." He pinches some flesh on her side and laughs. "Right, my little chubs?"

Everyone stops talking, and his wife's eyes fill as the camera zooms in on her.

Another woman gives him a dirty look. "I think Nina looks beautiful."

Nina gives her a grateful look.

Damon gets up and turns light on.

"You get the idea."

"What's entertaining about that? Why would anyone watch that garbage?"

"I've only shown you the highlights. We'll make them care about the people. By the time a scene like that airs, the audience will already be invested in their stories. We'll make them sympathetic to the couple having the affair, make it seem justified. But there's more. That's just the beginning."

I sit riveted over the next several hours watching all kinds of shows that promote promiscuity, the occult, perversion, abortion, prostitution, criminal lifestyles, and more. The villains are the heroes, and I can see how people might root for them. He's right. Commercials are as bad as the shows: ads for condoms, sex aids, and pornographic materials abound.

Then he tells me about a drama—his favorite idea—one about demons. He calls it *Sympathy for the Devil*. It's about a cadre of demons exiled from hell due to an act of kindness. They are sent back to earth to prove that they are worthy of their roles in the dark kingdom. The twist is that these demons have a compassionate side they can't seem to shake. In each assignment, they start off doing what is expected of them, but somewhere along the way, they meet a human who sparks a seed of sympathy or empathy, thus beginning the cycle all over again. He says he'll make sure they cast actors with boyish good looks, rakish charm, and their transformation into demons will be mildly appealing.

"You see, Maya, after a few episodes, the fact that these are *demons* will recede to the background of people's consciousness. Some people will even like it. In the next few decades, less and less will be offensive. In fact, the only thing that will be offensive is intolerance to these things."

I glare at him. "You won't rest until you strip society of every shred of decency."

"There is no decency in humanity. All I'm doing is stripping away the facade."

At first, I find it utterly impossible to believe that people will ever accept this type of thing. Deep in my heart, however, I fear that he's right. Over time, and with the right framing, I think he will accomplish his goals. I shudder when I imagine this bleak future, beset with darkness and iniquity. My beloved child, I am more convinced than ever that I must release you from this dark destiny.

"I need to use the bathroom. I feel nauseated."

"Can't it wait until we return to your room?"

I pretend to gag. "No!"

He makes a face and leads me out to the hallway to the lavatory. "I'll wait here."

I go in. There are four stalls. I turn the water on, hoping the noise will be enough to keep him from hearing my screams until it is too late. I walk to the stall farthest from the door and go in.

"Forgive me, God."

One deep swipe is all it will take. Nick the jugular, and I'll bleed out before he can do anything. I pull out the long shard of glass and take a deep breath. I hold my hand in front of my neck, bracing myself. As I am about to do it, I feel a kick. An overwhelming anguish overtakes me. How can I do this? But how can I not? I position myself again and tell myself to get it over with. It's the only thing I can do to save my child. Another move inside my belly causes me to pause, and I hear my mother's voice inside my head. *Life is sacred. God has a purpose for each of us.* Can He really have a purpose for my child? The battle wages in my heart as I wrestle with myself. My shirt is damp with perspiration, and I am dizzy. What should I do? *God, what should I do?* A small, quiet voice stops me. If I am to embrace my faith, I must embrace it all. I have to believe that God is stronger—stronger than Damon and Dunst and the evil one they serve. I throw the glass into the toilet and flush it down. I stand and watch as it swirls away, disappearing—along with my last hope of saving my child.

CHAPTER FORTY-SEVEN

Damon Crosse sighed in annoyance at the persistent ringing. He hated being interrupted.

"What?" He barked into the receiver.

"We've located them."

His hold on the phone tightened. "Where are they?"

"A motel in New Hampshire. We just got a call from one of our men inside Jeremy's organization. They checked in last night."

"And I'm only being informed now?"

The voice on the other end grew quiet.

"Well?"

"My phone died. I forgot the car charger. I just picked up the message."

He clenched his jaw, swallowed, then spoke evenly. "Have you dispatched someone to intercept them?"

"Yes, sir. They're on their way now. They'll arrive within the hour."

"Contact your people and tell them to call me once they have them."

"I can take care of it, sir I—"

"Have them contact me directly." He terminated the call and pressed the button on his desk.

Jonas entered.

Damon handed him a piece of paper. "Give this to Dakota. Tell her she can indulge herself with this one."

"Yes, sir."

"Tell her to make sure there is no mistaking her work. I want it to serve as a warning to the others that we take carelessness very seriously."

"Very well, sir."

When the door had closed behind Jonas, Damon picked up the crystal goblet and threw it across the room. It smashed against the brick wall, and Peritas jumped up, startled.

"Come here, my boy." Damon pushed his chair back from the desk to allow room for the dog.

Peritas put his head on Damon's leg and wagged his tail while his head was rubbed.

Damon closed his eyes and continued to stroke the lush fur. It would do no good to lose control, he reminded himself. They would be in his possession and then Taylor would play her part in leading him to Jeremy—all in good time. In the meantime, he *must* keep a cool head.

CHAPTER FORTY-EIGHT

They pulled into the empty lot of the Fiske Library.

"That's strange," Taylor said.

Jack pulled around to the entrance, and she got out to read the sign. "Closed on Sundays." He sighed. "Great."

The upside was they got one more night together, although he wasn't sure Taylor would see that as a good thing. They had been extremely lucky that no one had recognized them yet. Even though they were in small town USA, it would be prudent to take more precautions. Jack knew what they had to do. They returned to the motel.

* * *

Taylor stood in the small motel bathroom. "I thought you said we didn't have to?"

"Let's just say my gut is telling me it's a good idea."

"My hairdresser's not going to be happy. May as well get it over with." She braced herself while he began to cut her hair. When he was finished, she looked at him with surprise. "It actually isn't half bad."

He took a bow. "One of my hidden talents. My mother taught me how. She thought paying for hair cuts was wasteful."

She arched an eyebrow. "You didn't always have such a steady hand. Remember when you butchered your sister's hair. I thought she was going to kill you. It was all uneven and spiky."

He laughed. "I had to sleep with one eye open for weeks." He took a deep breath and winced. "My turn." He made broad cuts to his blond hair, cutting it close to his head. Then he picked up the razor.

Taylor winced. "You're not going to shave it all are you?"

He made the first swipe right down the middle. "Yup. Guess we'll get to see what I look like bald." He grinned. It didn't take him long to finish. Wow. Who knew hair made such a difference? He wondered what Taylor thought.

"Well?"

Taylor ran her hand over the smooth surface that was now his head. "At least it will grow back."

"Not exactly a ringing endorsement." He shrugged. "We're not done yet." He grabbed the box of hair color from the drug store. "I don't know how this will turn out." He paused and took a long look at her. "I always imagined I could see the reflection of the sun in your hair. I'm sorry to have to do this." He lifted a strand and held it between his fingers.

She flicked his hand away in obvious annoyance. "Just do it."

What was wrong with him? Just when the tension between them started to dissipate he acted like an awkward teenager rushing in for his first kiss.

"Here goes nothing."

Chapter Forty-Nine

The Institute, 1975
December

Today is Christmas. The only one I'll ever spend with my baby. I sing carols to him and tell him of the love of Christ. I continue to pray for him and for myself. I must believe that a mother's prayers count for something—it's the only thing that keeps me going. I've been thinking of my parents too. Can they see me from Heaven? Are they able to offer some protection, some prayer for me? Long-forgotten Bible verses, recited to me as a child by my mother return to me and give me some comfort. I lay my hands protectively on my belly and rub them back and forth, imagining I am stroking my child. How I wish I could hold him against me. It is agony to realize he will never know my love in this life. All the more reason for me to put my hope in the next.

I am singing "Joy to the World" when I hear his footsteps. I make my voice louder, forcing a jubilance to it that I don't feel. I refuse to allow him to steal Christmas from me, and I wait, almost eagerly, for his reaction to my praise. He says nothing when he opens the door, merely stares, his expression inscrutable. I look away and back down at my stomach, continuing my song. It takes every bit of resolve I possess to keep singing and pretend he isn't there. As I finish the last chorus, he begins to laugh.

"Well, Maya, quite the little convert."

"Can't you leave me alone on this day, of all days? Is there nothing sacred to you?"

He raises his eyebrows. "This is not a holiday I feel the need to celebrate. Now, the birth of *my* son, that will be cause for celebration. Only a fool would give his life for the world. My son, he will give the world what it deserves."

"What if he doesn't?"

"Doesn't what?" His tone becomes hard.

"Doesn't follow in your twisted footsteps. What if he has plans of his own? Noble plans?"

He stands up and turns his back to me. "That is no concern of yours. I am quite confident his upbringing will have the desired outcome." As he opens the door and steps from the room, he calls over his shoulder. "Oh, Merry Christmas." I hear his laughter echo as he walks away.

CHAPTER FIFTY

Taylor was now a blonde. Beau started whining and turning in circles.

"Aw, baby, it's okay. It's still me." She knelt and called him over to her.

He approached her tentatively and began to sniff. Tail wagging, he licked her face until she was laughing and had to push him away.

"Good job, Jack. My own dog didn't recognize me."

He had to admit that her appearance was quite changed. Even with his hack job, she was still beautiful. The familiar longing returned, burning in his belly like a shot of Jameson.

"It's almost dawn. Why don't you take him out, and then we'll hit the road before the sun comes up?"

With his face plastered all over the news, Jack was keeping the lowest profile possible.

"Come on, buddy." She put the leash on Beau and stepped out into the bracing air.

Jack frowned. "Be careful."

Taylor walked Beau to the back of the motel and gave him enough leash to find a satisfactory place to relieve himself. Why were dogs so particular about that? It seemed to her that one blade of grass was as good as another. She hopped from one foot to the other trying to keep warm. The temperature had dropped suddenly and sharply. Now she wished she had some gloves. She shoved her free hand in her coat pocket and tugged on the lead. Enough was enough. "Come on, boy. Go!"

He finally obliged and trotted back to her with a contented expression as they walked toward the front of the hotel. Then, he growled, a deep, suspicious snarl from the back of his throat.

"What is it?" she whispered.

He was still growling, and she stood still, paralyzed by indecision.

She pulled on the leash and tried to coax Beau slowly forward, but he refused, seemingly rooted the ground.

Then she saw them. Two figures in black skulking in the shadows, moving in the direction of their hotel room. What should she do? She had to warn Jack, but how?

As if reading her mind, Beau bolted upright, tore away from her and went bounding at the two men at full speed.

He leaped and sunk his teeth into the first man's arm. The man screamed as he tried to shake loose of the determined canine.

"What the hell?" he screamed.

The man next to him lifted the hand holding a gun and pointed it at Beau.

"No!" Taylor yelled, and instinctively ran toward them.

The motel door flew open, and Jack flung himself at the man with the gun. It went off, just as Taylor collided with Beau and fell onto the pavement.

CHAPTER FIFTY-ONE

The Institute, 1976

January

I spent New Year's Day thinking of resolutions, and of years past, when I had my entire life in front of me. This New Year will be my last. I think of how different things could be if I were free. My precious son would have an entire family to love him. It is too unbearable to ponder. I try to relish the little time I have left and use it for some good. When my thoughts become too torturous, I pray.

My stomach lurches as I hear the familiar clicking on the cold, marble floors. He is coming.

His boasting begins again.

"Maya, how is it possible that you are still so naïve? Do you really imagine the throngs will resist me? I have Madison Avenue in my back pocket. The fools believe whatever we tell them to. Slowly, very slowly, we have been shifting society's values. Small steps, moving the line ever so slightly until they don't even realize the gigantic leaps we have taken. Just a few years ago we couldn't show a married couple sleeping in the same bed. Soon, they'll be watching strangers having sex, during the so-called family hour, and no one will blink an eye. By the time we're through, morality will be a distant memory and the very few that try and hold on to it will be classified radical fanatics."

His arrogance is infuriating. "What's in it for you?" I blurt out.

He looks right through me. "I am serving my master. He desires the ruination of souls. It is my pleasure to assist him in that quest."

"Enjoy it while you can. I can assure you, eternity is not going to be fun for you."

"Don't preach to me, Maya. You have no idea what you're talking about. Too bad you won't be around to see your son serve the master."

He knows exactly what to say to shut me up.

CHAPTER FIFTY-TWO

She looked up from the cold concrete when she heard a rapid succession of popping noises. A different man was standing across from Jack with a gun in his hand. Where was the man Beau had attacked? She turned her head. There he was, lying on the ground, blood pooled around his middle, eyes closed. Was he dead? Jack held his own gun to the head of a third man, at whom Beau was growling, ready to pounce again. Taylor winced as she put her weight on her arm and pushed herself up and stood.

"Who are you?" Jack was glaring at the man.

"Jeremy sent us."

Jack still held the gun trained on him. "How do I know you're really with Jeremy?"

"Saint Christopher is on your side."

"I'll be a son of a—"

"Come on, we've got to move before someone sees us." He motioned with his head for them to look behind him, and Taylor saw a van with its back doors open and engine running.

Jack didn't hesitate. He pulled the man he was holding over to the van. Three men jumped out. One cuffed Jack's prisoner, while the other two retrieved the body. It was all cleaned up within a matter of minutes.

"How did you find us?" Jack asked.

"There's a tracking device in the St. Christopher medal. We've been keeping tabs on you. Jeremy got inside intel that we've been compromised. We found the traitor but not before he alerted The Institute."

"The what?"

"No time. We've got to get going."

"Can you take us to Jeremy?"

The man shook his head. "Don't know where he is. We were dispatched for this only. No one has his location. It's safer for him that way."

Jack felt inside his jacket pocket for the medal and handed it to the man. "Take it back. I don't want to throw it out, but I'm not keeping it on me in case you're compromised again." He hoped he wasn't bringing back luck on himself by giving the medal away. He shook his head. *Don't be a superstitious idiot*, he thought.

The man took it, ran back to the van, and they drove away.

"What was he talking about? What's all this with the Saint Christopher medal?" Taylor asked.

"It was a code. I didn't realize when she said it, until I heard him repeat it.

"What do you mean, a code?" she asked.

"I'll tell you in the car. Are you okay?"

She nodded. "Yeah, hurt my arm a little, but I'm fine."

"What were you thinking diving in front of Beau like that?"

She shrugged. "I guess I wasn't."

Jack looked down at Beau. "Come on fur ball. You deserve a big treat." He opened the back door, and Beau jumped in.

Taylor put on her seat belt, still trying to catch her breath and steady her shaking hands. She looked out of the back window as they drove away.

"So are you going to tell me what that was all about?"

"A nice old lady gave me a Saint Christopher medal the other day when I helped her to her car. The last thing she said was "Saint Christopher is on your side."

He continued to surprise her. "When did you help an old lady?"

"When I went to the drugstore for supplies, she was in front of me in line and fell. I walked her to her car."

"Still the Boy Scout." She grinned at him.

He narrowed his eyes at her good-naturedly. His stint in the boy scouts had lasted exactly one meeting. He'd said it was a little too gung-ho for him. "Funny."

"I can still see you in your uniform, your cute neckerchief slide around your neck."

"Thanks for reminding me. I had to pay my parents back for that uniform out of my allowance when I refused to go back."

She leaned back against the seat and closed her eyes. The image of the man lying on the ground filled her mind and she sat up.

"Jack? Was that man dead?"

He ran his fingers over his lips then nodded.

She shivered. The bodies were stacking up. "It's strange. I know they were there to kill us, just like the man at the cabin." She swallowed. "But I still feel bad. I mean—they were people. Two days ago, all I could think about was getting ready for my baby. Now we're being chased by killers. How can that be?" She turned and pressed her forehead against the cold window. Her eyes fixated on the yellow line on the road stretching out forever, toward nowhere. What was in store for her now? Her future unrolled before her like a foreign scroll, inscrutable and indecipherable.

CHAPTER FIFTY-THREE

"What do you mean, they got away?" Damon Crosse barked into the phone.

"We didn't know the girl and the dog were outside. They snuck up and attacked us."

Damon shook his head in disgust. "A dog and a pregnant woman *attacked* you?"

"They had help. Four men showed up out of nowhere. Lucky for me, they threw me out of the van instead of killing me."

"Too bad they didn't. They would have spared me the trouble." Crosse hung up. They must have been Jeremy's men. No one else would be stupid and sentimental enough not to finish the job. Threw him out of the van. How disappointing. Jeremy was weak. How did he think he could ever win when he couldn't handle the simple matter of disposing of an enemy properly?

"If they're in New Hampshire, Jeremy's facility must be close. I want aerial surveillance over the whole state and the surrounding ones. Find them."

CHAPTER FIFTY-FOUR

This time, the library was open, and Taylor entered the brown brick building. She scanned the signs on the shelves, looking for the fiction section. The facility was small, and it didn't take her long to find the *M* shelf.

She found the book immediately and blew the dust from the top of it. She held it close to her, suddenly irrationally fearful of it being snatched away. Sitting down at the empty table, she opened it and began to slowly turn the pages. There it was. A plain white slip of paper with one word written on it. She took the paper, returned the book to the shelf, and left.

She got back in to the passenger seat. "Do you see a road called Clayton?"

"Yeah, here it is, Clayton Drive." He pointed to it on the map.

"Then we are off to Thirty-Seven Clayton Drive."

"Great going, T." He held her gaze and smiled broadly.

"Well, what are you waiting for? Let's go!"

An hour later, Jack and Taylor pulled onto Clayton Drive. It was another long and dusty road that seemed to go on forever. Just when they thought they had hit another dead-end, they pulled in front of a small Cape Cod that backed into woods. There were no other houses around. Jack turned to Taylor and raised his eyebrows.

"Not what I expected, but here goes nothing."

She unlatched her seat belt, but he put a hand over hers.

"Wait here until I assess the situation. I don't know what we might be walking into. Get in the driver's seat—that way you can take off if you have to."

"Seriously? We're in this together. I can take care of myself."

"Sorry."

They approached the front door, and it opened before they had a chance to knock. Standing before them was an older man with white hair and wire-rimmed glasses. He smiled warmly.

"We've been expecting you. Certainly took your time getting here." He chuckled at their shocked expressions.

Jack held out his hand. "I'm Jack—"

The man interrupted him. "I know who you are." He turned his attention to Taylor. "You, child, must be Taylor. Come in, come in."

Taylor gave Jack a bemused look as they walked into the foyer. Now that they were inside the house, she saw that it was actually quite large—she could see into a long, eat-in kitchen and beyond it another large rectangular room. Before the door was shut, Beau began to bark from the backseat.

"Well, well. Who is that?"

"My dog," Taylor replied.

"Go get him. Poor thing must be going crazy all cooped up."

Taylor smiled gratefully and went immediately to retrieve him.

Beau ran into the house whimpering and licked the man's hand, his tail swishing in a frenzy.

"Are you all going to stand in the hallway all day or come in the kitchen and have something to eat?" a voice called from the other end of the house.

The man smiled. "That's Gilly. Come on, she's eager to meet you."

They were greeted by a sweet-looking older woman who was bustling around the kitchen and setting out a variety of scrumptious-looking desserts. She held out her arms and insisted on giving each of them a warm hug.

They sat at the round, wooden kitchen table. Jack cleared his throat, ready to start asking questions, but the man spoke again.

"Guess you'll be wanting some explanations. I'm Professor Carl

Rittenhouse and this is my lovely wife, Gilly. I taught at Harvard for the past thirty years. Retired last year, so I could devote myself full-time to my research and writing." He leaned back in his chair.

"Jeremy was one of my students many years ago. One of the brightest but also the most troubled. He hated my class, didn't think it applied to him, even sought to get it removed as a program requirement."

Taylor looked at him with interest. "What do you teach?"

He smiled. "Glad you asked, my dear. I teach medical ethics. I have my PhD in bioethics, but I'm not your typical bioethicist. You see, most in the field are working to push the limits, see how far they can go to optimize care, allocate limited resources by building a hierarchy of who deserves what. I'm what they consider a fringe lunatic. Prolife, anti-euthanasia, anti-embryonic stem cell research, and anti-assisted suicide."

Beau ambled over after drinking from the bowl Gilly had set on the floor for him and sat at Carl's feet. Carl stroked his head while he continued.

"Jeremy was not aligned with my views—many of my students weren't—but he harbored a hatred I'd not come across very often. Only way I can put it—he had an evil aura about him."

Jack couldn't keep the skeptical expression from appearing. Carl noticed.

"I don't use that word lightly, Jack."

Gilly set a plate of coffee cake on the table and joined them.

"I knew the only thing I could do was pray for the boy. Nothing I could say or do on my own was going to influence him, although I tried. An angrier atheist I have never met. After he graduated, I thought I had seen the last of him."

Gilly patted her husband's hand. "You'd have to know my husband to understand. He lives his faith more than anyone I know. Over the years, there have been some complaints about him professing his faith, but it's never stopped him. Did you know that Harvard was named after a Christian minister?"

Jack and Taylor both shook their heads.

Carl continued. "It's my belief that as long as we still have the power of free speech, no one should have the ability to stop us from sharing our convictions. My belief in God is so intricately wound up in my philosophy, my view of medicine, that to leave it behind would mean leaving all that behind as well. Of course, I didn't preach to the class, but I would not skirt any questions on the issues of faith and how they affected my beliefs. It worked for everyone, except for the occasional rabble-rouser that felt the right to his or her own beliefs supplanted my own. But I digress. Jeremy. The Lord let me know that I needed to keep on praying for him. So, I did. A few years ago, he showed up on campus. I took one look at him and knew something had happened to change him."

CHAPTER FIFTY-FIVE

The Institute, 1976
March

You are coming. I wake up in a cold sweat, and with a jolt, I feel another contraction. A moan escapes my lips, and I roll to my side and grip the edge of the bed. *It hurts, it hurts.* I didn't know it would hurt so much. I scream and try to bring my knees to my chest, but my belly is too big. I remember what I learned about the Lamaze method in medical school, and I rock and breathe, rock and breathe. It helps a little. The contraction passes, and I push my sweat-drenched hair back from my forehead. I look at the clock on the table to time my contractions. I sit up, trying to work out the dull ache in my back. Ten minutes and another one starts. The pain snakes its way from my toes, up my legs, and to my belly until it feels like there's a vise inside me smashing all my organs. I push on my stomach. It is rock hard. I feel like my bowels are going to explode. I need to bear down, push, but I know it's too soon. *Breathe.* It will be over in a minute. I clutch the sheets and bite my cheek. It stops again. Eight minutes this time. A spasm in my back makes me jerk forward, and another scream flies from my mouth. Sweat stings my eyes, and I swipe at my face with my sleeve. I start to shake and the whole bed seems to move with me. Why I am so cold now? Another convulsion and I'm racked again. Only four minutes. No. You're coming too fast.

I cry out as another wave of pain overtakes me and fall back on the bed. My knuckles are white as I squeeze the pillow. The contractions are faster now, each one leaving me more breathless than before. Something is wrong. A searing pain rips through me and a wetness spreads down my legs. Blood, there is too much blood. Someone needs to come.

"Help. Something's wrong." I push the call button over and over.

The door bursts open, and I'm thrown onto a gurney. He is there, panic written all over his face.

Time is running out. Once you are born, I will die. He'll kill me as swiftly and as easily as he did his own father—as he did my parents. But I don't fear death—not anymore. I know my Savior awaits me and that he will shepherd me from this hellish existence into paradise. But leaving you? This is a pain so deep, an anguish so terrible it slices through me like a knife. I love you my child. There is nothing more to say.

They rush me to the elevator and down to the first level. I'm wheeled into a cold room with shiny steel tables and counters and bright lights. He has his own operating room. The pain is excruciating now. I can't stop the screams. My eyes are clouding, and all I can hear is the clang of instruments and the voices shouting all around me. From the corner of my eye, I see him. Dunst. He is sitting, directing them.

A nurse hooks an IV up to my arm, and I beg for some relief. I know it's too late for an epidural and I don't want to be knocked out—I want to see my baby if only for a second—but I need something for the pain.

"Please, give me some morphine," I gasp.

She looks in the direction of Dunst.

"Dr. Dunst?"

He doesn't hesitate. "No. She can get through it. Medicine is not good for the baby. Give her nothing."

The doctor is yelling. "There's no time. The placenta is abrupting.

We have to deliver now!"

My God! They can't really be going to cut into me with no anesthesia. They don't even bother to put a drape up, so I see everything unfold. Betadine is thrown on my stomach; the scalpel is out and the pain is white-hot the second the knife touches my skin. I howl, and the nurse clamps her hand down hard over my mouth. I feel my organs being jostled and almost pass out from the pain. I'm trying to hold on for a glimpse of my baby—just one look. I am being torn in two. The agony is indescribable, and I yearn for the release of death. Everything begins to fade, and I know I'm bleeding out. It won't be long now. A cry pierces the air, and I see him lifted from me. I try to raise my arms, but they don't move. I long to hold him—to kiss him.

"Please, let…see." I can hardly speak.

The doctor hands my child to Damon. He is walking away, then stops, turns around, and holds him in front of me, close enough to touch if I had the strength. He is beautiful. So beautiful. *I love you*, I want to say, but nothing comes out.

And then it doesn't hurt anymore. The pain is gone and a warmth washes over me. Arms of love embrace me, and there is no more fear. I'm lifted, beckoned from this dim and fading room to another place that shines so bright, like going from darkest night to brightest morning. I'm free! I turn back for one last look, and the last thing I see before I leave is my son's beautiful, beautiful face.

CHAPTER FIFTY-SIX

Jack and Taylor were enthralled as Carl continued his story.

"Jeremy had discovered the truth about his father, Damon Crosse, who he really was and the extent to which he had sunk to attain his goals. After Jeremy finished medical school, he began working at a research facility on germ line genetic engineering. You have to understand; Jeremy was raised in an emotional vacuum. He attended boarding school from age six, summers in overnight programs. The only affirmation he ever received from Crosse was for his academic achievement. Friendships were discouraged. He was groomed for one purpose. To one day take over the Institute."

"What's the Institute?" Jack asked.

"A training facility. And so much more."

"What happened next?" Taylor asked.

"Jeremy fell in love. His father was furious, told him he had to give her up. They had a huge argument. Jeremy wanted to know why it was okay for his father to have a wife and family but not him. You see, Jeremy never knew his mother. That's when Crosse told him everything."

Taylor shook her head. "I don't understand. What does this have to do with Malcolm and his vote? With the people trying to kill us?"

Jack put his hand on her arm. "I'm fairly sure Damon Crosse is who Malcolm worked for." He looked back at Carl. "What truth?"

Carl drew a deep breath. "That he had kidnapped, imprisoned, and forcibly impregnated his mother, then left her bleeding to die after he'd been born."

"Oh my God! Are you serious? Why would he do that?"

Carl nodded. "It's a very long story, and it's Jeremy's to tell. He came to me after this happened. Instead of Crosse's revelations bonding him to his son, they alienated him. He poured out his heart to me, asked how he could continue to live knowing that half his DNA belonged to such a monster. He desperately wanted to believe that his heredity was not his destiny. I reminded him about the other half of his DNA and how the Lord had impressed upon me to pray for him. We spent hours talking and praying and at the end of it, he committed his life to God. We devised a plan together. He would go back, pretend that nothing had changed, begin to take his place and slowly, discreetly, gather the information necessary to bring Crosse down."

Carl continued. "It took every bit of strength he had to go back and face his father, knowing what he had done, but Jeremy knew that he had no choice. Crosse wanted Jeremy back, needed him to continue his research. Jeremy had to appear as single-minded and ruthless as his father. He used that time to amass information, get to know the players, and determine who would be open to switching loyalties."

"What kind of research?" Taylor asked.

"Gene therapy."

Jack and Taylor exchanged a look.

"Another scientist began to get suspicious. You see, Jeremy knew what his father was planning on doing with the research so he backtracked, made intentional mistakes. Damon questioned him about it and Jeremy either had to give him what he wanted or get out fast," Carl finished.

"Where is he now?"

"I don't know exactly. All of us have limited information, just what we need to help you reach the next way point."

Jack stood up, pacing. "Hold on. Doesn't Jeremy trust you?"

"Of course, but if Damon found us…well, he would stop at

nothing to get his hands on Jeremy." He arched a brow. "No one is immune to torture."

Taylor's eyes widened. "The more I learn, the more incredible this all is."

"It's true. Believe me. Once you get to Jeremy, you'll get the answers you seek." He stood. "I'll go and get your information."

Gilly got up and cleared the table. She looked at Taylor with warm eyes. "How are you feeling, my dear?"

"I'm doing okay."

"How about a quick cup of tea before you get going?"

Taylor and Gilly went into the kitchen together and Taylor sat at the table while Gilly made tea.

"Here you go."

Taylor felt strangely grateful for these small kindnesses and swallowed the lump in her throat. She wanted to sit in this kitchen all day and pretend that this sweet woman was someone who loved her, an aunt or a grandmother. Why was she being so silly? She had just met her. Taylor put her hands around the steaming mug and enjoyed the feeling of the warmth on her fingers as Gilly sat across from her.

"Gilly, do you and Carl know anything about my husband? About his role in all of this?"

Gilly stared at her for a long moment. "I think it's best if you wait to ask Jeremy."

Taylor looked up to see Jack and Carl come in.

Jack cleared his throat. "It's time to get moving. We've still got a few hours to drive."

She nodded. She took a last sip of her tea and pushed back in the chair.

"All right." She looked at Gilly. "Will I see you again?" She was reluctant to leave her.

Gilly smiled warmly. "You bet. Our home is always open to you. We'll talk again after you've seen Jeremy. We're here to help."

Carl looked at Taylor. "I think it would be best if you left Beau here while you visit with Jeremy."

Taylor began to object, but Carl put a hand on her shoulder. "I promise we'll treat him like he's our own, and he'll be here waiting for you when you return."

Taylor nodded reluctantly. It *would* be better for him here. Safer. "If anything happens to me, you will take care of him?" Her voice caught.

Carl's eyes were kind. "Nothing is going to happen to you." He put his hand on Beau's back. "We'll take good care of him no matter what."

"Thank you." Taylor bent down and embraced her beloved dog. Tears spilled from her eyes as she stroked him and whispered, "I love you, boy. I'll be back for you—don't worry." She laid her head on his and then turned away. It was unbearable.

"Here's your next set of instructions," Carl said as he handed the paper to Jack. "Godspeed, son." He gave Jack's shoulder a squeeze.

They turned and walked to the car. Taylor glanced back for one more look at Beau. He was watching her from the door, a somber expression in his wise eyes. She blinked back tears and tried to ignore the feeling that she would never see him again.

Chapter Fifty-Seven

Melancholy enveloped Taylor. She stared out the window and took in the bleak surroundings as they drove down what seemed to be a never-ending road. She felt like the trees—stripped of their leaves, bare and vulnerable, their insides exposed for the world to see. When she thought of her baby, she was overwhelmed with a sense of helplessness. A week ago everything made sense. Now, her very survival depended on her partnership with the one man who had broken her heart—the man she swore she would never trust again.

"Jack?"

"Hmm?"

"Did the two of you discuss me?"

He exhaled slowly. "No, Taylor. Never."

"I met her you know?"

"What? When?"

She exhaled. "When I found out you'd gotten married, I drove up from Maryland. She answered the door. You were in the shower. She knew my name, mocked me."

"She never told me. She knew who you were, but I didn't talk about you. I swear."

She didn't know whether she believed him or not. She plunged in. "Why did you let her take you from me?"

He looked at her. "Are you sure you want to hear this?"

"No. But I can't stand having it between us anymore. We can't keep pretending everything is okay. You broke my heart, Jack." Her voice caught, and she turned away.

"I know."

A heavy silence filled the car for a long while. And, then, finally, he spoke.

"You can't imagine how often I've gone over it in my mind—back to when I first met her—changed the scenario. Walked away. Never gone to her show. I wish to God I could go back in time and undo it."

"You still haven't answered my question."

"I don't know how! God knows I've spent years regretting it. She took me by surprise, knew exactly what to say and how to get under my skin. She was an addiction. One that nearly destroyed me."

"I know what she did to you. But you were supposed to be committed to me. How could you turn your back on us so easily? How could you sleep with her in the first place?" Now she was sorry she had started the conversation. Far from breaking down any walls, she felt new resentments and hurts arise.

He shook his head. "It wasn't about the sex. There was something else—"

"Stop." Of course it was about the sex. How many times had she imagined the two of them together? "I don't want to hear anymore. I guess I'm not ready to discuss it after all."

He tried again "I really wish I could make you understand—"

"So do I," she responded sharply, then she softened her tone. "How much longer?"

Jack glanced at the map on his lap, then up at the road. "About another hour. Then we go to back roads."

"I need to use the bathroom."

"Okay. Keep your eyes open for a gas station or restaurant. It's pretty deserted. Not sure when the next one will appear."

Taylor leaned back against the headrest. She missed Beau. She missed her marriage. She missed her life.

CHAPTER FIFTY-EIGHT

Taylor held the handwritten directions. "Turn there."

Jack slammed on the brakes and made the sharp left-hand turn down the narrow dirt road.

"Wait. Take note of the odometer. We have to go exactly one point seven miles and then take another left. There's no road."

A few minutes later, Jack parked in the small, round dirt enclosure. He took the paper from Taylor.

"We have to follow this trail and there will be a four-by-four waiting," she said.

"Here, put these on." He handed her the hat and gloves Carl had given him before they'd left.

Taylor slipped them on, and they got out of the car.

Jack reached out to take her arm. "It's a little slippery here. Hold on to me."

They walked arm in arm into the woods.

"Feels a little like Hansel and Gretel," he joked.

She smiled in spite of herself. "Let's hope our story has a happy ending too." Taylor pointed. "According to Carl's map, the truck should be up ahead about a hundred feet."

The trees seemed to close in upon them, the brush growing denser with every step they took. It was impossible to see anything but the branches around them.

"I have an idea. Give me the keys," Taylor said.

Jack handed them to her.

She depressed the panic button and immediately a loud blaring filled the air.

"Brilliant," Jack said.

They followed the noise, got in and began the descent down the mountain towards Jeremy's hideout. Taylor held tightly to the handle hanging above her door as they bounced down the hill.

Jack looked at her apologetically. "Going as slow as I can."

She grimaced. "I know."

They finally reached the bottom of the steep hill and got out of the truck.

"This is getting a bit tedious," Jack mumbled as Taylor read Carl's instructions aloud.

They counted aloud to the prescribed number and came to a hill. They reached a tree with a birdhouse hanging from it.

"That's it."

Jack put his hand in the box and retrieved a key. They walked another hundred feet and came to a small cabin. Using the key, they entered, and Jack turned on the flashlight and looked around the small one-room building.

"What's that?" Taylor asked, pointing to an envelope taped to the wall.

Jack snatched it down and tore it open. It was another set of directions and a compass. They went back outside.

"We need to go east twelve hundred feet and we'll be there. Are you okay? It's a lot of walking."

She arched an eyebrow. "I may be pregnant, but I'm not out of shape. I'm fine."

He held his hands up in surrender. "Sorry."

They reached the entrance to what looked like a cave, the opening large enough to accommodate one person. There was a wall blocking it made of a smooth plaster. Jack pulled the phone Carl had given to him from his pocket.

He dialed the number on the sheet of paper. A male voice answered.

Jack spoke the words as instructed: "This is the day that the Lord has made."

A whirring filled the air, and the door slowly opened as it slid into the wall.

"After you." Jack moved aside for Taylor.

As soon as they were both inside, the door closed behind them.

Chapter Fifty-Nine

Taylor looked around at the bright and cheerful surroundings. She didn't know what she had expected, maybe something more ominous and akin to the underground hideouts she'd seen in James Bond movies. Instead, the foyer was painted a light yellow, and the shiny hardwood floors were covered with vibrant oriental rugs. There was no one waiting to greet them, so they began to walk in the only direction they could—straight ahead. When they reached the end of the hallway, they came to an elevator and pushed the button. Immediately, the door slid open.

"What floor?"

Taylor exhaled. "I don't know. Pick one."

He depressed the top button, and they ascended.

When the doors opened, a man was waiting. He was tall and trim, with light brown hair worn on the longish side. He looked to be only a few years older than Taylor. He gave them a wide smile that transformed his face from merely nice-looking to handsome.

"Thank God you made it! I'm Jeremy."

So this was the mysterious Jeremy. He looked at her like he already knew her, and Taylor didn't know what she was feeling. When he got closer, she realized that he reminded her of someone, but she couldn't put her finger on who.

She held out her hand, and he grasped it in both of his.

"I'm Taylor."

They followed him to a living room, where an assortment of

snacks and drinks awaited them. "Would you like to freshen up?"

She didn't want to wait another minute to find out what he had to say. "We're fine," Taylor answered.

"Let's sit down."

They had made it! She should have felt a tremendous sense of relief, but she still felt suspended in anticipation. Jeremy looked so normal. After what Carl had told her, she had been expecting someone who looked more tortured. *What a silly thought*, she chided herself. Did she think she'd find someone in sack cloth and ashes? A warmth emanated from him, and she felt immediately comfortable with him. She took a seat in the plush chair closest to the fireplace so that she could see the fire and also enjoy the view of the outside from the floor-to-ceiling windows. She liked seeing nothing but the tall evergreens and mountains in the distance. It made her feel far away from danger, hidden away and safe from the faceless enemies they were running from. She took a deep breath and looked at Jeremy.

"Who was my husband?" That's what it all boiled down to after all—why they were here in the first place.

Jeremy took a seat across from her, his expression neutral.

"That's a complicated question. We'll get to it, I promise, but I think it may make more sense if I tell you who I am."

"We know you're Damon Crosse's son," Jack said.

Jeremy nodded. "Yes, my father is Damon Crosse. He runs a research and training facility but it's a front for much more. In private circles, it's called the Institute, and its graduates are placed in positions of power in all spheres of influence."

Taylor leaned forward. "So Malcolm was one of these graduates?"

"He was. Groomed for his position and firmly in Damon's pocket."

She was still having a hard time wrapping her head around it. "Was Malcolm even his real name?"

Jeremy stood up and paced. "I don't know what his real name was." He stopped and put a hand on Taylor's shoulder. "I don't think he did either. He was an orphan, raised at the Institute."

"What? How old was he when he was orphaned?" She thought of

the parents he'd told her he'd lost to an accident when he was fifteen, the way they'd shared their grief at experiencing a sudden and devastating loss. That was his way into her heart—and it was all one big lie.

"According to his file, he was brought to the Institute by nuns when he was a baby."

"Liar," she whispered as she clenched and unclenched her fists.

She caught Jeremy and Jack exchange a look.

"For what it's worth Taylor, he did love you," Jeremy said.

"How could you possibly know that?" It was ludicrous to think that this stranger knew more about her own husband than she did.

"It's why he did what he did—to protect you and your child. Let me explain. Carl has told you about my upbringing. When I graduated high school, I entered Harvard, where I earned my undergraduate degree in biology. I continued through their doctoral program, where I attained my PhD."

He continued. "During my visits home, my father began my indoctrination into the dark world of magic. He taught me the spells and incantations that he knew, the secret books that he referenced. I had been raised with no religion and had always assumed he was an atheist. But he was suddenly showing me an unseen spiritual realm and teaching me of its power. He made me do things and say things that I will never be able to forget. He wanted me to believe that I could never turn back, that I was beyond redemption. I helped him blackmail people, made them commit crimes. When I finished my studies, I returned home to begin my work full-time. I fell in love. I will never forget the look on his face when I told him about her. The combination of indignation and outrage took me completely by surprise. *No* was all he said. I asked him why, but he wouldn't answer. He got up from the table and left. The very next day, when I went to the lab, she was gone. No one would give me any answers. I went to her apartment, and it was empty. There was no trace of her anywhere."

She felt her earlier anger at him evaporate. "I'm so sorry, Jeremy. What did you do then?" Taylor asked.

"I went to his study and demanded that he tell me what he had done. He looked at me with derision, asked if I was still so naïve as to think I could lead a normal life. He told me there would be no wife, no family, in the cards for me. I was to be the heir to something far greater. 'You have a role to play in the shaping of humanity,' he said. 'You will be instrumental in undoing the unselfish sacrifice of the one who thinks he has won. You were chosen for a specific purpose.'

"Then he showed me a video of my mother." Jeremy grew quiet and looked off into the distance. "He explained how he had lured her to the Institute for a medical fellowship, then impregnated her and locked her up. She begged him to let her live. He told her that I didn't need a mother, that her role in my life would end the moment I was born. The look of despair in her eyes will haunt me forever. He thought I would see the weak, disposable tool that he saw. Instead of binding me closer to him, it turned me against him. The last thing he said was how she had been weak until the end, couldn't even give birth without making a mess. Apparently, something happened during the delivery, and she bled to death."

Taylor gasped.

Jeremy was whispering the story to himself as much as to them. "He did nothing to help her, nothing to ease her pain. I hated him then with every fiber of my being—for what he had done to her, and what he had made me into. I left then, driving aimlessly, and before I'd realized it, I was back at Harvard, outside the office of my Ethics Professor."

"Dr. Rittenhouse," Jack said.

Jeremy nodded. "Yes. He didn't even look surprised to see me. It was like he had been waiting for me to come. I told him everything. I don't know how long I was with him. He listened without judgment. When I was finished, he asked me what I wanted, why I had come. He was the only person I knew from the university who had no shame in publicly declaring his faith. I wanted to know if his God could forgive me."

Both Jack and Taylor were leaning forward in their seats.

Jeremy smiled. "He told me that, yes, he could. That his God was a loving and graceful God who had sent His Son to die for me. For *me*. What about everything I had done, I asked him. Could God overlook blackmail? Could he overlook my involvement in the occult? Carl told me that He would forgive all of it—all I had to do was ask from a sincere heart. Carl and I worked together to devise a plan to bring him down. I had to go back, to pretend that I was still on board. Then, I slowly began to amass my information, to make lists, target those who didn't want to be under his influence but were forced to and those who he had tried to win over but didn't. I had to know who I could and couldn't trust."

"How could you go back there? Couldn't he tell that you had changed?" Taylor asked.

Jeremy tented his hands. "He sees what he wants. I went back and told him that I hated what he had done to my mother but that I knew I had to live up to my purpose. I convinced him to let me spend most of my time in the lab, working on his pet project. That way, I didn't have to do any more of his dirty work. He was eager for the breakthrough I promised him, and I made sure, over that time, to come close but never complete it.

"This is the research Carl mentioned?" Jack asked.

"Yes. My father's behind Alpha Pharma. It's a blind trust but he's the owner. I was working alongside the vaccine researchers, trying to figure out a way to incorporate the germ-line genetic material into the vaccine."

"Hold on," Taylor said. "Is Alpha Pharma developing a TB vaccine with the TB Vaccine Initiative?"

Jeremy nodded.

Jack jumped up. "So Crosse is behind the bill to mandate his vaccine?"

Taylor's eyes narrowed. "I've read about gene therapy. It's wonderful. Diseases are being cured, people helped. Are you saying there's something wrong with that?"

Jeremy shook his head. "No, of course not. It's vital work that has the potential to help thousands. Alpha is working on finding cures and doing good work. But Damon has a secret project; he's trying to change the germ-line—genes down to future generations."

Taylor was puzzled. "To do what?"

Jeremy put his back to them and stared into the fire. Taking a deep breath, he turned back around to face them.

"He wants to eradicate the conscience."

CHAPTER SIXTY

"Are you nuts?" Jack was flabbergasted. "What kind of mumbo jumbo is this?" He was starting to think Phillips *was* insane and had sent them on a wild-goose chase. "How do you get rid of the conscience?"

Jeremy put his hands up. "I know it sounds crazy, but there's actually a scientific basis for it."

"Come on Jeremy—"

"Jack, let him talk," Taylor cut in.

"Fine."

"Scientists believe there is a so-called 'sociopath gene,' markers that are present in sociopaths that aren't there in healthy people. The point of isolating this gene is to eliminate it. But if it can be eliminated—"

Taylor's eyes widened. "It can be replicated!"

Jeremy nodded. "Exactly."

She was horrified. "Are you saying he wants to genetically engineer a society of sociopaths?" she asked.

"Yes."

"But I don't get it. Why would he want sociopaths working for him? Wouldn't they turn against him?" Jack asked.

Jeremy shook his head. "He isn't trying to turn *his* people into sociopaths. He wants to figure out how to manipulate the gene pool so he can pervert future generations—make them have no moral compass. By the time they grow up, he'll be gone anyway. He's doing it as his mission for the occult."

Taylor ran her hand through her hair. "I don't get it. Is he a megalomaniac that thinks he serves the devil? He sounds insane."

Jeremy waved his hand. "Whether or not he's crazy, he believes in what he's doing, and he's brilliant and he's dangerous. His scientists think they're working on gene therapy breakthroughs. It's only a handful of post-Nazi scientists that know what he's really doing and that all takes place far from the main institute, in a secret facility."

"Let's get back on track," Jack said. "So this gene manipulation, the delivery system is the vaccine? That's why the bill was so important?"

"Yes, exactly. But the research isn't finished, and I took it with me. I'll die rather than let him get his hands on it. I would have stopped him entirely, but he got suspicious, and I ran out of time. When I wasn't making enough progress, he knew something was going on. I had to leave before I could get the proof I needed."

"If the research is so dangerous, why not destroy it? Taylor asked.

"It's not that simple. If his other scientists do find a breakthrough, I may need my research to counteract what they come up with." He shook his head. "Besides, the work has value if used the right way, I would hate to destroy all that work. It's a part of me."

"Just how many people does Crosse have working for him?" Jack asked.

"Thousands. He's been running the Institute for over forty years. His people are everywhere."

"Thousands." Jack shook his head.

Taylor couldn't imagine a world where people had no consciences. "How close is he to making this a reality?"

"There's still a lot of work to be done. As long as he doesn't get his hands on my research, it's many years away and even then, there's no guarantee it will work. But he's trying to get everything in place for when he has it."

"Do the scientists realize what his intent is?" Taylor asked.

"Very few and he only gives them part of the story. He doesn't trust anyone well enough to share his true agenda. I was the only one he shared that with. Most of them think they're working on a better future. It's all through Alpha. But you're not understanding."

"Understanding what?" Taylor asked.

"This genetic therapy—it's his back up plan. He's already begun his assault on morality using every means at his disposal. If and when the vaccine becomes possible, it will just be icing on the cake."

"I don't understand. How can one man launch an attack on society's morals?" Jack asked.

"He's got lobbyists, politicians, advertising people. Take a look around—at television, the direction our laws are moving in. He's like a maestro, orchestrating it all from his fortress in the woods."

"I don't have a problem with our laws, Jeremy. You're starting to sound a little paranoid to me."

"Jack." Taylor gave him a look.

"Well, seriously, come on. People aren't sheep. One man cannot be manipulating an entire society."

"You'd be surprised at how easily people are influenced, Jack," Jeremy answered. "The decline in church attendance is something he's gleeful about."

That raised Jack's hackles. "If you're trying to tell me that church is the answer to society's problems, don't waste your breath. In my opinion, organized religion is the cause of most of society's ills."

Jeremy looked at him for a long moment before speaking. "I won't argue with you, Jack. Church attendance is merely a symptom of a greater problem. I'm talking about the loss of faith, the elevation of self, and the move in society away from good."

"Let's get back to the issue at hand—stopping Crosse. He admitted to murdering your mother and even recorded it. Do you know where he keeps the tape of your mother? Can you use that against him?" Jack asked.

Jeremy nodded. "I'm sure it's still at the Institute. I tried to find it before I left. I'm thinking it's in his private chambers. He has too much pride to destroy it, and he likes his trophies."

"We need to get our hands on that tape," Taylor said.

Jeremy shook his head. "Impossible. We can't go there. We'd

never make it out alive. The only reason I have been able to stay in hiding all this time is because of the generosity of my benefactor. He helped me to find and finance this place."

"Who?" Jack asked.

"The man who has been the CEO of Damon's pharma company for the past twenty years. When I told him the truth about what Damon is doing, he agreed to help me."

"Is he still heading up the company," Jack asked.

"Yes. Damon has no idea that he's helping me. He's keeping a close watch on the TB initiative and the work on genetic therapy."

"That makes me feel a little better," Taylor said.

He looked at them. "I have something to show you. The quality is very poor. I did my best to enhance it, but it was converted from tape that is over thirty years old."

The television screen came to life and the image of a young woman, visibly pregnant, filled the screen. She was sitting in a plush velvet chair with a stained-glass window behind her.

"You'll never get away with this."

A melodious voice answered her.

"Don't you see I already have? Your parents are gone. Your sister thinks you don't care about her."

"My sister will never give up."

He laughed. "She'll forget about you."

"Never."

"Trust me, Maya. She'll find a new family. Now that your parents are dead, and you've abandoned her, she'll move on. We'll send her a letter from you saying that you never want to speak to her again, that you've made a new life in Europe."

She shot up from the chair. "She'll never believe that!"

The man rose and walked toward her, his back to the camera. He put his hands on her shoulders and spoke slowly and deliberately to her. "She thinks you've run off with someone you met from here. She's very hurt that you missed her wedding."

She hung her head.

"Eva got married?"

Taylor looked at Jeremy. "Eva?"

Jeremy hesitated. "Your mother."

Jack looked back and forth between the two of them, bewildered.

Jeremy turned the television off and sat next to Taylor. "My mother and your mother were sisters," he said.

Taylor looked up, trying to remember. "My mother told me about her parents being killed before she got married, but she never mentioned a sister. Why would she keep it a secret?"

Jeremy shook his head. "I don't know. Maybe it was too hard for her."

"We can use that tape to prove he kidnapped her," Jack said.

"It's not enough. It'd be impossible to authenticate. He could say it was fake. Plus, you never see his face," Jeremy answered.

He handed a piece of paper to Taylor. "This is a letter she wrote to your mother. I guess she knew it would never get mailed, but she wrote it anyway."

Taylor took the paper from Jeremy with a shaking hand, and read aloud.

February 11, 1976

My darling Eva,

He has shown it all to me. It is appalling how easily he has managed to manipulate the people who work for him. They are zealots who actually believe in the philosophical rhetoric he uses to blind them. There are already dozens of his graduates placed in key positions— politicians, judges, doctors, captains of industry, media executives. They are everywhere. There are files on all of them, evidence of his empire and all those who have done his bidding to build it. Brainwashing, torture, even murder—there is no method that is beneath him. He took great pride in sharing his collection of memoirs with me.

His favorite topic though is how, through his efforts, it will one day be legal to decide who should live or die based on their worth to society. Life will have no intrinsic value. The so-called bio-ethicists, a term he uses with malicious irony, will succeed in convincing otherwise intelligent people that the greater good is served by weeding out the weak. Those with incurable illnesses and diminished mental and physical capacity are better off being released from this world, so resources can be better used for the healthy and firm.

My time is coming to an end. I have so many regrets. I never got to say good-bye to you and to Mama and Papa. I wish I could tell them that I returned to my faith—and that I love them. How difficult it can be for a person of intellect to accept the things of God. If it couldn't be scientifically proven, I had no use for it. Now I see how small we are in relation to God, yet how interested He is in us personally. The magnitude of His grace is beyond my comprehension. I am grateful that this temporary detour to hell has brought me to my senses. I know, beyond a shadow of a doubt, that when my usefulness to Damon is gone and he kills me, I will be sent into the arms of Jesus. And I will be at peace at last.

All my love always and forever,

Maya

"I'm so sorry. So very..." Her voice broke and the tears fell. She took a deep breath and put her hand on Jeremy's. "They're together now."

"Your mother was a believer?"

Taylor smiled. "Yes. Her faith defined her." She gave Jeremy a long look. "So our mothers were sisters? We're first cousins?"

Jeremy didn't answer.

She leaned over and embraced him. "I thought I felt a connection when I met you." She laughed. "Not to mention that we have the same color eyes. Must be from our grandparents."

Jeremy looked at her somberly.

"I have something else to show you." He opened a drawer in the table next to her and pulled out a photograph. "This is my father, Damon Crosse."

Staring back at her was a man with emerald-green eyes—eyes the exact color of hers.

CHAPTER SIXTY-ONE

The man in the trench coat tried to ignore the twitching in his eye. *Count to ten,* he reminded himself. *Shut up. Shut up. They're looking at you. One, two, three four, five, six seven. Breathe, breathe, look normal!*

He'd gotten out a few days after she did. The first thing he did was what she'd told him. Go to the Beans and Leaves Coffee shop in Woodstock, New York. He was in line, getting ready to give them his order. *Regular coffee, no sugar, light on the cream. Regular coffee, no sugar, light on the cream.* It was his turn.

"Regular coffee, sugar, no cream," he stammered. "No! Wait! No sugar, light cream." *Phew.* He'd almost messed up. *Think right, think bright, light, sight, might. STOP IT! One, two, three, four five, six, seven, eight. Breathe, breathe.* "Thank you."

He looked around suspiciously. There were lots of them everywhere. He could tell. They thought they were so smart, that they could fool him. Ha! He knew better. He narrowed his eyes at a particularly tricky one. She was masquerading as an innocent old lady, but he saw through her. He thought about smacking her right in the head, but he had been warned not to make a scene.

He found a seat at one of the tables in the back, just like she told him. He tapped his foot while he waited, his eyes darting around the room, surveying everyone in the crowded café. Where was she? *Wouldn't wait forever. Couldn't wait for never. Thought she was so clever. Someone's head to sever. STOP! One, two, three, four, five, six. Breathe, breathe, breathe.*

"Hello, Nathan."

His head jerked around. She had come! He grinned, and a relieved laugh escaped his lips.

She sat down across from him. "Good boy. You did exactly as I asked. I'm very proud of you."

He beamed.

"Did you bring it?"

He nodded his head excitedly. "Yes, wanna see it now?"

"Not here!" she snapped.

He tensed, and a scowl replaced his smile.

She patted his hand with hers. "What I mean, my dear, is it's not safe here. I wouldn't want you to get in trouble."

He relaxed, and his shoulders fell back into their usual slump. "Okey dokey, smokey. Where should we go?"

"Come with me and I'll show you."

They walked outside into the bracing air. Nathan had no coat and shivered as the cold wind nestled under his thin shirt.

He began to sing. "Freezing, wheezing, cold, old, sold, fold."

She stopped at a black Jaguar. "Here we are."

He backed away from the car as if it were alive.

"No black. I don't like black. It's black, it's black, attack."

She grabbed his arm hard.

"Ow," he yelled.

"Stop it now. Count. Do you hear me? Count. It's fine. Get in."

He gave her a terrified look but obeyed. She was being mean. Now he was mad. She wasn't supposed to be mean to him. He would ignore her. That would teach her not to be mean. They drove in silence for the next twenty minutes. She stopped the car at a warehouse.

There was a big car sitting there. He pointed to it. "What's that?"

"That," she said, "is your gateway to freedom."

"I don't understand."

"I'm taking you to a place where the doctors can help you."

He screamed. "No doctors! No needles! Needles! Beetles! No more!"

She turned to look at him. "Eyes."

He looked at her.

"Have I ever hurt you?"

He shook his head.

"These doctors are different. They're going to help you think clearly. No medicine. No machines. No needles."

The door to the large car opened and the driver emerged. "Mr. Crosse would like to know the reason for the delay. He is eager to be on his way," the man said. He talked funny.

Dakota gave the man a fast nod, got out of the car, and walked around to open the passenger door. "Come."

He looked around. She was moving toward the car without him. He didn't want to be left alone.

"Wait." He hurried to catch up and followed her into the big car.

Chapter Sixty-Two

Taylor went cold. "Are you trying to tell me that Damon Crosse is my father? How can that be?"

"He is nothing if not thorough. He had his people spy on Maya's family—your mother, your grandparents. He arranged for your grandparents' death. When your mother married Warwick Parks, your father, he placed people in their lives to keep an eye on them. When your mother couldn't get pregnant, their family doctor steered them to a fertility clinic in England that performed the IVF treatments. It was one of Damon's clinics. Instead of your father's sperm, they used Damon's."

Taylor's hand flew to her mouth. "How do you know this?"

"He bragged about it to me. He said he wished Maya could have known that he was the father of her sister's child too."

"But, why? Why did he want my mother to have his child? He's never been in my life."

"He had a twisted obsession with my mother. Once she was gone, he still wanted a connection to her."

Taylor cradled her stomach protectively. "Oh my God!" Her eyes widened.

Jack and Jeremy exchanged a glance.

Jeremy nodded slowly. "Yes. You are pregnant with his grandchild. It's one of the reasons you have not been harmed. It's also the reason Malcolm agreed to help me."

Her eyes narrowed. "What do you mean?"

"When I told Malcolm what Crosse was really doing, what his real intentions were and how he would draw Malcolm's own child into it if left unstopped, it broke him. He never imagined that the powerful cadre of men who gave him orders were anything but in it for the money."

"What's Crosse's end game?" Jack asked.

"Control. Manipulation. Corruption. He serves a dark master, and his mission is nothing short of the obliteration of all that is good. He wants to destroy the family, the individual, and, most importantly, all connections to God."

Jack and Taylor both stared at him, openmouthed.

"You're joking, right?" Jack said.

"I've never been more serious."

"You're telling me he's doing all this just to get rid of morality? That he has a bunch of Satanists working for him?"

Jeremy stood up and began to pace.

"No. There are many different motivations he uses. Some have venal motives." He cleared his throat. "And some of them have what they consider to be altruistic motives. He uses people's beliefs, or greed, or vulnerabilities—whatever is the most expedient to gain allegiance. He has true believers in a certain philosophy— those that fight for end-of-life choices, euthanasia, women's rights, freedom— and they serve him out of allegiance to their cause. Others are simply power hungry or greedy and work for their own advancement." He took a seat again and leaned forward, looking Jack in the eye. "He has all the money he could ever want. He's behind the scenes pulling political strings, influencing the media and advertising. He does it all for one purpose—to deceive and distract people from their true purpose."

There was no mistaking the look of skepticism and incredulity in Jack's eyes.

Taylor furrowed her brow. "Are you saying he's the Antichrist?" Now *she* was starting to wonder about Jeremy's hold on reality.

Jeremy shook his head. "No. But he is heavily involved in the occult. He considers himself a prophet—not for the benefit of mankind, but for its destruction. He believes that man deserves to be destroyed. His machinations have been behind the legislature responsible for legalizing drugs, mandating pregnancy screening and forced abortions, euthanasia, assisted suicide, legalized prostitution, relaxing of the ratings system—all of it his. He revels in it."

"How did he get started? Where did he get the money to do all this?" Taylor asked.

"His adopted father, Fred Crosse, was a scientist. He started it. I don't know where he got his money. He was German. I still remember the thick accent, and Damon calling him 'Father', but in my mother's journals, she refers to a man she met once, named Friedrich. She wrote about my father's obsession with him. It must be the same man."

"So, this Fred was alive when Crosse kidnapped your mother to give him an heir. If you are not going to carry on for him, who is?"

Jeremy's eyes went to her belly.

As the realization dawned on Taylor, she stood up and began to back away. This couldn't be happening.

"Oh no! No. No! What am I going to do?"

Jack put his arms around her. "Nobody is going to take that baby from you."

Jeremy walked over to them and put his hand on Taylor's shoulder. "Your baby is in great danger. Damon has a long reach. I believe he is trying to engineer a way to get your child, with no one ever finding out."

"Then what are we going to do?"

"I have the proof now. The file—the one he had bragged about, his people file—it has the name of everyone under his control, what they have done for him, and what he has on them. It's taken me almost a year to find a way to get it. I finally have a connection inside the Institute. He got the file a few weeks ago."

"What kind of people are in the file?" Taylor asked.

"I haven't been able to decrypt it, but it should have the names of judges, politicians, business magnates—people in all areas of influence."

"Okay, so why not take it to the FBI?" Jack asked.

"Because he has his people everywhere. I can't be sure who to trust, he has connections everywhere, and they're not all in his file." He looked at Taylor. "We need your father's help."

They both looked at him. "What are you thinking?" Taylor asked.

"You need to stay here in hiding. Jack can take the information I've gathered to your father. He's the only one in the press I think we can trust. As head of the largest Washington paper, he has the resources to investigate the names on the flash drive, to put together the evidence linking them to Damon and show that they've taken bribes and committed crimes."

"What if Damon's people have infiltrated his paper as well?" Taylor asked.

Jeremy shook his head. "It's a chance we're going to have to take." He looked at Jack. "You're going to have to impress upon him the need for his greatest discretion, to use as few resources as he can, and only ones he feels certain he can trust."

Jack rubbed the back of his neck and looked at floor. "Is there enough on that file to really get any evidence that will stick?"

"I believe so. It should have evidence of bribes. The problem is that the file is encrypted and it has a digital timer that measures how long it's been opened and I don't know what he set it for. We'll be able to validate it quickly, but we'll have to let Warwick read it because it'll expire if we keep it open too long. That's where the two of you come in."

Taylor looked at him quizzically.

He explained. "I've run all sorts of computer programs to break the encryption, but nothing has worked. My source has just gotten information on the password and how to get into it.

"How?" Taylor and Jack both asked in unison.

"It's our DNA. That's the key."

"Huh?" Taylor had no clue what he was talking about.

"He has a sick sense of humor," Jeremy said. "He, the man with no paternal allegiance whatsoever, has used our DNA sequence as the code breaker. I have it on good authority that he has combined the letters of the codon from each of our DNA sequences."

"Hold on. DNA fingerprinting wasn't discovered until the eighties. You were born in 1976," Jack pointed out.

"Yes. It would have been easy for him to get a sample from me without my knowing it."

"How would he have gotten mine?" Taylor asked.

"Most likely kept a blood sample, a hair, something from your birth. As I said, he likes his trophies."

Taylor was nauseated at the thought.

"How are we going to get our DNA sequence?"

"My lab will run the test. I can take the samples now." He pulled out a kit containing gloves, cotton swabs and envelopes. "Just swab your cheek. We'll have it in a few hours. Once we have the information from the flash drive, we can move forward with the plan."

"And what of the Institute?"

"Once he is out of the way, I will fight to take over as his legal heir."

Taylor's head was spinning. She thought of something. "Did Crosse orchestrate my meeting Malcolm?"

Jeremy uncrossed his legs then crossed them again.

"This is not easy to tell you—either of you." He sighed. "You and Jack were deliberately kept apart. But it wasn't just Malcolm." He turned and looked Jack in the eye. "Dakota was a set up. You were her mission. She knew all about your background, your mother, and she played her part to bewitch you. She—"

Jack jumped up from the sofa and grabbed Jeremy by the shoulders. "Are you insane? What are you talking about?"

Taylor sprang up and pulled Jack off Jeremy.

"Jack! Stop it. It's not Jeremy's fault. Sit down."

Jack shook his head, then put his hands over his eyes. "I'm sorry. Sorry." He sat next to Taylor, and she grabbed his hand.

Jeremy gave him a sympathetic look. "I understand. He had to get you out of the way, so that Taylor could marry Malcolm."

Taylor gulped for air. The room began to spin, and then there was nothing but darkness.

CHAPTER SIXTY-THREE

Nathan's nostrils were burning. The smell of the leather interior of the car nauseated him and he felt as if he were drowning. *Stop, stop, drop. Stop, drop, and roll. One, two, three, four, five, six, seven, eight, nine.* "Smell!"

Dakota was giving him a mean look. Why was she looking at him that way? He breathed in the way the nurse had taught him—in through the nose, out through the mouth. In and out. In and out. The car stopped in front of a gigantic house. It looked scary. The big gates opened and Nathan put his hands over his eyes.

"Huge, huge, huge. Where are we?" His voice rose, and he felt a firm hand come down on his arm. He looked at Dakota. Her mouth was a straight line. He didn't like that. He was scared. *Laired. Faired. Mared.* They kept driving down the long driveway until finally the car stopped. Dakota opened the door and came to fetch him.

"We're here. Come with me."

"This place is too huge. Too huge. Like a luge. Deluge. One, two, three, four, five." He tapped the side of his head with his hand.

"NATHAN!"

His bottom lip trembled, and he looked up at her from the corner of his eye.

She lowered her voice. "Focus. I'm right here. We are home now. Everything is going to be okay."

This wasn't home. "Don't want to."

Dakota smiled and took his hand. "Have I ever lied to you?"

He shook his head.

"Come on now. It's all going to be fine. No one will hurt you."

She was being nice now. He followed her to the front door.

They were greeted by another stranger who led them into the tremendous marble foyer.

Within seconds a big, bearded man appeared and nodded at Dakota. He looked like a grizzly bear. Nathan didn't like bears. He backed away as quietly as he could.

"I will take it from here," the bear said in a funny accent.

Dakota let go of Nathan's hand.

What was she doing? He looked at her in shock and began to stammer.

The bear stuck him with a big, long needle.

Before he passed out Nathan's eyes widened, and he gave Dakota a pitiful look.

"You promised no needles!"

"I lied."

CHAPTER SIXTY-FOUR

When Taylor came to, she was in a bed. Standing next to her was a woman in a white coat.

Jeremy walked over to her and picked up her hand.

"Taylor, this is Dr. Haller. I'd like for her to examine you if that's okay. Jack told me about the spotting."

Relief filled her. "Yes, thank you."

"When's the last time you ate?" the doctor asked.

Taylor thought. "Breakfast."

"Well, if you don't want to faint again, I'd suggest you eat more regularly. Let's do a quick finger prick and make sure your sugar's not out of whack." She took Taylor's finger and stuck it with the glucose meter. "Looks okay, but I'll run a blood panel to rule out any other issues."

"I'm fine. I just forgot to eat."

"Even so, I want to be thorough."

Taylor sighed and stretched her arm out to let the doctor draw her blood.

The doctor pulled a portable sonogram machine next to the bed, and Jack and Jeremy left to give her some privacy.

When she had finished with the exam, she called them back in.

"I'm happy to report that the baby is doing fine. There's a strong heartbeat. She's eight weeks along, and everything looks good. Spotting in early pregnancy is more common than you may think and is not always cause for alarm. Her blood pressure is fine; we'll have the blood results in a little while."

A grin broke across Jack's face. "Whew! That is a huge relief."

"Thank God," Taylor whispered.

Jeremy walked over to the bed. "You'll be well looked after here. We have our own medical facility and staff."

"It's like its own little city."

Jeremy pulled a chair up next to the bed." I think it's time I told you the rest of the story." He looked at Jack. "Get comfortable, this will take a while. Let me start where I left—"

"I'm not going to lie here like an invalid," Taylor interrupted.

They both turned to look at her.

"You heard the doctor. I'm fine. Now get out of here so I can get dressed, and let's go somewhere else to have this conversation."

Jack looked at Jeremy. "You heard her." Then, turning back to Taylor, he said, "Good to have you back."

* * *

They gathered together in the study where Jeremy had had some sandwiches brought in.

Jack rose from his seat. "Jeremy, you said earlier that Dakota was a set up. I need to know more."

Jeremy nodded. "You and Taylor were together, and Crosse had someone else in mind for his daughter."

"Please don't call me that," Taylor cut in. She would never be his daughter.

"I'm sorry. He's kept tabs on you all your life. Dakota works for Crosse. They arranged for her to meet you. She was the third one they tried. Apparently, you resisted the other two women they sent your way."

"I don't know what you're talking about. What other two women?"

"Your senior year of college, a girl in your study group made a pass at you. She was one."

Jack's mouth dropped open. "You really know how to make a guy feel like a loser. So much for thinking I had charm."

"The point is, you said no. Then, there was another woman at the Associated Press when you first started."

Jack shook his head. "I remember. Nancy. She was relentless. I thought she'd never leave me alone."

"You have to understand that when they want something, nothing gets in their way. They do deep background checks, psychological evaluations, and they make sure that the health professionals in your life are in their pockets. They knew what kind of environment you grew up in, Jack, the depressions and mood swings your mother experienced. They use profilers to help them when they have a delicate mission."

"Why not just kill me?" Jack asked.

"Because they wanted to break Taylor, to drive her into Malcolm's arms. What better way to induce her to fall for an older, stable man, than to have you betray her? It was easy for Malcolm to insinuate himself in to Taylor's affections."

"But why did he care if I married Malcolm?"

"So that he could have access to you when he wanted it. He considered Malcolm his property. He raised him, set him up with his life. Crosse thought Malcolm wouldn't stand in the way if he ended up wanting to have you in his life. He considers you a pawn, his to manipulate."

Taylor ran a hand through her hair. She felt like she was going to explode. "I want to kill that monster."

Jack went over and sat next to her. He took her hand in his, and she grasped it. "Does my father know?" she asked Jeremy.

Jeremy rubbed his chin. "He doesn't appear to know anything Taylor. He's been played just like you have."

She frowned. "So, what you're telling me, is that Damon Crosse has single-handedly assigned Jack and me handpicked spouses?"

"When you say it that way, I know it sounds crazy. But—"

"It's like we're all a bunch of lab rats," Jack said bitterly.

"He may have manipulated parts of your lives, but not any more. You've both gotten free, and you're going to help me take him down." He walked over to Taylor and spoke gently. "I only found out that you existed after Damon and I had our fight about my getting married. You weren't pregnant then, but he knew you were trying. He called you his contingency plan. He thought it would save me having to provide an heir."

"Are you telling me that he has been watching and waiting for me to breed? That all along, he was waiting to take my child?"

"It's not that simple. If I hadn't betrayed him, he probably would have just watched the child from afar. Nurtured him through others and, when the time was right, brought him into the fold. Eventually, he would be told of his true identity."

"Did Malcolm know that I was Crosse's daughter?" she asked.

"No. When I went to Malcolm and told him everything, that's when he agreed to help me. He did it to save you and your child. He wasn't an evil man, Taylor. He never really had a chance."

Taylor felt her anger rise again. "This is like some sick joke. Everywhere I turn has the taint of his handprint."

Chapter Sixty-Five

She knew Nathan was furious with her. After lying to him, Dakota had to earn his trust back. She smoothed the tight skirt and admired her shapely legs in the mirror. Pleased with her appearance, she descended to the chamber where he was being kept.

He looked up from his breakfast, then back at his plate, making a point of ignoring her.

"I know you're mad at me," she said.

"Liar, liar pants on fire. Lied, tried, fried, died. One, two, three, four." It took everything she had not to roll her eyes. *Friggin counting. Enough already.* She took a seat across from him. She wanted to look nervous, so she bit her lip and made her eyes wide.

"He made me do it." Her voice cracked.

Nathan looked up.

"I'm his prisoner. I needed your help, and I didn't know what to do." Tears fell from her blue eyes.

"Who made you do it?"

"The man with the big, black car. He won't let me leave here unless I do what he asks. I'm afraid."

Nathan puffed out his chest.

The rube was falling for it.

"What does he want you to do?"

She cleared her throat. "I don't know if I should tell you."

"Tell me, sell me, bell me. I want to know."

"There are people. These people are hurting babies. He wants me to stop them."

His eyes grew huge. "Hurting babies is bad. Bad, bad, sad, mad."

She nodded. "Yes, but I'm afraid they'll hurt me too, if I try to stop them. I'm not brave enough."

"I'm brave."

"Yes, you are, Nathan. That's why I thought you could help me, but now I'm not so sure."

"Why not? Don't you think I'm brave?"

She covered his hand with her own. "Of course, I think you're brave. You're the bravest person I know. But I don't want to be unfair to you."

"I want to help—kelp, melp. What do you want me to do?"

She smiled.

"You will be driven to the place where they hurt babies. You will need to leave a package there. Then, you will leave a note saying you did it to save the babies."

"That doesn't sound hard. Easy, peasy, leasy."

"That's because you are a brave, brave man."

He leaned towards her.

"Then he will let you go, and we can be together?"

She licked her lips. Like taking candy from a baby. "If you do a good job."

He sat up straighter. "I will. Good. Hood. Should."

CHAPTER SIXTY-SIX

Jeremy pressed a button next to the fireplace. A few minutes later a staff member carrying a tray of tea and cookies came in. Jeremy poured a cup of tea and brought it over to Taylor.

"Thanks." She took a sip of the amber liquid and tried to gather her thoughts.

Jeremy cleared his throat. "Taylor, do you know anything about some silver coins?"

"What?"

"My mother's journal talked about them. Crosse wanted to know what her family had done with them. Our mothers' parents were born in Greece, right?"

Taylor nodded. "Yes, the island of Patmos. They came over right after World War II. The island was occupied by the Germans before the war ended."

"Isn't Patmos the island where Saint John lived in a cave?" Jack asked.

"Yes, in fact, my great uncle was a monk at the Monastery of Saint John," Taylor said.

Jeremy spoke. "According to my mother's journal, Crosse was obsessed with finding the thirty pieces of silver that Judas received for betraying Jesus. He believed some of them were hidden by Saint John on that island."

"I've never heard anything about them," Taylor said. "Can I see the journal?"

"I don't have it. He let me read it when he decided to enlighten me about my origins, but he wouldn't let me take it, and when I tried to find it before I left, he'd moved it from his study. But I remember it. I can still see the pages in my mind—I have an eidetic memory."

"Okay, so he was looking for these thirty pieces of silver?" Jack asked.

"He was convinced that my mother's family had them, that they'd brought them to America when they left Greece."

Taylor's heart began to pound. "Wait. How did Crosse know about this?"

"It must have been Friedrich. She wrote of Friedrich coming to her room to question her about it."

The thoughts were coming too fast now. She took a deep breath. "What year did this Friedrich come to the United States?" Taylor asked.

Jeremy shrugged. "I'm not sure. He was completely bedridden for as long as I can remember. He had MSA-A, multi system atrophy, a debilitating illness resembling Parkinson's disease. I used to call him 'Grandfather' and go visit with him in his bedroom when I'd come home from school on breaks. He talked about the Old Country sometimes, and made mention of the war, but nothing coherent. I think he came after the war and worked for the government for a while before he got sick."

"You say he was a scientist?" Taylor asked.

"Yes."

"What kind?"

"A geneticist."

"Have you ever heard of Operation Paperclip?"

Jeremy had a blank expression on his face. "Operation what?"

"Paperclip. It was a covert operation where the United States smuggled in Nazi war criminals, whitewashed their histories and made them citizens."

"Why would they do that?"

"Because they were more afraid of Russia at the time and wanted to get the best scientists and spies before Russia did. I'm wondering if

Friedrich was one of those scientists," Taylor said.

"I remember pictures of him from his youth. I think I'd recognize him. Besides, how many geneticists named Friedrich could have come over?"

Jack walked over to the corner of the room where their belongings were huddled in a corner and got his laptop.

"Can we narrow it down through a search?" he asked Taylor. "Look for geneticists and see the names?"

"Maybe, but the rocket scientists are the most famous and easy to identify. There were over sixteen hundred scientists and doctors, and I don't know that we'd find them easily using Google. But I do have all the names from the piece I did on it. I save all my research." She exhaled. "Of course, it's all at home, filed. I did that story almost ten years ago."

Jack's fingers were tapping the keys. "Let me see what I come up with."

"We need to figure out who Friedrich was. Do you remember anything odd that sticks out? Anything he had that could be tied to the Nazis?" Taylor asked.

Jeremy jumped up. "He had a ring. I remember because it fascinated me as a kid. He told me I'd have it one day. But when he died and I asked my father about it he said it belonged to him now. He wears it all the time. I got so used to it, I almost forgot."

"What did it look like?"

"Silver. Like a large signet ring with a symbol in the middle, a sort of stick with a line wrapped around it and it had two German words, one on each side."

"Were the words *Ahnenerbe* and *Deutsches*?" Taylor asked.

"That sounds right! How did you know?"

"That's the ring given to members of the Ahnenerbe, a Nazi occult group. Friedrich was a Nazi! He must have indoctrinated Damon into the occult. If we can prove that the Institute was founded by a Nazi, that will bring it under scrutiny, shine a light on what's been going on there," Taylor said.

"The Ahnerbe? Isn't that the Nazi group that hunted down

religious relics—like in Indiana Jones?" Jack said. "Why did they want the coins so badly?" he asked.

"They believed the coins would give them power. The lore surrounding these religious relics is very potent. It says the coins represent evil triumphing over good and that whoever possesses them has the power to accomplish whatever they desire."

"According to this, the coins were hidden in the temple of Solomon." Jack slid the laptop over to Jeremy and Taylor, and they leaned in to look at the Web page.

Taylor read aloud. "*Medieval apocryphon.* What is that?"

Jeremy answered. "A Greek term for secret teachings that could not be shared publicly," Jeremy answered.

Taylor continued to read, fascinated. "According to this, the coins originated with Abraham. Abraham's father made them, and Abraham gave them to his son Isaac to purchase a village. From there the coins were given to the pharaoh who sent them to Solomon for the temple he was building. Solomon placed them around the door of the altar."

Jeremy broke in. "That's where they stayed until Nebuchadnezzar took over and enslaved the Israelites. He took the coins with him to Babylon where he gave them to some Persians who gave them to their fathers. When Christ was born, they took the coins with them to give as gifts with the frankincense and myrrh but fell asleep and left the pieces there without realizing it. Some merchants found them and used them to purchase a beautiful garment to give to King Abgar. When the king questioned how they had come upon such a beautiful garment, they told him they had found the money. He sent for the shepherds who now had the pieces and took the silver from them and gave both the garment and coins to Christ, who kept the garment but gave the coins to the Jewish treasury because he knew they would be used to secure his betrayal."

Jack gave a low whistle. "So the coins that Judas received to betray Christ can be traced back to Abraham, the father of the faith? That's some history."

"Yes, many powerful hands have touched them. But what makes

them evil is that Satan entered Judas and when Judas held them, Satan's power was conveyed to the coins."

Taylor was staring at Jeremy. "You seem very familiar with this story," she said.

"I've heard it all my life from Crosse. He has twenty of them now. He's determined to find the last ten, and he believes our family is the key."

Jack's expression grew worried. "He's not going to rest until he finds Taylor and those coins. Do you think her family knows about them?"

"According to my mother's journal, he interrogated and tortured our grandparents. They wouldn't tell him where they had hidden them, but admitted that they had brought them over from Greece and hid them."

Taylor turned white. "Oh my God! He *tortured* our grandparents?"

"What exactly does he believe he'll be able to do once he finds them?" Jack asked.

With all seriousness, Jeremy replied, "Unleash the power of Hell."

CHAPTER SIXTY-SEVEN

Dakota was driving them to their mission. He was going to be a hero. She told him so. He couldn't wait to make her proud.

"Now remember, you walk in, go to the waiting room, and sit down for ten minutes."

He remembered. They had gone last week, and she showed him where to sit.

"After exactly ten minutes, you go to the bathroom and leave the package in the trashcan. Okay?"

"Okey dokey, lokey, smokey."

"Nathan!" Her voice was too loud.

"Don't yell! Tell. Bell."

"Tell me again, exactly, what you're going to do. No rhymes!"

He folded his arms across his chest and jutted out his chin. He didn't like it when she talked mean.

She sighed and reached out to put a hand on his arm. "I'm sorry. I'm just nervous. Please, dear, tell me again." Her voice was nice now.

"Go to the waiting room. Sit. Ten minutes. Bathroom. Trashcan. Man. Stan. Lan." He couldn't help it.

"Okay. When you leave the bathroom, you wait for me outside to pick you up. Wait for the policeman and then give him this note." She handed him an envelope.

"Policeman are scary. Very. Merry."

"It's okay. You are very brave. It's important that you give him the note. I can't pick you up until you do. You just wait until he comes, and then you'll see me."

She dropped Nathan off a block away from the clinic. He knew where to go; they had practiced.

"I'll see you soon."

He walked the block quickly, staring straight ahead. The briefcase was heavy and he shifted it to the other shoulder. What was he supposed to do with the briefcase after he dropped the package in the can? *Man, shan, lan, tan. One, two, three, four, five, six, seven. Stop! Think!* Did he keep it or leave it too? He didn't want Dakota to be mad at him. What had she told him? Keep it. That's it. Put the box in the trash and keep the briefcase.

He arrived at the clinic and opened the door. A woman was coming out and smiled at him. He squinted his eyes at her. She couldn't fool him. She was another snarkie. He pushed past her and walked over to the seat closest to the bathroom. Someone was sitting there. *No, Lo, Mo, Bo, So. Stop! One, two, three, four, five, six, seven.* Deep breath. In and out. What to do? He gave her a mean look. Maybe she would get up.

"What are you looking at, weirdo?"

A lady came over and whispered something to her. The stupid girl got up and followed her. Good. Now he could sit.

The lady turned back around. "May I help you, sir?"

He spat out the line he had rehearsed. "I'm waiting for my girlfriend."

She smiled and turned back around again.

He looked at the watch Dakota had given him. 10:15. He had to wait until the numbers read 10:25. He tapped his foot and tried not to look at anyone. Too many snarkies were in here. If he looked at them, they would read his thoughts. Reaching inside his coat pocket, he found the rubber ball and started to squeeze. Breathe and squeeze. Breathe and squeeze. He looked at his watch again. 10:19. Six more minutes. He was good at math. *Math, bath, lath, tath.*

A woman came and sat next to him. Her stomach was fat. He slid away from her to the edge of his seat. He didn't like people sitting near him. What if she touched him? *Cooties, mooties, booties. Stop! One, two, three, four. Stop!* He checked his watch. 10:24. Time to get up! He walked over to the bathroom door and stood, watch in hand, and waited. When the numbers changed again, he pushed the door open and walked in. Unzipping the briefcase, he pulled out the heavy box and pushed it in the trashcan. It didn't go in all the way. There was too much paper in there. He shoved with all his might. The top closed. Good. He picked up the briefcase and went outside to wait.

He didn't see a policeman. He hoped they would come soon. He wanted Dakota to pick him up. After a while, he looked at his watch again. 10:31. He was trying to decide whether to walk down the street and look for her when he heard a loud boom. He crouched down and covered his ears. Why were all these people screaming? And the building was on fire. It was so loud. *Smoke. Smoke. Evoke. Provoke.* All he had done was put a package down. Why was everything on fire?

Nathan was scared. Where was she? When was he going to get to go home? People were running past him, and he looked for the policeman. Where was the policeman? Now there were lots of them, running up the steps.

"Stop!" He jumped in front of one of the policeman. "Take this." He shoved the envelope at him and the policeman grabbed it and gave him a funny look. He opened it and read it. Then he put a silver bracelet on Nathan. "Where are you taking me?" he wailed.

The policeman pushed him hard toward the car. He put his hand on Nathan's head and pushed him hard again. Nathan landed with a thump on the seat. The policeman stuck his head in the car and gave Nathan an angry look.

"To jail, where I hope you rot forever," he said.

Nathan looked at him bewilderingly. "No! I have to leave. Cleave. Retrieve. Where is she? She said I was helping babies." His voice rose with each syllable until he was bellowing like an injured animal.

"Shut up!" A second policeman yelled.

Nathan started to cry. He looked out the window as the car pulled away. The smoke faded into the background, and he wondered where they were taking him. He didn't want to go back to the hospital, especially now that she wasn't there. What would he do? *New. Flew. One, two, three, four, five, six, seven, eight, nine. Stop!* She would come for him. She had promised.

CHAPTER SIXTY-EIGHT

Taylor's blood work was fine. They had just finished breakfast and were watching the news while waiting for the DNA results. Taylor looked up when she saw the commotion being covered.

"Can you turn that up?" She pointed to the remote next to Jack.

"This is Sally Mason reporting for News 15. Late this afternoon a family clinic in Kingston, New York, was bombed," the anchorwoman said. "So far, there are nine confirmed deaths and numerous injuries. The alleged bomber has been arrested but not yet identified. All police can tell us is that he handed them a note from the group claiming responsibility for the bombing. They are called the Voice of the Victims and claim to be Christians bringing God's wrath down on those who, and I quote, 'are responsible for the massacre of the God's children.'"

Smoke and screaming filled the screen as cameras captured the horror of the attack. First responders were shown coming out of the ruins carrying stretchers. There was a close-up of a stretcher carrying a body covered by a white sheet. A woman stumbled from the front door with blood running down her face, and fell into the street. A crowd had gathered outside the clinic, and the horrified onlookers watched as more victims were brought outside.

The male anchor shook his head. "I'll never understand what would drive anyone to do something like this."

"These fundamentalist groups are out of control." Sally Mason cast a steely look at the camera. "We'll bring you more news as soon as we have it."

"What the...how do these people expect to be taken seriously when they do horrible things like this?" Jack felt the fury fill him. "It's disgusting."

"It may not be what you think," Jeremy said.

Jack jumped up from his chair, his face red. "What are you talking about? Please don't tell me you've turned into some religious nut who thinks these kinds of tactics are acceptable." He'd met enough of those freaks to last a lifetime.

Jeremy didn't appear rattled. Without raising his voice, he said, "Of course not. What I'm saying is that it might not have been done by who you think. My father hires people to commit atrocities and then blames them on groups he wants to damage."

"What?" Both he and Taylor said at the same time.

Jack was aghast. "Please explain. Because I know for sure that there have been plenty of occasions when these insane groups *have* done things like this. I've done stories on them."

Jeremy nodded. "Yes, that's true. I'm not saying they're all set ups. I'm just telling you that I've seen him manipulate the news and frame groups for things they haven't done. He hates the church, so anything he can do to give Christians a bad name, he does. Do you remember the story a few years back about the prostitution ring being run out of a local church?"

"Of course," Taylor said. "It made national news."

"That was Crosse's doing."

Jack was skeptical. "Come on, Jeremy. There were lots of girls involved. Are you telling me they all lied? You can't do something like that without someone leaking it."

"Well," Taylor said. "maybe you can if you pay someone well enough. And once the story's out, if someone comes back later and recants, no one really notices."

"The more I learn about this Damon Crosse the more I want to take him down. We need to see what's in that file," Jack answered.

* * *

The lab had their DNA results.

Jack was hunched over, staring at the computer screen. Taylor's hand shook as she held the paper with their DNA fingerprints. Now they just had to figure out in what order to input everything to open the file.

"Ready?"

"Go."

"Should I read yours or mine first?" Taylor asked Jeremy.

"Mine. I was born first. He's a stickler for order."

She read the letters aloud as Jack typed.

"Didn't work. Maybe he only used a part of it."

"The strand is cut into four pieces. The possibilities are endless," Taylor commented.

They tried combination after combination for the next three hours.

Jeremy rubbed his eyes. "He would have chosen something meaningful to him, something ironic. Let me think. Try every sixth letter in each one."

"Still nothing." Jack said.

"Try only three for each—from the first eighteen letters, and pick the sixth, twelfth and eighteenth letter. It would represent 666 to him."

Password successful: Do you wish to proceed?

"Bingo," Jack said.

Jeremy leaned back in the chair, looked up, and gave her a wide smile. "We did it."

"Well, let's see it," Jack said.

Jeremy shook his head and typed *Later.* "Let's not run the clock out. We have to let Taylor's father open it. It can't be printed. All his files have an automatic self-destruct if they're printed anywhere but the main computer. He'll have to take screen shots with his phone."

"Can't *we* do that?" Taylor asked.

"Sure, but do you really think your father's going to print a story based on some fuzzy screen shots. Better for him to see for himself."

"What if there's nothing on it?" Jack asked.

"There will be. It's the right file. You just have to trust me. There'll be names and dates, and once investigated, I'm sure those dates will correspond with bank deposits. Once it goes public, the FBI can investigate. But it's more important that your father has a chance to look at it so he'll believe it. Better close it now."

Taylor thought of something "Does he use one of those data destruction software programs?" remembering Malcolm showing one to her. It was an application you could use for an encrypted file where you could have the file self-destruct within a specified amount of time or it could be triggered by the sharing of the file.

"Yes. He has custom software."

Taylor shook her head. "I hope there's enough information for my father to authenticate it."

Jeremy sighed. "They'll be enough information to convince him. He's kept records on senate votes, inside information he couldn't make up. We also have the tape he kept of my mother, it could be enough to get a warrant to search the Institute. Just need the papers to make enough stink so whoever he does have in law enforcement can't cover it up."

Jack raised an eyebrow. "We really need to get into that institute and get our hands on his real files. Do you think he has printouts anywhere?"

Jeremy nodded. "I'm sure he does. He always has a back up. But this is what we have to work with for now."

"I still think I should go with you," Taylor said. She couldn't stand waiting around like a damsel in distress.

"Once Jack has delivered the file and it goes public, we can leave here. We can't risk Crosse finding you. It's better for you to stay here for now."

Jack exhaled. "I'll make Parks believe me." He looked at Jeremy. "You take care of your sister until we're together again."

Taylor saw a wistfulness come into Jeremy's eyes, and the full realization of his emotionally barren life broke her heart. Here he was, this lovely man, who had suffered such atrocities, yet he hadn't allowed them to destroy him. He had found a way to salvage his humanity.

She took his hand in her own. "You are my family Jeremy. Nothing is ever going to keep us apart ever again. I promise."

He looked back at her with a solemn expression. "And I will never let anything hurt you or your baby."

* * *

It was almost time to leave. Jack enjoyed the hot water beating on his back while he soaped his body. He scrubbed hard, imagining that he was washing away all the mistakes he had made. He would go to Taylor's father, and everything would be brought into the open. This was the story of a lifetime—but he couldn't care less about that. All that mattered was that he was going to bring down Crosse. He got out of the shower and quickly dressed.

He walked into the hall, and knocked on the door across from his.

It opened.

"Hi."

He entered the room. "Well, this is it. I'm heading out."

Their eyes met.

"Jack, I never thanked you for dropping everything to help me."

He shrugged. "You don't owe me any thanks, T. I should've been there all along." He sighed.

She placed a hand on his cheek. "Oh, Jack." Her voice broke. "It's not fair. Both of us, manipulated like puppets. It wasn't supposed to be like this."

He took her hand in his. "Our lives aren't over. We've got a chance to set things right." They moved closer toward each other at the same time and their lips met. Jack's insides melted. He wanted to stand there forever and keep kissing her. He tore himself away and took her face in his hands.

"I'll fix it, Taylor. I promise. This isn't the end."

She wiped a tear from her cheek and squared her shoulders.

"I can," she said.

"Can what?"

"Forgive you. I can forgive you."

He pulled her to him for another embrace and kissed her again. "See ya later." He winked and left.

Jeremy was waiting for him in the downstairs hallway.

"Ready?" Jeremy asked.

"Ready as I'll ever be," Jack said. He tapped the pocket of his jeans where he'd put the flash drive.

Jeremy put his hand on Jack's shoulder. "Remember, that file is all we've got. Remind him that it can't be copied, and that the security protocols prohibit printing out the contents. You've got to make sure it gets to him safely. I've vetted him the best I could and still believe he's our safest bet. Tell him to guard it with everything he's got. Once he's run the story, he can take the file to the FBI and their people can figure out how to secure it."

"Who would've thought a little flash drive could bring down an entire empire." He grinned at Jeremy, then grew serious. "You'll take good care of her?"

Jeremy nodded. "Of course." His eyes met Jack's. "I love her too you know."

CHAPTER SIXTY-NINE

If Jack drove straight through the night, he would be in DC by morning. Jeremy had given him a late nineties Ford Escort, and he'd left his brother-in-law's truck at the facility. They hadn't called Warwick Parks in advance in case any of his phones were tapped. Jack saw a convenience store up ahead and pulled in at the last second. Walking to the counter, he nodded to the cashier.

"Pack of Lucky Strikes," he was surprised to find himself blurt out. *What the hell*, he thought. If being hunted by killers wasn't reason enough to fall off the wagon, he didn't know what was. He took the cigarettes, got back behind the wheel, and lit one up. He took a deep drag and inhaled deeply. Man. It still felt good. He smoked it fast and leaned his head back to steady the dizziness that washed over him. He crushed the pack in his hand and threw it on the seat next to him. Maybe it hadn't been the best idea after all.

He got back on the highway, thoughts racing as fast as the car, and planned his next move. He'd been given an untraceable smartphone. He would text Taylor's father when he got into town and ask him to meet him at East Potomac Park. Taylor had come up with the message.

"Text—*Taylor enai endaxi. Then m'les tipota. Ela sto East Potomac Park.*" Which meant "Taylor is fine. Don't say anything. Come to the East Potomac Park."

Jack had looked at her with confusion. "He knows how to read Greek?"

Taylor nodded. "When he and my mother were first married, they lived in Athens. He was a foreign correspondent. He became fluent, and since my mother had learned Greek as a child, they continued to speak it to keep it alive. They would talk in Greek when they were out and didn't want anyone to know what they were saying."

"I hope he doesn't answer in Greek," Jack joked.

Taylor rolled her eyes. "Ever heard of Google Translate?"

A siren wailed behind him.

He looked into the rear-view mirror, then glanced at his speedometer.

"Crap!" He was going eighty.

The flashing lights got closer.

Jack slowed the car, pulled over, and waited for the officer to approach.

CHAPTER SEVENTY

The man stood in front of Damon Crosse's desk, looking pleased with himself.

"We found his hideout."

Damon flashed a rare smile "Where?"

"Vermont. An underground facility in the Green Mountains."

"How long ago did you discover it?" Damon asked.

"Just now. I've dispatched a team. They'll arrive within the hour."

"Remember: treat her with kid gloves. I don't want one hair on her head harmed. And keep Jeremy alive. I want to talk to him."

"Yes, sir."

When the man left, Damon looked at Dakota. "You need to be gone when they bring Taylor here." She'd done well orchestrating the clinic bombing, but her usefulness was beginning to pale in comparison to her elevated opinion of her importance. In fact, he was quite displeased with her attitude of late. She had demanded to be kept apprised of the situation with Jack and Taylor. He had gone along, not wanting to disrupt the clinic plan by upsetting her—it had been in motion for too long, and she was the only one Nathan trusted. Dakota had always been a volatile asset.

She made a face. "As you wish. Imagine, Jack going back to *her* after he'd had me. I suppose his tastes really are as banal as I thought."

Damon had no interest in discussing her sex life. She was a loose canon that needed to be capped. That was the problem with

247

sociopaths—they were incapable of true loyalty and one never knew what they had hidden up their sleeves. It was a pity, really. She was interesting and held a certain fascination for him. But it was time to say good-bye.

He depressed the red button and his men appeared. "Please come collect Ms. Drake."

Her eye narrowed, and she gripped the sides of her chair. "What do you think you're doing?"

"Saying adieu."

He nodded at his men, and they grabbed her and carried her, struggling and screaming, from the office.

He smiled. How he did enjoy tying up loose ends.

CHAPTER SEVENTY-ONE

Jack put down the window and looked up at the police officer looming above him.

"Do you know how fast you were going?"

"No, Officer. I'm sorry. I was lost and looking at my GPS instead of paying attention to the speedometer."

"Then you should have pulled over. It's dangerous to be distracted while you drive. You were going eighty-two. The speed limit is sixty. License and registration."

Jack leaned over and pulled the registration from the glove compartment. He fished in his pocket for his wallet and pulled out his license.

"Here you go."

He took them from Jack and returned to the police car to run them. Jack tapped the steering wheel and watched him from the rearview mirror.

He returned ten minutes later with his ticket pad in hand. He handed Jack a slip of paper.

"I'm only giving you a warning since you have a clean record but make sure you're more careful in the future, Mr. Morris."

Jack nodded. "Thank you so much. I certainly will."

He waited until the cop had driven away before starting up the car again. He exhaled the breath he'd been holding and took a long swallow from the can of Coke next to him. Boy, was he grateful for Jeremy's foresight. He had been surprised when he was presented with a new identity and the credentials to go along with it. Still, he'd better drive the speed limit the rest of the way.

CHAPTER SEVENTY-TWO

Jack arrived in Washington at six in the morning. He waited until eight to send the text. He got a response almost immediately—a simple *on my way*. He was sitting on a bench at East Potomac Park, facing the water. The breeze blowing off the Potomac was cold, and he pulled his collar up against the frosty bite. He expected Parks to arrive at any moment. His hand rested on the inside of his jacket, curled around his SIG. He wasn't taking any chances. He saw Parks approach and was surprised when he walked right past him. He guessed the beard and bald head had thrown him off.

"Mr. Parks," Jack called.

"Jack? Is that you?" Parks walked over and his eyes bulged. "Where's Taylor?"

"She's safe," Jack replied evenly.

"That's not what I asked."

"Sit down," Jack commanded.

"Don't tell me what to do. What have you done with Taylor?" His voice rose and people around them started taking notice of the two men.

"If you want to know, sit; otherwise I'm out of here."

Parks grunted and took a seat on the edge of the bench.

"I'm sitting. Where is she?"

"With a friend."

Parks looked like he wanted to kill him. "What friend? Damn it,

Jack, you break her heart, then come back all these years later and I'm supposed to trust you?"

"There's no time to rehash the past. I wouldn't be here right now if her dead husband hadn't dragged me into this. He's the one you should wonder about."

"What did Malcolm get himself involved in?"

"I can't go into all of it now, but Malcolm worked for a man named Damon Crosse. Malcolm turned on him and Crosse had him killed. Now, Taylor and her baby are in danger."

"What are you talking about? Murder? You're crazy! Malcolm's death was accidental. I think you're delusional and you've caught my daughter up in your fantasy world. Do you know there's a national manhunt for you? They say you killed a man."

He was getting nowhere. "I was set up. I killed him in self-defense. Taylor will tell you herself when she comes out of hiding."

"Hiding? I want to see her now."

"It's not safe. I'm trying to explain if you'd just listen. The recent bill on the vaccine expansion was created for something more insidious. Malcolm sponsored that bill until he discovered that Brody Hamilton was sneaking in a clause to mandate vaccinations for everyone. When he voted against the bill, they had him killed."

"Who had him killed?"

"A secret organization run by Crosse—he's got politicians, judges, all sorts of people, all in his pocket."

"Jack, you sound terribly paranoid. Do you have any proof to back up your outrageous claims?"

Jack handed him the drive. "Take this. It'll explain everything. It's got the names of everyone on Crosse's payroll and all their illegal activities. Don't show it to anyone. It's the only proof we've got. We're counting on you to investigate the people on that file. See if you can tie them to Crosse's organization. Check their bank accounts, look at their phones. There has to be a trail leading back to Crosse."

Parks took the drive from Jack.

"You have to guard it with your life."

"What?"

"The drive that can't be replicated or it will self-destruct. You can't print it out either. You have to bring it up on your computer and take screen shots with your phone. Bring a witness you trust. Make sure your computer is completely disconnected from Wi-Fi when you do. It's the only way that Taylor will be safe. Once we can get some dirt on Crosse and expose him, he won't be able to get to Taylor." Jack gave him a card. "Here's the passcode to open it." Jack hoped he was doing the right thing giving it to him.

Parks nodded. "All right. I'll check it out. Where are you going to go in the meantime?"

"I don't know," Jack said.

Parks gave him a hard look. "I'd like to believe you. I've known you since you were this high." He held his hand to his hip. "But after what you did to her." He shook his head. "I've hated you for a long time." He reached in his pocket and pulled out his key ring. "But you *have* kept her safe, and if what you say is true, that was no easy feat." He took a key off the ring and handed it to Jack. "I've got somewhere you can stay until I can verify this information. Our cottage on the Eastern Shore. Stay there until I contact you." He scribbled something on a business card and gave it to Jack. "That's the address."

"Thanks, Mr. Parks."

Jack stood up. "You can reach me on the same number I texted you from. It's a secure phone. I'll wait to hear from you." He walked away then stopped and turned back.

"Mr. Parks."

"Yes?"

"Please be careful who you share this with."

CHAPTER SEVENTY-THREE

"We've got to go!" Jeremy was pounding on Taylor's bedroom door.

She hurried to open it.

His face was ashen. "They've found us. We have to leave now."

"They're here?"

"Yes. A helicopter. We shot it down, but they would have radioed him. More will be coming."

He grabbed her hand and she followed, running, down the long corridor.

"Where are we going?" Taylor panted.

"Maryland."

"Why? I don't understand."

He pulled her into the elevator, then grabbed her hand when it opened as they ran down another corridor, then through a large garage and into an open field. There was a small prop plane waiting for them.

"Come on. Get in."

Taylor got in first, and within minutes they were both strapped in their seats, doors locked, the plane beginning its taxi down the runway. Once they were in the air, Jeremy let out a big breath and turned to Taylor.

"There's a safe place we can stay and we'll be close to your father. When the time is right, we can get in touch with him."

"Jeremy, something you told me about your mother's journal

keeps nagging at me. Was the cripple in the big house Friedrich?" Taylor asked.

"Yes."

"Well, you said that Maya talks about meeting a man with a cane, not a wheelchair."

"So?"

"So, how did he start walking again unless the coins actually worked?"

He looked up as if trying to remember. "I was sixteen when Friedrich died. He was bedridden for as long as I can remember."

"Could Crosse's obsession with the coins have been out of devotion to Friedrich. To try and make him better?"

"Absolutely. He worshipped Friedrich. I think Friedrich was the only person he felt anything for. When he died, he left everything to my father—his estate was in the billions."

"If Friedrich's gone, why does he still care about the coins so much?"

"They can do more than restore health. They give whoever has them the power to accomplish their greatest desire—if the person is on the side of evil, that is. I've told you. He wants to pervert society. To eradicate morality—to win souls for Satan."

"I understand that he was brought up to believe in all this occult nonsense, but he's a grown man now. He still thinks it's real?"

Jeremy looked Taylor in the eyes. "It *is* real."

"Come on. The devil made him do it? It's a little clichéd don't you think?"

Jeremy shook his head, and a sadness filled his eyes. "Taylor, the devil is not a figment of your imagination. Do you believe in God?"

She nodded. "Yes."

"Then how can you discount the existence of the devil? The Bible is not fantasy. Adam, Eve—they were real. The fall was real. And ever since, there has been a battle for souls. Ephesians 6:12: says, 'For our struggle is not against flesh and blood, but against the rulers, against the authorities, against the powers of this dark world and against the spiritual forces of evil in the heavenly realms'. Some believe the thirty pieces of silver contain the power to call forth more of these demons to earth. Damon has twenty. Whoever possesses all of them will command the power. Look how far he has gotten. With all thirty, there will be no stopping him."

"Why not destroy the coins back then?" Taylor asked.

"Because they can't be destroyed. They can be neutralized, but it's not easy and we have to travel out of the country to do it. Just as the hands that channeled evil gave them a dark power, hands that have turned away from evil and toward God, hands of someone who has been redeemed, may be able to deactivate them."

"Do you mean someone like you?"

He nodded. "Once we bring Damon down, I'll explain it all. For now, if we find them, we'll have to hide them. We need to focus on that, not get bogged down in the rest of it. If we can hide them in a holy place the destructive power is said to be made inactive while there. That's why they were hidden in Saint John's cave, and in the Virgin Mary's house in Ephesus."

"Did you say a holy place?"

He nodded.

Taylor smiled. "I think I might know where they are."

CHAPTER SEVENTY-FOUR

Jack arrived at the small, white cottage and was relieved to see that there were no other houses in sight. He walked around the back, to the wooden deck, and took in the two rusty chairs and rickety plastic table. Cobwebs covered everything, and the top of the table had clumps of dirt on it. The house backed up to woods and he could imagine how relaxing it would be to sit on the deck in the morning with a cup of coffee. But right then, it looked uncared for and desolate. It was clear that no one had been to stay there in months. Once inside, he had to try two lamps before he found a working bulb. His text tone sounded, and he swiped his phone to see a text from Taylor's father checking to see if he had arrived. He sent a quick text back.

Too full of nervous energy to sit still, he went back into the house, stripped down to his boxers, and began doing push-ups. It felt good to exert himself, and before long, perspiration covered his back and chest. He got in the shower and closed his eyes while the water beat on his head. He stepped out, pulled a musty towel from the rack, and dried himself. Grabbing some clean clothes from his duffel, he got dressed. He opened the refrigerator to see if there was anything to eat. An open box of baking soda sat on a bare shelf. There was a bottle of white wine lying on its side and some shriveled lemons. He grabbed the wine and looked through the drawers until he found an opener. Foraging through the cabinets, he was able to find some crackers and jar of peanut butter. He took the plate with his meager dinner and sat down on the worn chenille sofa. He tasted the wine, pretty awful, but he drank it anyway. He wanted something to steady his nerves. He drummed his fingers on the armrest and tried to slow his racing mind. He was worried about Taylor but knew he couldn't jeopardize her by calling. He had to trust Jeremy. He drained another glass and put his legs up on the sofa. He may as well try and get some sleep. He was just dozing off when the glare of bright lights, and the sound of sirens roused him.

CHAPTER SEVENTY-FIVE

When they landed in Maryland, a car was waiting for them.

"Can we stop by my father's house?"

Jeremy shook his head. "It's far too dangerous."

Taylor wouldn't get in the car. "Jeremy, my christening cross is there. It was my mother's. It's still in my old bedroom. I didn't care before, but now, after everything I've lost, I need it. I'll be fast. No one would think to look for me there. It's too obvious, don't you think?"

He shook his head. "I don't know."

"This might be my only opportunity. Please."

"I'm probably going to regret this, but okay. Do you have a key?"

"No, but I know where they hide the spare."

* * *

They were in her old room.

Jeremy looked at his watch.

The room looked exactly as it had when she had been in high school, the combination mirror and dresser paint-chipped and worn. She walked over to the dresser and lifted the top of the monogrammed mahogany jewelry box. There it was. She picked up the delicate gold cross and leaned in toward the mirror. She fastened it around her neck and turned to Jeremy.

"Thank you. Okay. Let's get out of here."

"Taylor?" A deep voice startled them.

"Dad!" She ran to him and his arms encircled her in a tight embrace. Jeremy said nothing and stood back until she pulled away.

"I've been worried sick about you," her father said. "Jack said you had to stay in hiding. What are you doing here?"

"They showed up at Jeremy's facility. We had to leave. There's so much I have to tell you. I assume Jack filled you in on what's going on?"

"Yes. I've got him stashed at our cottage on the Eastern Shore. He'll be safe there."

Jeremy held out a hand. "I'm Jeremy."

Parks appraised him with a long look then shook his hand. "What are you two doing?"

"We have to find something."

"What?"

"Dad, it's not safe to stay here. I'll explain later."

"I'm not letting you out of my sight again. I'm coming with you, and you can explain. We'll take my car," Parks said.

"All right. Can you grab the tool kit from the garage?" She asked her father.

"Why?"

"If I'm right, I'm going to need it retrieve what we're looking for."

"Okay, I'll meet you in the driveway."

Taylor got into the front and Jeremy into the back of the Mercedes. Parks started the car and turned to look at her.

"You look pale. Are you okay?"

She put her hand on his arm and gave it a gentle squeeze. "I'm okay. Dad, listen, you know the shelter Mom's parents started? The one run by the nuns?"

He nodded. "Of course. I never liked your mother going there, but she always insisted. The few times I went, I could see what a dangerous element was there. It was like skid row."

Taylor had forgotten about the arguments her parents used to have about the place. Because Taylor's grandmother had founded it, it had held a special place in her mother's heart.

"I think Mom's mother may have hidden something very important there."

He turned to her look at her. "What?"

Taylor hesitated, and Jeremy answered for her.

"It's something my father is looking for. Silver coins."

"We need to go check it out," Taylor added.

"Okay. Tell me about these coins," her father said.

Jeremy repeated the story for him.

"That's the most ridiculous thing I've ever heard. And your mother never mentioned a word about any coins or silver pieces."

"Dad, trust us. Please?"

He sighed. "Fine."

"Did you have any problems with the file?" Jeremy asked.

Parks cleared his throat. "No, it opened fine. We're following all your precautions. Two of my top investigators are working on it."

"Dad, there's so much to tell you. Jeremy's mother and Mom were sisters! She had a sister. Did you know that?"

The color rose in his cheeks. "Yes, Taylor. It was something she didn't like to talk about. Her sister ran off with someone she met at a medical fellowship, never bothered to get in touch with your mother again. She didn't even come to our wedding. Eva searched for her for years and years. It was only when you were born that she finally let it go. That's also when she gave up practicing medicine. Her sister and she were going to practice together. I think she just wanted to put it all behind her. She never spoke of her again. It was too painful."

"Her sister didn't run off, Dad. She was held hostage by Damon Crosse, the man Jack told you about. She gave birth to Jeremy and then Crosse let her bleed to death. Jeremy found this out when his father showed him a journal that he'd been holding on to all these years," Taylor said.

"She was held *hostage*? How do you know?"

"It's a long story. We'll explain it later," Jeremy answered.

"Dad, you missed the turn."

"Damn." He made an abrupt left and drove around the block. A minute later, they were in front of the shelter, a two-story worn, brick building. "Now what?" He looked at Taylor.

"I'll go inside. It won't take me long to figure out if I'm right." She left the two of them in the car.

Parks turned to look at Jeremy in the back seat. "Well, son, you've been through the mill. I admire your tenacity in gathering everything you did." He shook his head.

"I'm just doing what's right. I appreciate your willingness to go out on a limb. You're going to have a lot of powerful people against you when that story breaks."

Parks shrugged. "I gave up worrying about what others think of me a long time ago."

Taylor opened the car door, her face red with excitement.

"I knew it! Come on." She pulled the tool kit from the back seat.

Jeremy and her father followed her into the building.

"Dad, Jeremy, this is Sister Carlisle. She was a friend of Mom's."

The slight woman held out her hand in greeting, then looked at Taylor. "Your mother was a good friend to me and to Agape House. If it wasn't for her family and their endowment, we wouldn't be here right now."

Taylor clasped Sister Carlisle's hands in both of hers. "Thank you. I'm afraid I have a strange request. My mother had something belonging to our family that she left here."

Sister Carlisle raised her eyebrows. "Oh?"

"When she had the bathrooms redone, she inserted some special tiles into the shower. I need to remove them." Before the woman could respond, Taylor continued. "Of course, I'll have workers come by and repair it."

"Whatever you need, dear. Go ahead."

Jeremy and Parks followed Taylor into the dark locker room. The entire wall was tiled and in each tile was a pattern of five coins.

Jeremy looked at Taylor, disappointed. "There are hundreds of coins here; they're just decorative."

Ignoring him, she walked to the farthest end of the long wall, sat on the floor, and ran her hand over the tile. "When I was little, I used to come here and pretend I was locked away in a castle. I remember these tiles, that the coins felt different from the others. They're so low, no one ever looks at them."

Jeremy crouched down and looked where Taylor was touching. "You're right."

"My grandmother must have had the other tiles custom made to look the same, so no one would notice the real ones." She hesitated. "Should we leave them here? They've been safe all this time and only we know about them."

Jeremy shook his head. "We need to take them. Now that the three of us know they're here, it could be used against us if the wrong people tried to interrogate us. Besides, I have a plan for them."

"All right."

Taylor used the claw end of the hammer to try and dislodge the first tile. The mortar began to crumble, and the ceramic material started to crack. She kept at it, until the first one was dislodged. The space left next to the second tile made it easier to pull it away from the wall in one piece. Taylor ran her hand over the silver coins and looked at Jeremy. "This *is* them, right?"

He took the broken tile from her and peered at one of the coins closely.

"Yes. They look like the other ones." He opened his satchel and they placed both tiles in it.

They returned to the car. Parks looked at Jeremy and asked, "Now what?"

"I need to think. Ultimately we have to get them back to Greece."

"What?" both Taylor and her father asked.

Jeremy sighed. "I didn't want to get into it now, but we need to take them back to Patmos, to the monastery, where the priest can perform a ceremony to mitigate the evil of the coins. My hands are needed because of my redemption from evil to good, and Taylor and I together are from the same bloodline that has protected them over the centuries."

"How do you know this?" Taylor asked.

"When I read about our great uncle, the monk in Greece, from my mother's journal, I wondered if he was still alive."

Taylor's heart skipped a beat.

"Is he?"

Jeremy smiled. "Yes. He's still there. I spoke with him on the phone after I'd tracked him down, not long before you and Jack found me. We need to take them to him. The three of us, all with the same blood flowing through our veins, can do together what we can't do apart. He quoted Ecclesiastes 4: 'Though one may be overpowered, two can defend themselves. A cord of three strands is not quickly broken.' But for now, I think we go back to Carl's and find a church or cathedral nearby him."

Taylor's father spoke. "Where does this Carl live?"

"New Hampshire," Taylor answered.

"That's a long way to drive with people trying to kill you. We need to get you somewhere safe, fast, until everything hits the paper and we can put these guys away. Then you can do whatever you need to do."

"How about the cottage?" She wanted to be with Jack.

Her father nodded, then looked at Jeremy. "That should work. Okay, with you?"

"Sounds good."

Parks nodded. "It's settled then. It's nearly a three-hour drive. Let's stop and get something to eat on the way and you can both fill me in on the rest of it."

As they were getting in the car, Parks stopped to look at his phone.

"Everything okay?"

He typed something then looked up. "Yes. Just letting Evelyn know you're with me and we're headed to the cottage."

CHAPTER SEVENTY-SIX

The door burst open and a swarm of green-armored and helmeted FBI agents poured in. Before he could get a word out, he was slammed to the floor, a knee on his back. As he cursed, he heard the click of the handcuffs and felt their bite on his wrists.

"Push on through. Once the house is clear and safe, I want the entire place searched from top to bottom." The agent turned back to Jack. "Sir, you are under arrest for the kidnapping of Taylor—"

"I didn't…" He stopped, coming to his senses. He would call Arnie.

CHAPTER SEVENTY-SEVEN

FBI Resident Agency, Salisbury, MD

Jack had been sitting in a wobbly chair, his hand cuffed to the table, for what seemed like hours. He had a dull headache from the cheap wine, and his mouth felt like cotton.

How had they found him? He looked up at the agent sitting across from him. He wanted to tell him to quit wasting his time. He had done nothing wrong, but even so, he wasn't going to talk without his lawyer.

"We're trying to get in touch with your lawyer now. It's in your best interest to tell us where Taylor Phillips is. Now. If we find her now, and alive, things will go much better."

Jack said nothing.

"Suit yourself. But you'll be out of options soon."

Jack knew his rights. They couldn't keep grilling him without his attorney, especially after he'd asked for one.

"Aren't you supposed to bring me before a judge?" Jack asked.

"You would think," the agent answered. "Things seem to have gone a little off script." He shrugged.

Jack wouldn't give him the satisfaction of a reaction.

The agent stood. "I guess I *am* going to have to let you go. The search gave us what we need, and I can't keep you much longer." Then he smiled, and Jack got a sick feeling.

The agent picked up his pen, his thumb clicking the top up and down. "When I say I'm going to let you go, I mean I'm going to let you go with…" The door opened and two men walked in. The agent made a sweeping gesture with his hand. "These nice detectives from New Hampshire. See, when we ran your name in NCIC before we came to get you, it set off some flags. These two have been driving non-stop from New Hampshire just to meet you. I guess they want to chat about a murder. Know anything about that, Logan?" The agent laughed. "You don't have to answer that. If your lawyer ever shows up, I'll tell him where you're headed. Enjoy the ride."

CHAPTER SEVENTY-EIGHT

The Ford Escort was parked in the driveway, and Taylor was overjoyed at the thought of seeing Jack again. She looked at the old clapboard house and marveled again at her father's fondness for it. She hadn't been here in years—she had hated it from the moment she saw it. Her father and Evelyn had bought it when they were first married and used it as their weekend retreat. She'd failed to see the charm. To her it was isolated and barren, and she spent as little time there as possible.

As soon as they were out of the car, she knew something was wrong. The door was ajar and when she pushed it open, she saw the chaos—drawers wide open, their contents strewn, the floor littered with papers and objects. The sofa cushions were scattered on the floor, and all the cabinets in the kitchen hung open.

"Jack," she yelled, as she ran to the bedroom, frantic. "Jack, are you here?"

"What the hell happened here?" her father yelled.

Jeremy looked around the room, taking it all in. "Looks like the house has been ransacked."

She ran back in the living room, out of breath. "He's not here. He's not here!"

Her father pulled out a gun and pointed it at her. "Sit down." He looked at Jeremy. "You too."

"Dad! What are you doing?"

His voice turned cold. "I'm not your father, and I think you know that."

This had to be a joke. Was he actually pointing a gun at her? She moved toward him, and he cocked the gun.

"Stay back."

"What are you doing? I don't understand."

"Taylor, do as he says." Jeremy's hands were up, and he sat on the sofa.

She continued to stand. "Why are you doing this? I'm your daughter. I love you." Taylor was too devastated to feel any fear. "Dad, please!"

Parks shook his head. "I never wanted kids. I had a vasectomy before I married your mother. Then she went on and on about having kids. Drove me nuts. I finally went along with the IVF just to shut her up."

She felt as if she'd been stabbed in the heart. "You mean she wasn't infertile? You let her think that she couldn't get pregnant and all the while you'd had a vasectomy? I don't understand. I thought you loved me." She sounded pathetic, even to her own ears. He didn't love her. Her father didn't love her. She had loved him. Still loved him. She felt her heart break into a million pieces and a cold lump take its place.

"He's not worth it, Taylor," Jeremy said.

Parks put his free hand over his heart and flashed a phony smile. "Aw. Your big brother coming to your defense." He looked at her coldly. "It all worked out. Crosse got an extra kid, and I got more money than I could ever spend, and no messy emotional attachments. My time at the Institute was well spent."

"*You* were trained at the Institute?"

He laughed, a humorless, odd laugh. "Trained, raised, made."

"You were one of the orphans?"

"Yep. How many poor throwaways do you know who have the power and money I have?"

She sunk to the sofa. "Both you and Malcolm were raised there?"

"Poetic, no? You've belonged to Crosse forever. Before you were even born."

A surge of adrenaline shot through her. "I don't belong to him and I never will. You're evil, and you're going to rot in hell."

He narrowed his eyes at her. "Just like your mother with the preaching and the fire and brimstone. How about you let me worry about my eternal soul? And by the way, thanks for finding the coins. Your useless mother couldn't tell me where they were. Even when my guy tortured her, nothing."

"I hate you!" she screamed.

"Don't you want to know why she died?"

Jeremy reached out and grabbed her hand.

"Crosse had me marry her so I could find them. Your grandparents wouldn't give them up. He didn't want to make the same mistake again. He figured after a while, she'd confide in me. All those years, she pretended to know nothing. Then one day I hear her talking to you. Right after your fourteenth birthday. Do you remember? You were having a crisis of faith."

Taylor thought hard and a memory came to her, of her mother sitting on the edge of her bed, talking to her before she went to sleep. Yes, it was coming back. She looked at the man holding the gun. Not her father—a stranger, an imposter.

"How could I have forgotten? The family's sacred trust. She said we were guardians of the faith, that we had to keep a relic hidden and that when I was twenty-one it would be my turn. But I had to have faith. It could only be entrusted to one with faith."

Jeremy gasped. "That's why they told your mother about them but not mine. My mother had lost her faith."

"I knew then she'd been lying to me all those years. I could pretend a lot of things, but going to church every week, pretending to be devout, that was beyond even *my* abilities. I wanted those coins. Why should Crosse have them? I'd researched them, figured if it was worth making me marry someone and wait to find them all those years, they had to be something special."

"So you killed her?" Taylor asked.

"I wasn't going to wait anymore. I hired someone to interrogate her. To torture her if necessary. She wouldn't tell him anything." A scowl transformed his face. "I couldn't let Crosse know what I'd done, so I had him rape and murder her, made it look random."

He extended the arm holding the gun and aimed it at her. "And now it's time for you to join her. Crosse will think that you two are still hiding somewhere, and he'll never know that I have the coins. Then *I'll* have the power. Maybe even immortality."

Jeremy flew from his seat and knocked Parks down, reaching for the gun. It went flying, skidding over the wood floor. They struggled, rolling on the ground, and Taylor jumped for it. The gun was a few feet from Parks's arm. He was reaching for it, but she got there faster, picked it up with a shaking hand, and, pointed it at him.

"Get away from Jeremy."

Jeremy was pinned on his back, Parks straddling him, a hand on his neck. She saw Parks reach into his pocket and pull out something shiny. There was a click and a blade popped out. He was going to kill Jeremy. His hand moved toward Jeremy's neck, poised to slice. Taylor got ready to pull the trigger when a voice made her jump.

"What in the world is going on here?" She looked toward the door. It was Evelyn. Her entrance had distracted Parks too. Jeremy took the opportunity to knock the knife from his hand and push him off him.

Parks ran to the door, shoved Evelyn out of the way, and jumped into his Mercedes and took off.

Evelyn ran out the door after him, but he was gone. She came back inside. "What happened here?" She started walking toward Taylor, but Taylor put a hand up to stop her from coming any closer.

"How did you get here so fast? He only texted you an hour ago." She pointed the gun at Evelyn. "I think you'd better tell us what's really going on."

CHAPTER SEVENTY-NINE

"You let them get away again?" Damon Crosse was livid. He had a bunch of imbeciles working for him.

"They shot down the helicopter and took off. They landed in Maryland but we lost them."

"Damn it to hell! I won't allow him to undo everything I've accomplished."

"We recovered the flash drive. Logan gave it to Parks and he's given it to us. We also swept Jeremy's facility. And Logan's been arrested."

That was one bit of good news. But Jeremy and Taylor were still free.

"Find them. Do you hear me? Find them and bring them to me. And remember: don't let anything happen to the woman."

"What about Jeremy?"

"Bring him too. He has information I need."

The man continued to stand there, looking at him.

"If I have to repeat myself, you won't live long enough to hear it. Get moving!"

After he had left, Damon opened the center desk drawer and pulled out the large black book. He turned to the familiar page and began to chant. Enough was enough. He should have known better than to ever show Jeremy Maya's journal. He was furious with himself that he had unwittingly played a part in helping her achieve her agenda. How was he to know she would turn to God? He had selected her so carefully, made sure that her position as an atheist was solid, her idolatry of science secure. She had reached out from the grave and converted his son. His *son*. He had been foolish to forget the power of prayer. He knew all too well what it could accomplish. He had devoted his life to convincing others of the absence of God knowing full well God's power. He had believed Jeremy was cut from the same cloth as he and that he would assume his role. The insolence! Plotting against him. *Him*! Jeremy had been conspiring with those traitors. It would stop now.

Picking up a rubber ball, he squeezed it in his left hand over and over. Frustrated, he threw it against the wall. He had one more chance and this time he wouldn't squander it. Time was running out. At best, he had another twenty-five years left—unless he got the final ten coins—then he could turn the clock back. He shook his head, and a slow smile spread across his face. It wouldn't be long. In a few more months, he would be holding the heir to his kingdom. And this time, he would do it right. This child would never betray him or search for his mother. Damon would provide a mother for him, one that shared his own ambitions. He would grow up in a stable environment and be more than willing to take his place when the time came.

CHAPTER EIGHTY

Evelyn put her hands up. "Don't do anything crazy. I'm not here to hurt you. I came here to save you."

Taylor was skeptical. "Did you know he was bringing us here to kill us?"

"Not until a few hours ago. Taylor, what happened? You need to tell me everything."

"Why should I trust you?"

She looked at the gun in Taylor's hand. "You've got me covered, at least, let's talk. Your father duped us both."

"That man is not my father."

"What do you mean he's not your father?"

"He admitted that he killed my mother."

Evelyn didn't look surprised. "I thought so!" She shook her head. "I suspected it when I heard him talking a few weeks ago."

"Wait, what are you talking about?" Taylor asked.

She looked up and gave Taylor her full attention. "He was in his study. I was about to come in when I overheard him on the phone with someone. He said, 'I'll use the same guys on Taylor who did her mother.' It all clicked. I thought back to the day she was killed. He had sent her to that mall. She and I were supposed to have had lunch. She cancelled because he asked her to pick up a tux he needed that evening. I didn't think anything about it at the time. Just a tragic coincidence. But then I began to wonder." Evelyn sighed. "I didn't know what to do. I searched around for evidence, anything that would prove me wrong. I didn't want it to be true. Then I found a burner phone. So, I cloned it and his regular phone."

Jeremy had a suspicious look on his face. "You cloned it? How does a psychologist know how to do that?"

"I have a friend who knows how. The point is, today I saw a text saying they'd taken Jack and the house was clear. The second text he sent an hour ago was to an unknown number, saying he had you and would need someone to come to the cottage and clean up after him."

"That still doesn't explain how you got here so fast. What aren't you telling us?"

Taylor walked toward her until she was only a few feet away. "If I have to shoot you, I will. Tell us the truth. Do you work from Crosse too?" Taylor knew she could never really shoot her, but hopefully Evelyn would believe her bluff.

"Who?"

"Come on, Evelyn, cut the crap." Taylor wasn't playing her game. "Were you in on the murder of my mother? Just waiting in the wings to marry her husband?"

"Of course not! I loved your mother."

"Really? It didn't take you long to become the new Mrs. Parks. Did he tell you that Damon Crosse is my father, not him?"

Evelyn's mouth dropped open. "Your what?"

"Jeremy is my brother. Jeremy's mother was a medical student at the Institute. Damon held her hostage, impregnated her, then let her die after Jeremy was born. He made sure his sperm was used when my mother did in-vitro at one of his clinics so that my mother would have his child too."

She looked up at Jeremy. "What was your mother's name?"

He narrowed his eyes at her. "Why?"

"Please, I have to know. Was it Maya?"

His eyes widened. "Yes."

"I thought she had left the program voluntarily. He told me that she'd run off with another man. Brian, I think. He left when she did. Are you sure about this? Held hostage? I can't believe Damon would do that." She looked like she'd seen a ghost and in her eyes, was the same shell-shocked look that Jack had had when he found out about Dakota.

"You knew my mother?"

"I was there when she came to the Institute. Damon hired me right after I got my PhD. I thought he was doing noble work. He said I was helping to shape the future. She was in the first group I worked with. I was so sad when she left. There was something about her that made an impression on me. I can't believe he would do something like that. All the work that he does, it doesn't make any sense."

Jeremy and Taylor exchanged a look.

"Let her read it," Taylor said.

Jeremy retrieved Maya's letter from his satchel and handed it to Evelyn. "My mother wrote this. You want to know about all the good he does at that institute? You'll see the truth. She also kept a detailed journal, but he still has that back at the Institute."

She took the letter, then looked up, panic-stricken. "We have to get out of here. Crosse's men will be here any minute."

"What? You called them?" Taylor asked.

"I thought I was doing the right thing. He made me believe that Jeremy was the evil one. He said he wanted the chance to talk to him again, work things out. And I didn't think he'd hurt you. He told me he just wanted to make sure you were safe."

"That's because he wants my baby," Taylor yelled behind her as they sprinted out the door.

CHAPTER EIGHTY-ONE

Hillsborough County Jail, New Hampshire

"Jack, it's bad. They say your fingerprints are all over that cabin. How did you get so sloppy?"

Jack's eyes went to the ceiling.

"I wasn't expecting it. I let my guard down. I didn't realize until the guy showed up that I'd been set up."

His longtime buddy and trusted lawyer, Arnie Thomas, chewed his lip. Jack waited for him to say something. He frowned at Jack. "It doesn't look good. We're going to need Taylor to corroborate your story that it was self-defense. She has to testify that you didn't kidnap her and that this man threatened your life."

Jack shook his head. "No way. She can't come out of hiding. It's too dangerous."

Arnie sank back into his chair. "Are you serious? How do you expect me to get you out of this without her help?"

Jack leaned forward. "Find a way. I'm not about to hand her over on a silver platter just to save myself."

"We might be able to use a deposition from her, plead the case that she has to stay in hiding. Can you contact her?"

"Maybe. If Jeremy's still got the same disposable, it's possible." Jack scratched his head. "Have you been able to find out anything about Craig?"

"No. Nothing. I'm sorry."

"What about the paper? Did the story get printed?"

Arnie reached into his briefcase and pulled out a newspaper. He handed it to Jack.

"That can't be," Jack sputtered.

"I'm afraid it is. There's nothing about the conspiracy. You're front-page news, though. And Parks never went back to his office. When I called, they didn't know where he was."

"Could Parks work for Crosse too? I'll bet we'll never see that flash drive again." He punched the table.

Arnie stood. "If you think of anything helpful, let me know. I've got a bail hearing to prepare for."

CHAPTER EIGHTY-TWO

"We can't take my car. When they get here and we're gone, they'll look for it. What about the Escort?" Evelyn said.

Taylor shook her head. "No, the FBI was here. They arrested Jack. They would have the plates, and Crosse might too."

"What are we going to do?" Jeremy said.

She had to think.

"About half a mile up the road there's another cottage. We know the family; they only come here in the summer and occasional weekend. They used to leave an old Volvo station wagon there. If we're lucky, it's still there."

"What about the keys?" Jeremy asked.

"There's a tool box under the kitchen sink. Grab it and bring it."

They followed Taylor down the gravel road and narrow dirt driveway that led to the house. There was a carport next to the cottage, and parked there was a blue station wagon.

Taylor tried the door. It was unlocked. "Get in." She turned to Jeremy seated next to her. "Give me the screwdriver, please."

He handed it to her. She inserted the flat end into the ignition.

"Hammer?" She took it from him and used it to smack the butt end of the screwdriver.

"What are you doing?" he asked.

"Unlocking the steering column so we can start the car." She turned the screwdriver and the car started.

"How in the world do you know how to do that?"

279

She gave him a wry look. "Things can get boring at boarding school when you don't have your own wheels. You learn a lot living with a bunch of girls."

"You're full of surprises."

"Let's get out of here."

"Where are we going?" Evelyn asked.

"I think the only safe bet is to go back to Carl's," Jeremy answered. "He's a good friend of mine completely off the grid," he explained for Evelyn's benefit.

"Where is he?"

"New Hampshire."

"That's a long trip."

"Well, we don't have much choice. We'll drive straight through, taking shifts," Taylor said. "In the meantime, we have to figure out our next move. Now that the flash drive is gone, all we have is the letter. I'm not a lawyer, but I have to wonder how it would be authenticated with Maya gone and everyone in her family dead."

"Evelyn's met her. And I'm sure there are handwriting samples from tests or essays while she was in school," Jeremy said.

Evelyn was shaking her head. "It's not enough. He'll figure a way to get out of it. He can claim that she was delusional—she made it all up. We need more."

"What if I went public with what we know? I have contacts in the press. Everyone knows Karen Printz, I was her producer for years. I'm sure she'd love to interview me on *Nightline*. We could tell them of our suspicions that the founder was a Nazi war criminal. It might be enough to get people looking into the Institute, Crosse. They could investigate his dealings, get people to come forward. Those stories always bring people out of the woodwork," Taylor said.

"Maybe," Jeremy said, "but his people are not your ordinary victim types. Remember, they are all well compensated for what they do or else they are zealots doing what they believe is their calling. I'm worried that such scrutiny would only drive him to get rid of any evidence of what he did to my mother and all his other illegal activity."

"I can attest to what Jeremy's saying. Being on staff all these years, he's very careful to make sure his key players have passed stringent psychological screenings."

Taylor looked around to make sure no other cars were in sight and swerved off the road into a wooded clearing and turned to face Evelyn.

"Give me your phone."

"What?"

Jeremy sensed what she was up to, and from the corner of her eye she saw him pull the gun out of the satchel where he'd stashed it.

"I want to believe that you're going to help us. But how do I know you don't just want us to lead you to Carl?"

"Fair enough." She handed the phone to Taylor.

"Now get out of the car."

"What are you doing?" Jeremy asked. You're not leaving her here?"

"Keep the gun on her. I want to search her."

They both moved behind the car and Evelyn put her hands up while Taylor patted her down.

"Okay, you can get back in. Give me your purse as well." Taylor threw it to Jeremy, then put the car back in drive. "Take out her wallet, then throw the rest out the window. We don't have time to look for a tracking device."

"Taylor, you have to believe me. Now that I know the truth, I could never work for Damon again. He truly never showed me that side of him. All I saw was his educational programs."

"Don't you think it's time you were honest with yourself at least? You had to know he was up to no good. You were the one administering the tests. What did you think he was doing?"

"A lot of companies use psychological testing on their employees. I thought he was a visionary intent on improving the world, that his work with doctors and lawyers was progressive. I believed in what he told me, that he wanted to relieve suffering through euthanasia, improve health, through genetic engineering."

"And what did you think he was going to do with Taylor?"

281

"He told me that Jack Logan had kidnapped her, that Warwick asked him to help. Jack's face was all over the news. I had no reason not to believe him."

Taylor still wasn't completely convinced, but Evelyn's words had the ring of truth to them. She needed to figure out a way to be certain. "I want to believe you, but you can understand if I'm having trouble trusting people these days."

"Record me. Record me saying that I'm helping Jeremy get back at his father. I'll say that I'm going to testify that I knew Maya and that I believe he killed her."

"What will that accomplish?"

"An insurance policy. You can email it to whomever you want, and they can send it to Crosse if I double-cross you." She threw her hands up. "It's all I have."

"You could always say we made you do it," Taylor said.

"I know my father, that'll be enough for him to doubt her and have her killed."

Jeremy swiped to video and recorded Evelyn saying the incriminating words. "Done. I've emailed it to three of my people."

"All right. We still have to figure out a way to take him down," Taylor said. "I think we need to get back into the Institute and try and get his files."

"Impossible. The video surveillance would pick us up before we got close and his security detail would get us," Jeremy said.

She drummed her fingers on the steering wheel. "What else can we do? We can't let him get away with all of it." She had an idea. "What if we don't sneak in? What if we're invited?"

"What do you mean?" Evelyn asked.

"I'll call him. Say I want to meet him. I'll go in, wear a wire, and get him to admit to everything." Even as the words left her lips, she realized she'd watched too many detective shows.

"No way," both Evelyn and Jeremy answered.

"You can't go near him. It's too dangerous. If anyone is going in, it's me. Problem is, he just wants me dead. After everything I've done to hamper his plans—turning Malcolm, finding you—he wants vengeance."

"There's something he wants even more," Taylor said.

"What?" Jeremy asked.

"The coins."

"The what?" Evelyn asked.

Ignoring her, Taylor went on. "If you call and say you want to talk to him and use the coins as a bargaining chip, he'd have to let you in. He wouldn't risk losing them forever. You'd have to prove that you have them though, bring some with you."

"I don't like that. If he gets his hands on them, it will only make him more powerful."

"He's not going to get to keep them. We have to figure out a way to get you in and then contain him while you download the file from the main computer."

"I think I can help with that," Evelyn said.

"How?" Taylor asked.

"The head of security. I practically raised him. If I call him and tell him I need to get on site undetected, I think he can rig the security cameras so that they play old tape—Jeremy could sneak whomever he wanted on site to help."

"Are you sure he'd do that? What would you tell him?" Jeremy asked.

"If I tell him I messed up on a dossier, that I need to replace it without Damon's knowing, he'll do it."

"What do you think?" Taylor asked Jeremy.

"I think it could work. I could have my men surprise his security and take them out. I also have a connection there, who will help me keep Crosse contained if necessary."

"Who?" Taylor asked.

"Jonas, his house manager. We've been working on him for the past few weeks. His granddaughter died. He blames Damon."

"What happened?" Taylor asked.

"She was one of the kids that died trying the choking game from that show."

Taylor looked puzzled. "I don't understand."

"He knew that Damon was behind fixing the Supreme Court case against the parents." He nodded. "This might actually work."

CHAPTER EIGHTY-THREE

"Bail denied. The defendant will be remanded to the custody of the Hillsborough County Sheriff's," the judge said as she slammed the gavel down.

Arnie's face went white, and the bailiff cuffed Jack and led him away.

Hillsborough County Jail—Valley Street Jail—as the locals referred to it, was no place for lightweights. Sure, it wasn't a prison, just a jail, but that made little difference. The worst of the worst started their journey in a jail before heading off to prison.

The cells were full of men on trial for murder, drugs, rape, and other assorted crimes. Arnie had assured him that, unlike Jack, most of them *were* guilty, and that Jack better show them he was more than a pretty face, or it would be a long year waiting for trial—if he made it that long.

The first night was the defining one. Jack had to make the transition quickly if he wanted to survive.

It was lights out, and as he lay on his back he waited for the initiation to begin. He figured it would happen in the next hour or so. He evened his breathing and completed a quick visualization. Every muscle in his body was tense, and he listened for telltale sounds. He pretended to be asleep. He was ready.

He heard Finley, his cell mate, first—the creak of the metal bed as he got up. Jack remained motionless, his eyes closed. The swish of coarse fabric—thigh against thigh—as others approached the cell. He estimated that there were three plus Finley, not counting the crooked guard who would be letting them in. The whining of the door as they entered was his cue.

He sprang up from the mattress and gave the first man a swift upward punch, smashing his nose. He went down. Jack shoved his fingers into the second man's eyes. He pushed until there was no more resistance, and the man screamed in agony.

Jack felt a searing pain in his leg and realized he'd been slashed. *Where did that come from?* He turned and saw Finley dancing in front of him, waving the weapon in the air.

"Come on, big shot. Come and get it." He was grinning at Jack.

The last man came up behind Jack and threw a meaty arm around his neck. Jack didn't resist but fell back against the man in surrender.

"Not so tough, now, huh Logan? It's Miller time." He recognized the voice. It was Albert Miller. He'd made himself known to Jack earlier in the day.

Jack bent his head forward, then snapped it back hard, gratified to hear the sound of cracking bone. Miller cursed as he released Jack and his hands went to his own face. It was now or never. Jack rushed in and grabbed Finley by the balls. He squeezed. Hard. Finley screamed as he swiped at Jack. He got two more swipes in, but Jack didn't let go.

"Get off me, you lunatic."

"Drop the knife," Jack said.

Finley opened his hand.

Jack leaned down and took it, releasing his grip on Finley.

"Tell your friends to get out of here before I finish them off and blame it on you."

CHAPTER EIGHTY-FOUR

Damon Crosse froze when he heard the voice on the other end of the phone.

"Hello, Father." The sarcasm was palpable.

Damon scowled. "Have you called to confess the error of your ways?" He couldn't wait to vent his fury on Jeremy. But first he would let him know that all his efforts at redemption were in vain. Yes, he would make him suffer for his betrayal.

A loud sigh. "I've no patience for these tiresome games. I have something you want."

"And that would be?"

"The last ten coins. You'll finally have them all."

His body tensed. "What do you want for them?"

"My mother's cross and her journal. I presume you still have them?"

"You presume correctly," Damon answered.

Jeremy continued. "And to work out a peace agreement. I'll leave you alone if you'll do the same."

He laughed. "You take me for a fool. You cannot seriously expect any peace between the two of us. You have betrayed me and everything I believe in. There is no peace." He felt the anger rise again and resisted the urge to smash the phone against the desk. The insolence!

"Fine. You'll never see them. Taylor and I will deactivate them so they will never do you or anyone else any good."

He clenched his teeth. "All right then. We shall talk. Perhaps we can come to some sort of cease and desist agreement. You must bring the silver pieces."

Now it was Jeremy's turn to laugh. "So you can take them and kill me? No, I'll bring half to prove they're authentic and to show my good faith. The rest will stay hidden. After we speak and you give me what I want, I'll text you their location when I'm safely gone again."

He was dying to get his hands on the silver pieces, but this was too easy.

"You are willing to give them up just for an old book and a piece of jewelry?"

"It's all that's left of her."

What a sentimental fool. "How do I know that you'll really tell me where they are after I let you leave? Why not just take her things and disappear again?"

"You'll just have to trust me. I'm the one with the coins, remember?"

"Fine." He hung up. What a fool. Jeremy was stupid to believe he'd ever release the journal to him. He'd trade him the cross for the five coins Jeremy brought with him, but he'd tell him he wouldn't get the journal until the last five coins were handed over. Damon would trade a journal for them, but it wouldn't be Maya's. He would soon have all the coins. And once he did, he'd never stop looking for Jeremy until he hunted him down and killed him. If Jeremy understood the power he was handing over, he would never make such a deal. Not only would they unleash demonic power that would be in Damon's control, but they would also restore his youth. Some even said they could make you immortal. He wasn't sure if he believed that, but with another forty or fifty years and to have more supernatural help, there would be no stopping him. Everything would be accomplished so much more easily, and the access he would have, oh the access—it was something he had only dreamed about. He thought of his beloved mentor and whispered, "Oh Father, if only you were still with me. What we could do together."

CHAPTER EIGHTY-FIVE

The first thing Taylor did when they reached Carl's and Gilly's house was to sit on the floor and embrace Beau. He licked her face as he jumped, delirious with joy. She was as thrilled to see him.

"So good to see you, baby. I missed you so much." She showered his head with kisses. He finally settled down and put his head in her lap. She looked up at Gilly. "I can't thank you enough for taking such good care of him."

Gilly shook her head. "Nonsense. It's been a pleasure having him. Truth be told, I hate to see him go."

Jeremy came into the kitchen. "Let's go find Carl."

Taylor followed Jeremy down the stairs to the basement. He walked over to a bookcase, pulled a book out, and the bookcase swung in, becoming a door.

"You're kidding?"

He shook his head. "Nope. Sometimes life does imitate art."

She followed him into the hidden room and watched as he replaced the book and the door shut. It was a tremendous space with lab equipment, computers and lots of machines that Taylor had never seen before.

"How have you managed to keep this place a secret? They found your hideout."

"They think Carl is dead. Knowing Crosse was likely to discover my connection to him years ago; I knew he'd have him killed. My people made it look like they were dead, that he and Gilly had a car accident. This isn't on their radar." He made a face. "Despite his delusions of grandeur, he's not omniscient."

Carl walked in from yet another doorway located at the end of the room.

He embraced Taylor and led her to a chair.

"My, dear. I'm so glad you made it back safely. I'm so sorry to hear about Jack."

Taylor's face clouded at the mention of him. It killed her not to be able to go see him, to try and help him, but it was too dangerous to come out of hiding. Jeremy put his hand on her shoulder. "You okay?"

She nodded. "What if he goes to prison? He needs my testimony to prove he killed that man in self-defense." She and Jeremy had argued about it. She wanted to go to the FBI to let them know the truth. But he reminded her that her priority had to be her child. And even though she knew he was right, she hated doing nothing while he sat in jail. After all, Jack's only connection to Crosse was her. She sighed.

"If all goes according to plan, I'll get the evidence we need, they'll arrest Crosse, and you can come out of hiding. Once you come forward, I'm sure they'll drop the charges," Jeremy said.

"I'll testify too, Taylor. I'll corroborate that Crosse was searching for you and you were on the run," Evelyn added.

Jeremy put a hand on her shoulder. "Try not to worry. You're a credible witness—the wife of a senator. Your word will hold enough weight for them to release him."

She looked at Evelyn. "Everything's all set on your end?"

"Yes. Jeremy will have five minutes to get his men on campus. My contact will text me when the tape is replaced. Jeremy will take my phone with him."

"Is that long enough for your people?" Taylor asked.

"Yes. They'll be hiding in the woods, waiting."

Taylor looked at Jeremy, then at Evelyn. "Just to be sure, we're going to need you to stay here, until Jeremy gives us confirmation that you've done what you promised."

Evelyn looked hurt. "You still don't trust me? Taylor, I've raised you since you were fourteen. I'd never hurt you."

"I didn't think Parks would either." She softened her tone. "I do think you're telling the truth, but I can't risk Jeremy's life or my baby's life. Carl has told me there's a safe room here. You'll be locked in it. If you *are* trying to double-cross us, no one will ever see you again."

Evelyn was studying her face, probably trying to psychoanalyze her right now. Taylor had to convince her that she was capable of carrying out her threat. "If I've learned anything, it's that the rules only apply to the weak," she said. "Don't forget, Crosse's blood flows in my veins. I don't want to hurt you either, but, if you're lying to us now, I'll know you were part of the plan to kill my mother. That, I won't forgive, and that, I will avenge."

"I guess we'll know by tomorrow night," was all Evelyn said.

CHAPTER EIGHTY-SIX

Jeremy pulled up to the iron gates and felt a shiver go through him. He was looking forward to the look on Damon's face when he realized Jeremy's true intent. He pressed the button on the video monitor and held his hand up, displaying the coins. The heavy gates opened, and he drove on to the property. Reaching the door, he was escorted to Damon's office by one of the security officers.

"You've aged." Jeremy looked at the man who had been the center of his universe for most of his life. He was surprised to realize that all he felt was a deep sadness. Where was his hatred? His anger? His thirst for vengeance? When he looked at him, all he saw was a tired old man. Frail almost. Then, his father blinked and Jeremy saw that steely glint of something otherworldly still there in his eyes. He recognized at last what had been there all along—the complete and utter absence of any goodness or humanity. His sympathy evaporated.

"Let me see them."

"My mother's things, first."

Damon opened a desk drawer and brought out the cross. He pushed it toward Jeremy, on the desk. "You get the journal when I get the other five."

"That wasn't the deal."

Damon shrugged. "It is now."

Let him think he had the upper hand. Jeremy would find the journal himself once he took over the facility. He played along.

Jeremy picked up the cross and put it in his pocket. He reached in his other pocket for the coins. He handed them to Damon.

Damon grabbed them eagerly, clutching them in his fist, then opening his hand to hold one up to the light. He studied the one side of the coin—a Grecian profile wearing an aegis—then turned it over to look at the eagle on the other side. He eyes shone with excitement.

"You must tell me where the others are." He clutched the coins to him.

"In good time. We have other things to discuss first."

His lip curled in a sneer, and he looked down at Jeremy. "Your conversion? You are weak. Just like your mother."

Jeremy laughed. "Your words don't have the power to hurt me anymore. I can't even summon enough feeling to hate you."

Damon laughed, a dry, mirthless sound. "Tell yourself whatever you want. You were never good enough, never came close to measuring up. I expected great things from you, but you're weak and soft."

Jeremy looked at him without flinching. "I suppose you think you're strong? Powerful? Were you powerful when your father killed your dog in front of you? Or when he beat you with his belt?"

Anger flashed in Damon's eyes. "You have no idea what you're talking about. My childhood is none of your business. It has nothing to do with who I am today."

"Oh, I disagree. I think it has everything to do with you. And it's not very original. The abused child grows up to be the abuser. Straight from the psychology books. You're a tired cliché. The only difference is that your second abuser turned out to be rich and adept at using the occult to his advantage. He manipulated you, and your entire life's work has been nothing more than the completion of another man's dream."

"How dare you! Do you know what I can do to you? What I *will* do to you? No one has manipulated me. No one controls me. I'm the one in control. It's my world, and don't you ever forget it." Spittle flew from his mouth, and his face contorted like an ugly purple balloon. "I'll kill you myself." His hands twitched by his side.

Jeremy remained calm. "You'd like that, wouldn't you? You can't touch me. I belong to God now. It must kill you that my mother's prayers actually worked."

Damon leaned forward. "You belong to me. You are nothing, and your God has no power here. He couldn't save your waste of a mother, and he can't save you." He pushed the button on his desk and looked at the door expectantly.

Jeremy laughed.

His father whirled around and demanded. "What's so funny?"

"No one's coming."

"What are you talking about?" Damon's mouth opened, but no words came out.

"Your security has been disabled. While we've been having this nice little father-and son-chat, my men have taken over your facility."

"How?" He finally managed to ask.

"You should take more of an interest in the personal lives of your employees. Then you would have known that Jonas's daughter was one of the plaintiffs in the Supreme Court case you rigged. He tipped me off about the DNA sequence. I'll get your dirt file. That'll be enough to take you down."

Damon ran to the door. It was locked. "What happened to my guards?"

"Oh, Evelyn helped us with that."

Damon shook his head. "It doesn't matter. There is nowhere you can hide. We will find you again. Go ahead and walk out the door."

"I want the tape of my mother. The one that proves you killed her."

Damon laughed. "You're insane if you think I'd ever give that to you. I'll kill you and add you to the collection."

"You're not going to kill me or anyone else. You're finished. You couldn't even produce an heir the right way. How ironic that your only two children are both on God's side now. We will fight you until our dying breath and do everything in our power to neutralize your insidious influences. I'll go through your files and prove what you've done. This time I'll take it to someone who will actually help us.

You'll spend the rest of your pitiful life in a cell."

Damon laughed again. "You fool. Do you really think you can undo decades of my seeds? Take a look around you. You've already lost. Look at this." He pulled a black leather book from his center drawer and threw it toward Jeremy.

Jeremy looked at the first page, which was a table of contents. Subjects were listed in alphabetical order: abortion, alcoholism, depression, divorce, drug addiction, murder, pornography, prostitution, rape, suicide, and trafficking. He turned to the first tab and saw that the abortion rates by state were displayed in a bar chart by year. The bars went up every year. He thumbed through more of the book and saw the same trend.

"There are also cross-referenced graphs. It's quite fascinating, Jeremy. As a scientist, you will appreciate the synergy. You see, as the laws governing pornography were eased, the depression and divorce rates spiked as well. There are correlations between so many of the laws and the corresponding consequences. And it's so easy to accomplish. In the beginning, it was more difficult. Especially the pornography. But now with the Internet, we can get it to kids. We've yet to see what that affect that will have on future generations." His mouth was a ghoulish slash. "Isn't it wonderful? You will never stop this train."

Jeremy's stomach lurched, and it took everything he had not to strike him. "We have stopped it. We'll be cleaning house in Congress and in the courts. You won't win. There are still good and decent people who don't want a world like this."

"My pawns in the government and business are icing on the cake. The real power is the media and entertainment world. They lead the cause and influence everything that happens. I have already won. Look around you. Turn the television on. Those good and decent people love to sit down and spend the evening watching vampires, zombies, cheating spouses, serial killers; those are the heroes of today's shows. Websites promoting adultery grow in popularity every day. Drugs are legal in more and more states. Anything goes. It's only going to get worse. Only a fool would waste his time trying to save the witless wretches. Leave them to rot in their own filth. It's what they deserve. You have chosen the wrong side."

"No. I will fight this with all I've got. And I've got God."

"God?" Damon snorted. "Where was God when you were growing up? When your mother breathed her last breath?"

Jeremy shook his head. "It's no use. I've met Him. I've felt His power, and nothing you can say to try and deceive me will work anymore. I will spend the rest of my life working for Him and trying to forget the horrible things I did when I was still under your control. I won't give up on humanity."

"Humanity deserves to be given up on. What does it tell you about humanity when a rape victim is better served by screaming *fire* than *help*? The instinct for self-preservation is immeasurably more potent than the instinct to help others. The selfish, amoral, ignorant masses care only for themselves. You are wasting your life on them."

Jeremy stood up. The anger and bitterness he harbored toward his father had resulted in a prison of his own making. Jeremy knew what he had to do and he stood there, grappling with the truth of it, fighting against what he knew was right but felt was impossible. Offering a silent prayer, he forced himself to remember God's grace toward him. He swallowed hard, then spoke.

"I forgive you."

Damon's eyes widened and he said nothing at first, thrown by Jeremy's statement. Then the surprise in his eyes changed to fury. "You forgive *me*? You are the one who abandoned your calling, betrayed your destiny. It is you who should be begging forgiveness from me."

He had done his part. Even though he would never have any sort of relationship with him, his words were a symbol of his faith, and he knew that he would have to continue to rely on God for them to become true. He had taken a step toward what he believed was required of him in the life he had chosen. Damon's reaction was of no concern to him.

"We are finished." He walked over to the desk and took Damon's laptop. He knocked hard on the door and it was opened. "Detain him in his office, until we find what we need to turn him over to the authorities."

Jonas bolted the door and resumed his station just outside it.

Jeremy walked out into the ornate hallway to Damon's trophy room. He was the only one who knew about it. It was where Damon had taken him to show him the tape of his mother. He knew exactly where he would find what he needed. Opening the door, he was struck by the starkness of the room. Nothing personal adorned the walls or the tables. He walked toward the tall, mahogany bookcase. He crouched down and pushed the gold book of Grimm's fairy tales and the bookcase opened. He opened the top drawer first, and his breath caught in his throat. A long braid, held together with a red ribbon, was lying atop a wooden box. He picked it up and rubbed it against his cheek. It had to be his mother's. But why had Damon kept it? He lifted the box from the shelf and opened it. A series of DVDs were inside. He pulled out one of them. It was labeled "9/75 – 10/75". He looked at the next and it was 11/75 – 12/75. He must have transferred everything to DVD and categorized them by month. He stood up and walked over to the DVD player and popped one in. His mother. His beautiful, beautiful mother. And that monster tormenting her. He had recorded it all. Every conversation, every heartbreaking moment of their interactions. He picked up the last one. It was marked "The End". He wouldn't watch it now. He put the discs into the duffel bag and put the braid on top. He went to the business office in case there were files there not on the laptop. He would make sure he had enough to implicate everyone in Damon's network.

CHAPTER EIGHTY-SEVEN

Damon fell back against his chair and heaved a deep sigh. Now that Jeremy had free rein to the facility, he would find the DVDs. Damn his foolish arrogance in keeping them. He shouldn't have kept evidence of her imprisonment and murder, but it had been a matter of pride. Proper record keeping. They were never going to be seen by anyone else. His blind spot was to blame again. He should have known about Jonas. Then he wouldn't have made the mistake that cost him the man's loyalty. It was all unraveling now, and he was smart enough to know when it was time to cut his losses. It didn't matter; his work would continue without him. He might not be able to prevent Jeremy proving he was a murderer, but Jeremy would never gain access to the files that would disband the network he had so carefully built. He pulled out his cell phone, punched in the code, and destroyed everything.

He opened the center drawer and took out a key. He rose and walked to the wall across from his desk. He pushed on the panel and put the key into the lock of the wooden box. The purple velvet pouch inside the box fit in the palm of his hand. He returned to his desk and took out a sheet of ivory stationary. With a trembling hand, he picked up the antique fountain pen and brought it to the paper. He wouldn't let anyone lock him up. He would never again be a prisoner to anyone. He opened the pouch and pulled out the capsule. Closing his eyes, he started chanting. He opened his eyes again and let them take in the room. It would be the last time he would see it.

Much had been accomplished here. He ran his hand over the rich wood, soaking in its sumptuousness.

It was time for Damon Crosse to make his final exit. He opened his mouth and swallowed the pill. Now, all he had to do was wait. He clasped his hands and bowed his head, again chanting the soothing prayers he had learned so long ago. When his speech began to slur and his mouth to numb, he knew it was coming. His head swayed, and he had the sensation of floating out of his body. He was a balloon gliding up, up, up. Nice. Smooth. Easy. He tried to move but found he was rooted to the chair. His brain and his body were disconnecting. He felt like a rock, heavy and blunt. And then, he felt nothing.

CHAPTER EIGHTY-EIGHT

Jeremy saw the body as soon as he opened the door. He ran over to the slumped figure.

"Call 911," he yelled to Jonas.

He felt for a pulse. Nothing. Then he saw the letter from the corner of his eye and snatched it from the desk.

Jeremy,

Don't congratulate yourself yet. You must have surmised that I would never allow myself to be imprisoned. I have no fear of death. I am assured of what awaits me and am eager to take my place. Peritas is to go to the shelter on Green Street. They will find him a good home and are expecting him. I will rely on your sense of morality to ensure he is delivered there.

Adieu for now. And, Jeremy, remember: you will never be free of me.

Your devoted father

Jeremy threw the letter back onto the desk. Even with death looming, his father had had to get his last licks in. He hesitated only a moment before putting his hand in Damon's pockets to get the coins. They weren't there. He searched his jacket pockets as well. *Where were they?* He had only brought them because he knew that Damon would be leaving in handcuffs. What could he have done with them in that short amount of time? Frantic, he ran to the desk and yanked the drawers open, pushing papers out of the way and pulling everything else out of them until they were empty. Nothing. He walked over to the bookcase and began pushing different books, looking for an opening. They had to be here somewhere.

Jonas came in and looked at the mess Jeremy had made and then back at Jeremy.

"I'm looking for something he stole from me." He straightened up as quickly as he could. Damon's black book had fallen open and a white paper was sticking out. A list of names in Damon's handwriting. Jeremy recognized some of them. Folding the paper, he put it in his pocket and looked at Jonas.

"Will you stay until the police come?" Jeremy asked.

"Yes."

"What will you do now?"

"If you'll have me, I'd like to work for your organization," Jonas said.

"Of course. I couldn't have done this without your help. Please feel free to stay in your quarters until we iron out the details of the estate."

Jonas shook his head. "Thank you sir, but I don't want to spend another night here. I'll go and stay with my daughter for now."

"Very well. I'll be in touch."

He needed to leave before the police arrived. He would have to come back later and look for the coins. He didn't want to have to answer any questions about what he was doing there, or about the things he had taken.

As soon as he had walked into the business office and seen the white screens, he had realized that all the data had been deleted. When he'd opened Damon's laptop he saw that it had been wiped clean as well. It hadn't occurred to him that his father could access anything without his laptop. He must have used his phone. He felt like a fool, but he was a scientist not a technology expert. He would bring someone in to try and recover the data on the computers. There had to be some way to retrieve it. In the meantime, he had the list of names. It was a start.

"You haven't won." He spat the words out.

He opened the ornate wooden door and walked through it. He was finally free.

CHAPTER EIGHTY-NINE

After Crosse's suicide, Taylor and Jeremy had come out of hiding, and she'd had to deal, finally, with Malcolm's funeral. The masquerade was the worst, everyone saying such wonderful things about him—what a great man he was—the asset he had been to Congress. She had wanted to scream: *It was all a lie!* She was still angry and didn't want to forgive him, to feel any understanding about what he had done. It was easier to hate him. It hurt much less. But then, she let herself remember the good he had done. In the end, he had sacrificed his life for her and their child. Despite the lies, she believed that she *had* known him, a part of him anyway—the part that hadn't been completely corrupted by Crosse and his brainwashing. The process had been cathartic, finally she was able to come to terms with his betrayal, and look upon his final actions as a sort of redemption.

Now she and Jack were finally going to be together. Even with Taylor's testimony, it had taken Jack's lawyer almost a month to get him out. The kidnapping charges had been dropped right away, but that was in Maryland. The New Hampshire state's attorney was not so easily convinced to drop the murder charges, even with Taylor corroborating that it was self-defense. Thanks to Malcolm, Taylor knew Senator Polk, the New Hampshire representative, and had gone to him for help. She didn't tell him the truth about Malcolm, of course. The story she and Jeremy had agreed on was that Malcolm had confessed to Taylor that he'd been harassed by Damon Crosse and had received death threats if he didn't vote the way Crosse demanded. Malcolm had asked Jack to intervene if anything happened to him. In their version, Malcolm was a hero, refusing to be bullied and paying the ultimate price.

She was scheduled to appear on the Karen Printz show next week, and that would be the story she would tell to the world. Malcolm *had* made the right choice in the end, and she saw no reason for her child to have to live with a legacy of shame. She had no idea whether Senator Polk was in Crosse's pocket too, but she had a feeling he would help her regardless, to make sure he came out looking clean.

She was waiting outside for Jack, thinking that the modern brick building looked more like a high school than a jail. She didn't want to think about what the inside was like. His release papers had been signed yesterday, and she had overnighted some clothes for him so he could feel like himself again. She checked her watch, and movement caught her eye. There he was. As he walked toward her, everything seemed to slow down, and she was afraid if she blinked, he'd disappear.

"Hey, you." He pulled her to him and covered her lips with his own.

She melted into him, feeling her body respond.

He cupped her face in his hands. "I love you so much it hurts. I am never letting you go."

She smiled. "You just try and get away."

She took his hand as they walked to the parking lot. "I have a surprise for you." She couldn't wait to see his reaction. She stopped in front of the car.

His eyes widened, and he smiled in delight when he saw the red Mustang.

"Sorry it can't be the original. But it's the same year and color," Taylor said.

He ran his hand over the hood.

"She's a beauty."

"We can't change the past, but I didn't see any reason we couldn't recapture the good memories." She threw the keys to him. "Just do me a favor, and don't get us killed. No faster than sixty-five."

He cocked an eyebrow. "Yeah, that's gonna happen." He got behind the wheel. "Where to?"

"Back to the old neighborhood."

"Put your seat belt on. It's gonna be a long ride."

CHAPTER NINETY

"Been a while since I've been here," Jack said as he pulled into her driveway. Looking at his old house next to Taylor's, he was jarred by the bright red door. His family didn't live there anymore, but in his mind's eye, it was still exactly the same. He wondered how much the inside had changed. It felt like eons ago since he'd lived there. For a minute, he pictured his young self bounding from that front door over to the house of his best friend.

"Evelyn's going to sell the house." Taylor interrupted his thoughts.

He looked at her, surprised. "Really? How do you feel about it?"

"I'm okay with it." She shrugged. "Most of my memories are tainted now anyway."

He hoped that didn't include the ones he was in.

The door opened as they approached, and Evelyn welcomed them in. "Jeremy's already here, waiting in the kitchen."

Jeremy stood and walked over to them. Jack held out his hand, but Jeremy was having none of that. He embraced him in a bear hug, then pulled back to look at him. "None the worse for the wear. Good to see you, Jack."

"I'm tougher than I look," he joked. *Things could have been a lot worse*, he thought.

"I brought Jack up to speed on the ride here. I just want to make sure we're all on the same page before the interview," Taylor said.

Jack already knew that Taylor was going to be interviewed live on

Nightline this Saturday. Everyone had been clamoring for her story since she'd surfaced. A kidnapped senator's widow makes for big news.

He spoke up first. "Crosse is dead, and he left no will. So, everything goes to Jeremy, right? The Institute, the pharmaceutical company, the works."

"Yes," Jeremy answered. "His death eliminates the worry about the genetic testing research being used for his purposes. I've already been working with the CEO, Sinclair Devlin. He's the one who financed my facility. When I went to him with evidence of Crosse's plan, he agreed to help me. He'll stay on as CEO. I'll bring Carl on as well." He looked at Taylor. "I've offered to split all the assets with my sister, but..."

She put her hand up to stop him. "I don't want any part of any of it. And I don't want my child to know he or she is related to Damon Crosse. We're going to go public with the fact that a Nazi founded the programs there. I was able to trace Friedrich to Operation Paperclip. His real name was Friedrich Dunst and he worked under Joseph Mengele. Jeremy recognized a picture of him from Germany. When they finally had the Nuremberg trials, no one could find Friedrich; he had managed to change his name from the alias the government provided. He was responsible for helping Mengele perform all kinds of horrible experiments. I won't go into the atrocities. But when it comes out, it's going to cast a long shadow over the work done at that institute."

Evelyn gasped. "I remember Dunst. A cold, cold man."

"When people find out, it's going to have them looking into the programs Crosse ran there. Even the main institute with the legitimate programs will be under scrutiny. It will turn things upside down for a while. Phase two, where his secret work was done, is most likely already shut down. With him gone, the professors will be running scared. The legitimate programs will continue until the semester completes, I'm guessing," Jeremy said.

"What about the journal, are you releasing it?" Jack asked.

"It's most likely going to be taken for evidence," Taylor answered.

"Here's the important part. We're not going to talk about Crosse's influence over power players. We're going to make it seem like Malcolm was a one-off. Nothing about Brody Hamilton being implicated by Malcolm. Nothing about his being in the orphanage. Nothing about the orphanage at all. Since it's been out of commission for the past twenty years, there's little chance anyone will discover it. Jonas has already pulled the paper records and Jeremy has taken them to Carl's."

"All the electronic files were destroyed when Damon executed the system delete," Jeremy added.

Evelyn cut in. "But if all you disclose is his training facility and nothing about how he's strategically placed his own people in government and business, no one will look any further than the Institute. There won't be an investigation."

Taylor and Jack had discussed this on the way back to Maryland and he had agreed with her.

"We have no proof, Evelyn," Jack replied. "All that will do is make his people run scared, cover their tracks. Now that he's dead, they'll feel safe. He has nothing over them anymore. Then we can quietly begin to investigate the list of names Jeremy found in his office. And of course, we'll begin looking into Brody Hamilton's dealings. We'll also try and trace where some of the orphans came from and see if we can find where they are now."

"Don't forget that we have Jonas too. He's overheard and seen plenty in all his years of service. He'll work with us," Jeremy said.

Evelyn nodded. "Okay. It just makes me sick that I enabled him all those years. I feel like I need to do something to make it right."

"You have. You helped us. If Jeremy hadn't confronted him, he would have kept going. He knew we had him, and he took the easy way out," Taylor assured her. She exhaled. "It may not be right, but I'm glad he's dead."

Jack steered the conversation back on track. "So, nothing about Malcolm's involvement. We say he told you he was being pressured; he resisted; they killed him. What about the letter he wrote to you?"

"I burned it."

"Good."

"The coins. They still haven't turned up?" Jack asked.

Jeremy's face darkened. "No. I don't know what he did with them, but they've got to be hidden in his office somewhere. I've searched and searched. There must a hidden compartment I haven't found yet. The only good news is that no one else there would know what they are."

"Could he have hidden them in his body?" Taylor asked.

"If he did, they would have been found after the ashes cooled from the cremation. I hired someone to be there when they manually inspected the ashes. Nothing."

"I guess that covers everything. We're not mentioning the coins either. Everyone's on board, yes?"

Yesses all around. He thought of something else. "What about Parks? Has anyone seen him?"

"No," Evelyn said. "He's disappeared. The paper hasn't heard anything either. He had money stashed everywhere. My bet is he's on an island far away from here."

"What are you going to tell Karen Printz if she asks?" Jack turned to Taylor.

"I'm going to tell her the truth: I don't know where he is but I worry that it's related to Crosse."

"Looks like we're ready." He looked around the room. Normally it would have made him nervous to be involved in a conspiracy with three other people, but he knew it would be okay. He trusted Jeremy and Taylor with his life. And Evelyn, well, he supposed she had proved herself by helping them. But that wasn't the only reason he wasn't worried. She had too much at stake to say anything to anyone. Public knowledge of her involvement in the Institute would ruin her professional reputation, and besides, she would have nothing to gain by not going along with them. Once they got this interview behind them, they could get on with the real work—figuring out who Damon Crosse's puppets were and exposing them.

CHAPTER NINETY-ONE

Brody Hamilton sat in his favorite chair, a plush leather recliner, holding a glass of Scotch in one hand while the other scooped up a handful of peanuts from the bowl perched on his lap. He loved being back in his Charleston home surrounded by all his comforts.

"Hand me that remote. Hurry up." His wife gave him an annoyed look and placed the remote in his outstretched hand.

"What are you so anxious about?" she asked.

"The interview. It's about to start. Sit down now if you want to watch, but hush up, you hear?"

His wife was an incessant chatterer and it drove him crazy. Couldn't get five minutes into a show without her big, loud mouth talking over the television. As his grandpappy would say, she could talk the hind legs off a donkey. He'd learned to ignore her over the years, but tonight, his nerves were raw and he had to stop himself from telling her to shut up. But of course, he didn't. There were fifty million reasons not to—all in her name right down the street at First Fidelity. Besides, she was a good old girl at heart. She knew when she'd married him that he was hard dog to keep on the porch and she didn't mind. He could have his fun, long as he came home again when he was done.

She sat her ample behind down on the sofa and pulled a box of Oreos onto her lap. Just as the program started, she piped up.

"What a pretty thing. I didn't know the senator's wife was so young. She his second wife?"

310

"Quiet, Coralee! I can't hear what she's saying. Ask questions later."

She gave him a wounded look and stuffed another cookie in her mouth.

Karen Printz was talking now.

"Taylor, thank you for agreeing to come on tonight. I know you're usually the one behind the camera." She favored the audience with a smile and explained, "Taylor and I used to work together. She was my producer." Here a tender look at Taylor. "Still miss working with her." Taylor murmured a thank you and looked duly humble.

"So, Taylor. The whole country believed that you had been kidnapped. Can you tell us what actually happened?"

"My husband, Senator Phillips, made a powerful enemy. He was approached by Damon Crosse who tried to bribe him in exchange for certain votes."

Printz was leaning in toward Taylor, shaking her head.

"When my husband refused, his life was threatened."

"Do you know what he wanted him to vote on?"

Brody felt his stomach drop and tightened his hold on the remote, then pushed the volume up. What had the damn fool Phillips done? How much had Phillips revealed before they killed him? Brody had been on pins and needles ever since he'd read about Crosse's suicide. He still couldn't believe that he had taken his life. Things must be pretty damn bad for him to off himself. He was left wondering who knew about his own connection to Crosse and if it would come out. He hadn't spent the last thirty years creating alliances and building his political career to have his own dirty laundry aired for the whole world to see.

"No. I don't think it was a specific thing. He more or less wanted someone he could control. I'm assuming for business interests. Malcolm didn't share the details with me, I don't think he wanted to upset me. When the threats didn't stop, he told me that if anything happened to him, I should trust Jack Logan."

Here Printz's expression turned mischievous.

"The same Jack Logan you used to date?"

Taylor's expression remained neutral. "That was a long time ago, Karen. Malcolm knew that Jack was an old family friend. And he trusted him to help us."

Brody took a long swallow of his Scotch and relaxed slightly. So far so good. Nothing about him. The interview went on, Taylor recounting the days in hiding, finding her half-brother, and the incredible story about his mother being held hostage.

A look of horror came over Printz's face. "Are you telling me that Damon Crosse imprisoned a young medical student and forcibly impregnated her?"

"Yes, Karen. It's all detailed in the diary of Maya Deering, Jeremy's mother."

Brody was flabbergasted. "Well I'll be a monkey's uncle." His wife started to talk, but he put his hand up to silence her.

Maya Deering. She must have been part of the medical group during his training at the Institute. Crosse had kidnapped her? No wonder Jeremy hated Crosse and had defected. Now it was all making sense. He looked back at the television as the interview continued.

"An investigation has already begun. The FBI is also trying to determine if anyone was complicit in helping Crosse when he kidnapped and murdered Maya Deering," Taylor said.

"Are there any suspects?" Printz asked.

Taylor folded her hands on her lap. "I'm afraid I can't comment on that while it's still an ongoing criminal investigation."

"All right then, let's talk about the origins of this institute," Printz began.

Taylor took a sip from the glass of water on the table next to her, then spoke. "We believe that Crosse's adopted father, Fred Crosse, was actually Nazi scientist Friedrich Dunst."

It was too much for Coralee. "Nazi's! What the heck? Can you imagine? What in the world was going on at the place? I never heard of the programs there. What has this got to do with the senator? You think that girl is touched in the head?"

Brody had never told his wife about his time at the Institute or anything about his dealings with Crosse. The way she ran her mouth, it would have been suicide. From what he could tell from the interview, Phillips had taken the same approach with his own wife. It was concluding now. He relaxed. There was nothing for him to worry about. He looked at Coralee, her eyes huge with amazement and black cookie crumbs around the corner of her mouth. He winked at her and said, "Truth is stranger than fiction, darlin. Stranger than fiction."

CHAPTER NINETY-TWO

Her son was perfect. Everything about him enchanted Taylor. Their eyes locked as he suckled, and she was filled with a rapture so exquisite, she thought her heart would burst. When he had had his fill, she laid him on her shoulder and rocked him, their hearts beating in concert. He was soon asleep and she stayed that way a long time, savoring his closeness and the peacefulness. Reluctantly, she stood and put him in his crib. Beau remained on the floor beside him like a sentinel, ever watchful and protective. He had been like that from the moment she'd brought the baby home.

She tiptoed out of the room, and into the kitchen, where Jack was going through emails. After the Printz show had aired, the station had been inundated with mail and e-mail from people claiming to have been brainwashed by the Institute. Jeremy, Jack, and she had read each and every one, and none seemed legitimate. As journalists, they knew these kinds of stories brought out the cranks in droves. But they couldn't dismiss the possibility that now that Damon was dead, some of his graduates might come forward. They'd put up a website specifically for people with information about the Institute. So far, nothing helpful had come through, but they weren't giving up.

In the meantime, they were working with Jonas and Evelyn to try and find the churches and orphanages that had brought children to the Institute. It was slow work, as so many years had passed, but they'd just gotten a call from Jeremy that he'd located a nun who remembered Crosse taking some of the children under her care. This was the first break they'd gotten so far. They were also looking into the backgrounds of the individuals on the list of names Jeremy had found. It had been six months, and they were still no further along than when they'd started.

Jack looked up as Taylor walked in.

"He sleeping?"

She smiled. "Like a baby. Any luck?"

He shook his head. "Nothing."

Pushing his hair back from his forehead, she leaned down and kissed him. "You've been at it for hours. Time for a break."

He yawned and nodded in agreement. "You hungry?"

"Starved."

"How 'bout I order some pizza and we watch a movie?"

"Perfect."

"What kind of movie are you in the mood for?"

She gave him a long look. "Anything that doesn't involve Nazis, conspiracies, or car chases."

"In other words, a chick flick?"

"Just for that, I get to pick." She walked into the family room and pulled out a DVD from the cabinet. "Here you go." She handed it to him.

He groaned. "*Gone with the Wind?*"

"That's right. And no falling asleep till the bitter end."

"Fine, but I'm getting anchovies on the pizza." He picked up the phone and ordered.

"Hey, what did you decide about the job?"

Karen Printz had called her last week. She'd recently taken on a new job as the prime host of a weekly news show on the UBC network. She wanted Taylor to come produce for her.

"I told her I didn't want to come back full-time. I don't want to take so much time away from the baby, and I can't get back into that crazy rat race."

"And?"

He could read her so well. She smiled. "And, she countered with an offer to let me produce one show a month. I was going to talk to you about it tonight, see what you thought."

"What do *you* think?"

"I want to do it. One show a month is manageable, and I love working with her. It would be good to get back into it. It will still leave me time to help you and Jeremy with looking into Crosse's empire, and it will keep me connected, so that when we're ready to go public, we'll have more allies."

He was nodding. "I totally agree." He grabbed her hand. "Come on, let's go see how Miss Scarlett's getting along."

CHAPTER NINETY-THREE

Crosby Wheeler perused the contract between Taylor Phillips and UBC while he reached under the desk and stroked Peritas' soft fur. It was all in place now. He opened the file drawer and placed the contract in the folder he had prepared weeks earlier.

He had been in the studio audience the night her interview was recorded, had been sitting in the very wheelchair that his beloved mentor had graced. His arms hung limply at his sides, his right hand curved like a claw, useless and slack against his stomach. He'd watched through thick glasses as everyone averted their eyes, avoiding looking directly at him. A "nurse" sat next to him, glancing over at him occasionally to make sure he wasn't in need of anything. He suppressed a smile, congratulating himself on his disguise. He may as well have been invisible.

Predictable—the shallowness of human beings. As if by acknowledging him, they might embarrass him or themselves. Better to pretend he didn't exist, then to confront the fact that he was a cripple while they walked around, able-bodied. Never mind. It all worked in his favor. He had to remind himself not to move. Most likely no one would notice, but one could never be too sure. Crosby Wheeler was used to personas. After all, no one had yet figured out that he was the same elusive gentleman otherwise known as Damon Crosse.

It had been risky but he was used to risk. He had to use the precise dose. The good thing about tetrodoxin was that if one recovered from the poison, it had no lasting effects. The bad thing about it was that it was highly lethal, and any miscalculation would result in a quick death. Its ability to mimic death to the degree that it fooled even EMS personnel made it the right choice. It was referred to in some circles as the "zombie drug"—those who were dead suddenly and inexplicably resurrected. The concept had a certain poetic irony. Of course, he didn't wait days to wake up on his own. He needed to fool only those transporting him to the morgue. The medical examiner had received a text alerting him to Damon's imminent arrival. The ME administered the necessary antidote as soon as his body was brought in. Damon's body was replaced by a nameless unfortunate, then sent on for cremation after the autopsy had been completed.

And the coins. They were safely in his possession. Peritas had been his courier. It hadn't been difficult to get them down his throat—they were small enough. A quick text to his connection at the dog shelter assured that they would be retrieved at the other end. Now he had twenty-five—only five away from the full set and then he would be invincible. With all of them thinking he was dead, it would be that much easier to employ his methods to find wherever Jeremy had hidden the last five.

He had watched Taylor, curious as to what she would reveal. She was quite good-looking he had thought dispassionately, appraising her as he would a piece of art or fine furniture. He felt nothing for her. She was his flesh and blood, yet he could muster no emotional connection. How interesting. She'd made Malcolm out to be a hero. And why not? It would only reflect badly on her and her child if the truth came out. She was smart to protect herself. The apple didn't fall far from the tree. Pity he hadn't raised her. Her portrayal of Friedrich and the Institute had infuriated him though. She had reduced him to a stereotype, had said nothing of his brilliance, his dedication to science and progress. But, what did he expect? She was a victim of her own mediocre upbringing. But his grandson would be different.

He would wait and watch, see what his interests were, what his passions became. When the time was right, he would use those interests to bring his grandson to him. It was what he did best. Let them have their false sense of security and believe that his threat had died with him. He could wait as long as he had to. After all, he was a patient man.

As for his fortune, it was safe. He kept most of his money in Wheeler's name. And no one knew that Catherine Knight was only a figurehead for his own vast media empire—he had owned it all from the beginning. Omega was the only outlet he ran publicly, under his Crosby persona. How he would love to tell Taylor that when she accepted the job with UBC, she had become his employee. Oh well, she would find it out eventually.

Damon Crosse had left no will, so the Institute would go to Jeremy, as would Alpha Pharmaceuticals which, he supposed, would continue to finance the Institute if Jeremy so desired. He hated walking away from Alpha, but in time, he would woo his key scientists away when he opened a new lab. As for continuing to exert his control, his political connections were all through Wheeler anyway. His work would continue. It was a shame that he had to walk away from the Institute, but it had already succeeded in its mission and nothing would stop what he had started all those years ago when Friedrich and he founded it.

He pressed a button and remotely engaged the lock on his office door. He pulled out his smartphone and tapped the icon. He watched as Taylor rocked the child. He was a beautiful boy, with curly, black hair and smooth, ivory cheeks. His eyes were closed and he sucked his thumb while his mother sang a soft lullaby. It had been easy to install the camera in the nursery. The real estate broker had been one of his.

"Sleep soundly, young master. One day, you will hold the world in your hands. Until then, sweet dreams."

ACKNOWLEDGEMENTS

Behind every endeavor is a group of supporters without which the journey would be much more difficult and lonely. I have been blessed with an abundance of encouragement and help from dear family, friends, and subject matter experts generous and willing to share their knowledge and resources.

First, I want to thank everyone who participated in my crowdfunding campaign from the bottom of my heart for your generosity, kindness, and support. It was scary out there on the ledge and your willingness to jump right in and join me made it much less so (a complete list of supporters follows these acknowledgements). To my platinum sponsors: Valerie & Colin Rees and Lynn & Stanley Constantine, my deepest love and appreciation for going above and beyond and contributing at such a high level. Your commitment to me and the project made its successful completion a certainty.

The insightful feedback from beta readers was another key component in improving the story. Thank you for reading and often re-reading Veritas with enthusiasm and providing valuable feedback: my husband, Rick Openshaw, my sister Valerie Rees, sisters-in-law Lynn Constantine and Honey Constantine, My nephew, Christopher Ackers, My in-laws Dorothy and Dick Openshaw, My dear friends: Eileen Arndt, Amy Bike, Tricia Farnsworth, Lia Gordon, Deb Nygard, Michele & John Perkins, Kim Torre-Tasso, Rivers Teske, Rich Schneider, and Diane Vara. Many thanks to Tracey Robinson and Valerie Constantine for proofreading help. Special thanks to Marie Diven for being my first reader and editor. To my good friends and authors Anthony Franze and Sandra Brannan, thank you for reading, encouraging, and providing me with endorsements for the book.

I continue to be humbled by the generosity of experts in their fields who were willing to take the time to answer my questions. Thank you: Anthony Franze for your legal expertise, Chris Munger for F.B.I. authenticity, Lori Cretella and Fady Sharara for medical advice, Lynn Drasin for television production information, Stanley Constantine for technical advice on escape hatches and hot wiring cars, Lieutenant John Thomas for information on Hillsborough County Jail, and Tony Burke and Slavomír Čéplö for information on the history of the thirty silver pieces used to betray Christ and Tony in particular for advice on elaborating on what could have happened to them. Any errors are solely my own.

To the master of the thriller, David Morrell, heartfelt thanks for taking the time to work with me on perfecting the back cover copy and for your encouragement and advice all along the way.

My deep appreciation to Jaime Levine, editor extraordinaire, who in addition to the extensive time she spent editing, sat with me at my kitchen table for fifteen hours straight refining story lines and plot issues. Thank you for helping me to find the story within the story and for making it shine. I will always be grateful for your wholehearted partnership.

To Nick and Theo, you inspire me to want to make the world a better place.

And finally, I would be remiss not to acknowledge the inspiration, empowerment, and grace from the divine Author without whom none of it would have been possible.

About the Author

Lynne Constantine is a coffee-drinking, Twitter-addicted, fiction writer always working on her next book. She runs her plots by Tucker, her golden retriever, who never criticizes them. Lynne has a master's degree in business from Johns Hopkins University. Visit Lynne at lynneconstantine.com. She loves to hear from her readers. She also writes with her sister under the pen name Liv Constantine.

Also by Lynne Constantine:

CIRCLE DANCE
THE DECEPTION, SHORT STORY
MOTHER'S DAY, SHORT STORY

Thank you for reading *The Veritas Deception*, I hope you enjoyed it.

Reviews help other readers find books. I appreciate all reviews, and every one matters, so please consider taking a little time to leave feedback.

THANK YOU TO MY CROWDFUND SUPPORTERS

Tracy & Malcolm Robinson, Amy Bike, Leo Manta, Michael & Honey Constantine, Lori Mattioli, Valerie & Colin Rees, Ron Kaine, Lynn & Stanley Constantine, Theo Openshaw, Sean Openshaw, Kim & Alex Torre-Tasso, Nick Openshaw, Tee Bond, Christopher Ackers, Marina & Jim Lillie, Carrie & John Diveris, Annitsa & Bruce Searles, Kathleen& Mark Greenhalgh, Sara & Mike Galullo, Demi Morekas, Dick & Dorothy Openshaw, Ted Stratakos, Edmund & Tawn Tribue, Paula Sparks, Teddy Constantine, Melinda & Gil Weatherly, Alexa Constantine, Donna & Stanely Pamfilis, Liz & Garry Wilcox, Valerie & Dave Bacchiocchi, Chris Constantine, Lisa Golia, Robin & Brian Phillips, Marie Diven, Kiko Teed, Michele & John Perkins, Carmen Marcano-Davis, Diane Kuczo, Andrew Openshaw, Teresa & Norman Loverde, Lynn & Ron Hazelton, Madeline Monde, Chuck Mason, Michelle Hydeck, Kris Seskunas, Marilyn Torre, Ellie & Paul Joslin, Charles Waechter, Diana Parsons, David Bike, Lori Cretella, Steve Tsihlis, Lori Smith, Rich Schneider, James Bothello, Jeff Goddard, Pat Shea, Christina & Nick Constantindes, Charles & Laura Constantine, Kathy Moscato, Nick Beezhold, Brian & Leslie Workman, Janet Liberati, Janine & Pietro Scotti & Lynn Kahlenberg

I COULDN'T HAVE DONE IT WITHOUT YOU!

Made in the USA
Middletown, DE
07 July 2018